KU-166-997

OSCAR OCTOPUS and the FISH FACES

Bright Sparks

Oscar Octopus was very popular with the fish. He could sometimes be a bit snooty, but most of the time no one really minded because he was so clever. There was very little he couldn't do - usually at the same time - and everyone was always impressed by the serious, important way he spoke.

Every evening Oscar could be found at home, reading,
practicing a lecture and playing the violin, all at the same time.

Oscar did his best to keep the younger fish in order.
He corrected their speech, watched their manners and tried to teach them
how to do all the wonderful things he could do himself.

Pearl the Curl thought that Oscar was **WONDERFUL.**

But Gary Glory was not impressed. Gary liked playing tricks and making lots of noise.
He did not like being told that reading was good for him,
and having to apologise when he had been rude.

“I don’t want to be like Oscar Octopus,” grumbled Gary one day, after he had been told off.

“I think it’s funny to tease the other fish.”

"Gary Glory is getting naughtier by the minute," thought Oscar.
"I must think of something to keep him busy."

So that afternoon - whilst he practised his recorder scales, prepared a seaweed casserole for Howie the Shark, corrected some sums and knitted a pair of riding gloves for Emmy the mermaid - he put on his thinking cap.

Then Oscar did what he always did when he really needed to think – he put aside all his other activities, sat down at the piano and began to play some red hot **boogie-woogie.**

"What's that fantastic music?" cried Gary Glory, who was passing by.

"I'd be the most popular fish in the sea if I could play something like that!

Can you teach me, Oscar?"

Oscar smiled to himself and kept on playing.

"It'll take hard work," he said sternly. "You'll have to practise."

"I'll do anything you say," promised Gary, dancing around Oscar's piano.

"Right," said Oscar. "Be here at eleven sharp for your first lesson."

At eleven o'clock the next morning there was a clamour outside Oscar's rock.

"I told everyone that you were going to teach me to play the piano," said Gary Glory. "And now they all want to play your music!"

"I want to play the electric guitar but I'll never be any good," said Vinnie Tuna in his usual gloomy way.

Buster Blowfish fancied the trumpet. Pearl the Curl was born to be a lead singer, and Sizzle and Slink were certain they could provide superb backing vocals.

"I'll teach you everything I know," agreed Oscar.

"But I expect everyone to work very hard!"

It wasn't easy teaching the unruly fish how to play their instruments. Gary had no ear for rhythm. Buster kept blowing himself up, instead of blowing the trumpet.

Vinnie Tuna kept missing rehearsals because he was certain that the noise would attract the shark gang (and sharks LOVE tuna steak). But Pearl was a model pupil and Sizzle and Slink were so keen to perform that they did everything they were told.

One day, Emmy the mermaid came to sit in on a lesson.

"What a great band you are!" she cried, clapping her hands. "You must come to the Enchanted City and play at the King's birthday party! We'll put on a surprise show - the King will love it!"

"Hmm," said Oscar. "I'm not sure we're ready for that."

"I'm ready," said Pearl the Curl with a flick of her crimped fins.

"We're ready too, **shooby dooby doo**," sang the eels.

"Rock on!" cried Gary Glory, hammering at the piano.

“We need a name,” said Pearl the Curl. “All the really good bands have wonderful names.”

“Oh dear,” sighed Vinnie Tuna, looking worried. “This will end in disaster.”

“Oh, you're such an old fish face!” said Gary rudely, sticking his tongue out at him.

"That's it!" cried Emmy. "We'll call you Oscar and the Fish Faces!"

Oscar looked pleased and everyone agreed that it was a wonderful name for a wonderful band.

The day of the party arrived and everyone was
feeling **REALLY REALLY REALLY** nervous.

"Now remember everyone - best behaviour! Gary, no pranks!
Sizzle, no electric shocks! It's not often that a set of rabble-rousers like you
gets invited to the King's palace! Now, is everybody here?"
Oscar paused and looked around. Oh dear - where was Pearl?

They searched high and low but Pearl was nowhere to be seen. "We'll have to cancel," sighed Vinnie Tuna, as if he had known all along that this would happen.

“Nonsense,” said Oscar. “We *must* simply play without her.
Sizzle and Slink, you will have to be the lead singers for tonight.”

Clutching their instruments, and feeling very nervous, Oscar and the Fish Faces entered the Enchanted City.

Right at the last moment Pearl and Emmy **ZOOMED** up on Emmy's seahorses.

"Look what we've got!" cried Emmy. "Costumes for everybody!"

Never had a lead singer looked more stylish than Pearl the Curl.

Never had Gary Glory looked so cool or Buster Blowfish looked so handsome.

"Showtime!" yelled Gary.

The King was soon beaming from ear to ear.

"What a wonderful birthday surprise!" he exclaimed.

Soon everyone in the Enchanted City was swinging their fins.

"Rock and roll!" cried Gary, who was having the time of his life.

And Oscar? Oscar conducted the band, played the drums, kept all the excited little shrimps off the stage, sipped his glass of seaweed surprise - and grinned.

And the band **boogied** on until dawn.

This is a Bright Sparks Book
First published in 2000

Bright Sparks
Queen Street House
4 Queen Street
Bath BA1 1HE, UK

This book was created by
small world creations ltd
Tetbury,UK

Written by Janet Allison Brown
Illustrated by Matt Ward
Designed by Sarah Lever

Printed in Spain

ISBN 1 - 84250 - 031 - 7

OUNTAINS
F MENACE

EXECUTION RIVER

ICE WA

ANDS

THE EASTERN REALMS

THE GREAT LAKE

LAKE REGION

E FOREST

THE THRONE
CITADEL

TAL LAKE

SNOW PLAINS

THE GREAT GARDEN
OF THE EAST

GAOL WATER

MYSTERY
WOOD

THE SOUTH POINTS

THE WILDERNESS
LANDS →

RDEN
ITH

Enchantica
THE REALM OF THE ICE LORD

J BLAKEMORE

Enchantica

The Well of Hope

by

Andrew Bill

Holland Studio Craft Ltd.,
156, King Street,
Fenton,
Stoke-on-Trent,
Staffordshire ST4 3EP,
England.

Acknowledgements
All characters designed by Andrew Bill.
All characters sculpted by Andrew Bill, Ken Fallon and Andrew Hull.
Colour illustrations by Jay Blakemore and Stephen Simmons.

ISBN 0 948511 75 3

Author's Note

Well, it has been a long hard struggle, but it is finally here; Enchantica Book II: The Well of Hope.

I would like to thank everybody who has helped and supported me in this latest endeavour i.e. Theresa (my right hand man!), Phil, Denise, Doug, Nan (thanks for the loan of the spare bedroom and the nosh!), various members of my family, friends and colleagues, who have chipped in; and anyone else who knows me!

Special thanks to Jay Blakemore and latterly Steve Simmons, for their skill, patience and hard work on the illustrations. Nice one lads!

Thankyou John (Woodward) for your sterling work on the finished book. Not to mention the classy little dragon motif, cute eh?

I must also give a mention to all those who have worked so hard here at Holland Studio Craft on the Enchantica range of figurines. A range that is constantly being expanded with new characters and complimentary projects.

Writing of which, Anthony Schaeffer, the experienced broadcaster and actor, has recorded an audio cassette tape of the first Enchantica novel: Wrath of the Ice Sorcerer. We are delighted with the result and cannot wait for him to have a go at book two!

At this point I feel I ought to mention that this novel is a straight forward continuation of 'Wrath of the Ice Sorcerer'. Therefore, anyone not familiar with the first novel, may find that their appreciation of the original characters suffers slightly from a lack of background information. This is not a cheap attempt to boost sales of the first novel, however (although that sounds like a great idea to me!) I just thought I ought to mention it.

One word of caution to anyone considering reading this novel to young children. At various stages in the novel Jonquil and Rattajack eat mushrooms and fungi that they find growing around them. I feel it ought to be pointed out to young children, that unless one is an expert, it can be highly dangerous to pick mushrooms and toadstools from the wild. I only mention this in case some impressionable youngsters should try to emulate their heroes. Thankyou.

On a lighter note, I hope this second novel and the wide variety of new characters and creatures it contains, brings enjoyment. I would like to take this opportunity to thank anyone who feels they have been left out, and Rush for making great music.

The adventure has definitely continued, for all of us, and I hope it will continue to do so.

So as the phrase has it;

Take the hand of the child within you,
And let the adventure begin..........!
A.B.

Do you know Enchantica?
You have been there . . .
In your dreams,
Your nightmares.
Do you know Enchantica?
Close your eyes,
Open your mind,
Escape the chains of disbelief.
Do you know Enchantica?
Then take the hand
of the child within you
And let the adventure begin . . .

Do you know Enchantica?
You are already there.

Contents

The Battle of the Bay of Voices

"Destroy!"

The blood chilling scream of the goblin prince tore through the air like a rapier and the mighty host surrounding the raft took up the cry with such ferocity that the very floor of ice beneath them seemed to tremble.

A wall of ugly creatures at least fifty bodies thick thundered towards the rescuers in the middle of the frozen bay. Another, even larger, ring of Winter warriors surrounded the first, and then another and another. The army of the Ice Sorcerer reached back across the bay like dark menacing ripples upon a pristine crystal pond.

Within the ranks of the enemy companies of goblins set poison-barbed, black-feathered arrows to their bows. Battalions of icedemons summoned forth ice javelins from the air. Huge blue skinned trolls waved great stone axes in furious circles, spitting dark curses and threats in their vile tongue whilst reaching into their armouries for rocks and newly forged spiked iron missiles to throw.

In the sky a blizzard of mighty snowdragons wheeled in impatient spirals, their white riders eager to join the fray. For as far as Jonquil's keen eyes could see, Vrorst's hordes came upon them in invincible strength; thousands perhaps tens of thousands of death dealing gargoyles all baying for their blood and the destruction of the precious vessels. The enemy bristled with spears, lances, clubs and scimitars and the banners of the assembled tribes and races slapped against their poles in the insistent sea breeze.

Rattajack's brilliant amber orbs, in which Jonquil had always found such comfort, held nothing for him now. The terragon's eyes only reflected the horror that lay around them. Jonquil noticed that a few remaining Fallon leaves were still attached to Rattajack's collar. He was just about to decide whether it was better for the terragon to be visible or invisible during the battle when a roar of alarm from Snarlgard wrenched his thoughts aside. A volley of black arrows clattered across the raft and its three priceless burdens. The Autumn dragon ordered the two companions beneath the shelter of one of his rapidly outstretched wings and they were alarmed to discover that they could follow the progress of the battle outside with sickening ease through the gaping holes rent in the leathery membranes, during the Battle Of The Green Oak. Another swarm of black arrows screamed towards the raft, deadly flights of ice-javelins fell silently from the air upon the dragons. The terrible sound of the enemy's battle drums beating out the attack carried from the bay like black thunder. The Battle of the Bay Of Voices had begun.

Arangast bade Gorgoyle stay on the ground to aid Snarlgard in defence of the Sacred Vessels. The Summer dragon then launched himself upwards to engage the gathering flocks of snowdragons threatening from the air. The Spring and Autumn

Guardians braced themselves back to back and filled their lungs in readiness for the coming onslaught from across the ice. As Snarlgard manoeuvred himself into position, Jonquil and Rattajack had to follow him closely, to keep beneath his shelter and avoid the worsening hail of arrows and rocks.

Suddenly a flight of snowdragons that had flown wide of Arangast's assault, stooped low at the two defending dragons at the raft. Their maniacal dragonlords, clothed in flowing white robes and gleaming silver helms, urged their white steeds faster and lower, and so they came, talons to the fore. Before either of the two dragons could react, the attacking skein were upon them belching great sheets of blue fire that could instantly freeze a banf's blood in his veins. Gorgoyle and Snarlgard broke free of the frozen coating spewed upon them, that threatened to chill their great bodies and extinguish their white hot flame, and shook the ice fragments from their scales. A freezing wind accompanied the white attackers as they roared on to turn again but the Guardians were determined that they would not be taken by surprise a second time and let their flaming torches fly.

Three white bodies crashed on to the frozen crust of the bay when the snowdragons returned, their wings stripped of skin by the searing kiss of the dragons' fire, their bodies charred and smoking. Another fell from the sky in a ball of flames, its deathflight sending it crashing into a charging column of goblins, scattering them across the ice in a flood of burning bodies and metal.

Icicles hung like crystal teeth from Arangast's wings and he knew that soon the sheer weight of ice breathed upon them by the blizzard of white dragons about him, would drop him from the sky like a stone. With a great roar he ploughed through the clouds of white beasts, shaking as much of the burden from his wings as he could. Despite the gnawing cold of the freezing cloak that clung to him, Arangast tried to concentrate his thoughts down to his two brothers on the raft. He had to be free of the ice.

With as skilful a twist as he could manage with his stiffened wings, he spiralled away from his attackers into a deathly fall. A stream of snowdragons surged after him in furious pursuit as Arangast gained yet more pace and then tipped himself into an uncompromising dive at the raft. Even Jonquil who had first hand experience of Arangast's stomach lurching aerobatics, had to gasp in wonder at the spectacle of the golden dragon approaching like a fury, a vast white arc of snowdragons swooping after him, gathering for the kill. Snarlgard and Gorgoyle's great reared heads came together as the golden dragon raced towards them. Suddenly they let forth a combined fountain of brilliant white fire that completely engulfed Arangast's body as he swept overhead, freeing him from his frozen shackles. Unharmed by his brothers' fire, and free to do more battle, he rose like an arrow on the generous sea draughts to breath more death to the enemy. The swarm of pursuing snowdragons were also carried into the plume of white fire and fell amongst their ground dwelling allies as a shower of burning corpses.

The dragons on the raft used flame, teeth, claws and thrashing tails to rip the charging creatures apart or hurl them as lifeless bundles to the wind. Armour was peeled away like smouldering paper under the intense heat of the dragons' furnace and the screams of the enemy lived on the breeze for long hours in that desolate place. Row upon row, rank upon rank of goblins, demons and trolls filed past their beloved prince to offer their blood to the Guardians of the Sacred Vessels. Rivers of fire ravaged through the columns like hungry beasts devouring all in their path but still the monsters continued. Bledderag knew that the breath of the dragons would claim many of his soldiers and that the raft on the bay would be piled high with smouldering bodies before victory was realised. However, as mighty as the three dragons were, they could not wield their swords of flame forever, eventually they would tire and the Vessels would belong to the goblin prince. The Lord of Ice had given the son of Hellbender the Great, the largest army ever assembled to claim back the precious chests and Bledderag was more than ready to send every last creature to his death to achieve that end.

A sheen of sweat glazed Jonquil's forehead and he suddenly realised how hot the air had become around the raft. He and Rattajack had been ankle deep in bloody water for some time as the bay's surface had slowly begun to thaw. Jonquil also noticed a few subtle cracks beginning to creep through the frozen floor beneath them and fancied he could almost feel the ice straining to hold together under the intense heat.

As Jonquil examined the ice beneath him, he became aware of a pale, oval shape in the darkness of the water far below. It looked almost like a face, soon to be joined by another. The banf had the strangest feeling that he was being watched, if not discussed by some unknown beings beneath the deep lid of ice, then the shapes were gone and the dark void empty once more.

The tireless advance of the enemy continued, there seemed no end to the walls of bodies that tramped forward to engage both dragons. Every now and then a small raiding party of goblins would slip past the dragons' arcs of fire and steal in towards the raft to lay hands on the precious vessels. Jonquil could only look on in horror as the goblins came upon their priceless quarry and raised high their scimitars to strike. The first of these worrying breaches caused Jonquil to grasp a nearby abandoned weapon and try to rush out from the safety of the red dragon's shadow to attack the goblins, thinking that the Guardians had not seen them. However, before the banf could do so, Snarlgard carefully held in his wing to keep Jonquil back and when satisfied that the banf could not escape, lashed his tail sharply across the raft, flinging the enemy attackers from the Sacred Vessels. Jonquil soon learned that the dragons were only too well aware of the movements of the enemy, especially when they dared to violate the sanctuary of the three chests.

There was a resounding crack. Despite the fury of the battle, all on the ice seemed to hear it. A thin rupture, beginning at Gorgoyle's feet, snaked across the glassy battleground, the enemy faltering slightly as the hairline fissure darted through their ranks. There was a moment's hesitation, as if the mob was waiting for a conclusion to the ice's warning, when none came the battle recommenced, the dark soldiers confident that it was safe to continue. As the air once more grew thick with the arrows and missiles of the enemy, another crack weaved its way from beneath Snarlgard, drawing a wavy white line right between Jonquil's feet and zig-zagging outwards into the bay.

Bledderag was not oblivious to the strains the great battle was placing on the ice. He knew only too well that it was a race against time. The Winter armies had to overpower the Guardians before the ice crust finally collapsed and his prizes sank forever out of reach. The goblin prince decided that there was no time for careful tactics or strategy, so he cast them to the wind and ordered a massed charge at the dragons. The regimented lines and formal columns of the enemy suddenly melted into a huge black wave of charging creatures that surged towards the raft and broke over the already beleaguered dragons. More and more white swarms flocked in to join the growing numbers of snowdragons assailing Arangast in the air. Bledderag held nothing back, this was his one chance for glory and he was determined not to lose it.

Jonquil and Rattajack were valiantly defending the narrow opening allowed by Snarlgard's wing. Crowds of bloodthirsty creatures were trying to force their way in to get at the lance-wielding banf. It began to get much lighter beneath the red dragon's wing and when Jonquil anxiously stole a glance upwards he discovered why. Scores of goblins and demons, using their fellows' bodies as ladders, had climbed up on to the giant leathery canopy and were viciously hacking great vents into its stretched membranes. Jonquil had to leave Rattajack to continue the defence of the narrow opening whilst he rushed to prevent further damage to Snarlgard's precious wings. Holding the long goblin weapon right at its end, he jumped upwards to try and stab at the foul creatures. Two of the attackers squealed as the lance thrust through the holes they had just made and found its targets. Jonquil's spear dislodged a further two and was just setting to work on a third, when the section of wing that the evil perpetrator was enthusiasticly ripping apart suddenly tore beneath him and he fell through on to the banf below.

In a flash the goblin leapt to his feet, blade in hand and made a rush for the surprised banf. Jonquil parried a vicious blow from the goblin's curved sword with the strong shaft of his lance and in return smashed the other end against the goblin's helmet. The creature was thrown hard into the dragon's flank, a stream of obscenities erupting from its mouth and it made as if to charge again. Jonquil braced himself and held the spear so that its point followed every move the tensed goblin made. The creature slowly circled the banf, now and then trying to dodge around the pike and make a thrust at Jonquil but the banf held firm and even pushed the creature back on to its heels once or twice to show that he was unafraid. After a last and rather half-hearted attempt to beat Jonquil's lance, the goblin narrowed its yellow eyes, reached inside its tunic and deftly tossed a short knife to grab the poisoned blade in his fingertips. Before Jonquil even had time to think the small dagger whistled past his head, almost nicking one of his large ears before it clattered harmlessly against the iron-plate scales of the dragon. The goblin cried out in despair, abandoned his attack and fled towards the opening, the wet ice punishing him for his haste and bringing the creature heavily to his knees. Rattajack, who was of course invisible by this time thanks to the magic of the Fallon leaves left in his collar, kicked the luckless goblin out into the light. The grisly spectacle of the poor creature being mistakenly set upon by its furious brethren caused Rattajack to shy away from the opening and seek the comfort of his beloved Jonquil.

The Battle of The Bay of Voices had begun.

The terragon scratched the magic leaves from his collar so that he would be visible to the banf and the two companions, both quite exhausted from their trials, stood together to await the next rush of the enemy. Three more goblins crept through the opening, wiping the blood of their brother, whom they had assumed to be Jonquil, from their swords. Their evil faces twisted into fang-bristled snarls as their eyes fell upon the two companions. Out of the corner of his eye Jonquil could see the jostling shapes of hundreds of dark warriors silhouetted against the skin of Snarlgard's wing. Many of them were using the numerous holes and tears in the mutilated membrane as a means of hauling themselves up on to the dragon's body to overwhelm him with sheer numbers. Jonquil tightened his grip on the spear and the three goblins began to close in, more of their kind stealing in through the opening behind to join the sneering execution party.

Bledderag had almost lost sight of the two dragons now, only their mighty horned heads, still breathing the last remnants of their fire, could be seen above the boiling black mass of his soldiers. The raft itself was now lost within the core of the battle, at least a hundred bodies thick.

Gorgoyle raked his head back and forth through the advancing forest of attackers, partly to halt their endless advance and also to try and wrench loose the more adventurous amongst the enemy that had scaled his neck to stab at his eyes. He thrashed his great wings which now crawled with hole-rippers and a score of bodies flew into the air to be swallowed up by the crushing black mob. Gorgoyle had one fat ice troll pinned beneath the talons of his rear left leg but was too occupied thrashing his tail against the stabbing clans on his back to finish him. Ice javelins that had jammed between his verdant scales were slowly thawing in the heat as hundreds more rained down upon him. Some of the enemy were using the half melted spears as makeshift ladders to climb up the great dragon's body to join the gathering along his back.

The ice had begun to groan again and a network of ominous fractures now radiated outwards from the raft. As thick as the crust on the bay was, there was a limit to its tolerance and the sheer weight of creatures piling on to the slaughter at the raft tempted it sorely.

Bogra and another ice troll were ploughing through the seething ranks before them in an effort to get to the dragons. They swatted badly aimed or deflected missiles away from their faces as if they were merely clouds of troublesome mosquitos and their eyes squinted to peer through the haze of flying weapons. Bogra was the only surviving Ice Troll of the original three that had breached the Sacred Chamber in the Throne Citadel and stolen the three Sacred Vessels. He had been instructed by Bledderag to steal away the chests once more but this time to a different end. The two Ice Trolls each carried huge stone axes and, after a great deal of barging, trampling, jostling and even cleaving some of their smaller allies aside, managed to clear a path for themselves and eventually draw near to the tree trunk raft and its precious cargo.

Surprisingly, the three vessels securely strapped to the raft were still very much intact. The two powerful dragons had so positioned themselves so as to be able to cover all entrances to the raft, first with their eyes and then with their lightning tail spears. The paths to the Vessels were littered with the disembodied or broken corpses of those who had tried to claim them so far.

Bogra halted before approaching too near to the dragons and, remembering the careful instructions his royal master had drummed into him, brought his foolishly compliant companion forward. Bogra then crouched behind the upright body of the other and ordered the first ice troll to advance. And so it was in this curious, horse-like fashion that they proceeded towards the killing tails. Bledderag had calculated that in the deep confusion of battle, the two ice trolls, thus positioned, would easily pass as one. Snarlgard caught sight of the menacing axe wielded by Bogra's companion as he waded towards the chests, urged on by the stooped Bogra concealed behind. The lumbering ice troll screamed his curse of defiance as he leapt into the dragons' coils and placed his first step on the wooden platform, axe held high. The troll may have seen a snaking flash of red, or heard a dull roar like a great blade parting the air but there was little he could have done. In a instant Snarlgard's tail spear had sliced through his waist, even halving the thick trunk of his stone axe with ease.

Bogra had not seen the approach of the killing tail either, but he had felt its draught through his hair and quickly dropped to all fours lest the murderous tail should return. Bogra crawled through the still standing legs of his dead companion and, as he wormed his way on to the raft, he heard the halved corpse of the other ice troll finally collapse behind him.

Arangast, mighty Guardian of Summer, was nearing total exhaustion and the enemy dragons were beginning to win. He was almost completely engulfed in ice, his white fire long doused by the freezing blue flame of his relentless assailants. His dagger-studded jaws were the only weapons left to him now but they ached with fatigue. All of his senses were gradually drifting into a chilling numbness and he could barely manage to hold himself aloft. The evil dragonriders, sensing the imminent decline of the golden dragon, urged their snowy steeds to pounce upon Arangast's back and bite into the iron-tough scales protecting his body. It would take only one of the white dragons' fangs to penetrate the Summer dragon's thick scales and breath their blood freezing fire into his veins to succeed in claiming his life.

Arangast hung his head in despair. He searched wearily for the raft on the great sheet of frozen water below. His eyes told him that Gorgoyle and Snarlgard had allowed an ice troll to break through to the Vessels. They themselves were overwhelmed with swarming black attackers. Disaster! All was lost!

Suddenly a familiar piping voice sharply invaded his doom-ridden thoughts.

"Cracks! In the ice!" it urged. "The ice! Crack the ice! Crack the ice!"

Arangast immediately recognised Rattajack's quietly persistent tones and appreciated the fear and desperation they carried with them. The golden dragon valiantly summoned his numbed senses together to form an idea. If it failed it would mean his doom but then death was already riding at his shoulder, waiting for a chance to breathe its eternal invitation into his heart. So what did he have to lose?

With the very last ounce of strength he could muster, Arangast broke free from the murderous attentions of the snowdragons and dropped from the sky. Talons bared, the golden dragon plummeted towards the throbbing heart of the battle, using the ice troll Bogra, who was now disobediently stuffing prised-off jewels and gold fragments into

Wargren on Snowthorn the Magnificent.

his pockets, as his target. Bledderag's jaw dropped in disbelief as Arangast's monstrous shape fell on to the battle. Was this victory? Surely the precious chests would be destroyed? This was not the ending he had planned for his glorious battle. This was not victory!

Bledderag's scream of protest was drowned by the thunderous explosion of bodies and ice as the golden dragon's desperate dive punctured the crust of the bay. A great upsurge of angry sea water rose like a white mountain from what had just been the scene of battle, towering over the terrified dark legions like a giant avenging angel before crashing down amongst them, dragging them back through its jagged jaws into its deep, dark, cavernous belly. The shockwaves that followed ripped into the lid of the bay carrying hundreds of small bands of the enemy on turbulent floating platforms out into the great chasm. Those that contained ice trolls were soon capsized by the clumsy creatures clambering this way and that in a frenzy of fear. Instead of moving away from the crumbling edge towards safety, crowds of archers rushed forwards to fire volleys of arrows into the raging pool, almost as if they were trying to kill the foaming water itself. The bowmen seemed oblivious to the pitiful sounds of their fellows who cried out to be rescued before the salt water poisoned them or they fell victim to their own archers' arrows.

The ice gradually became more unstable and the goblin archers failed to notice the extensive web of fine cracks beneath their feet begin to widen and drift away from the edge. At first Bledderag, who surveyed the chaos from a new, safer vantage point, thought the drifting of the ice fragments was due to the pulling of the liberated tide, but on closer scrutiny he observed that some of the fragments were actually moving against the waves. There were clearly other elements at work here.

In the heart of the commotion a small battalion of goblin warriors and rock hurling trolls, who had previously been employed to great effect in the warring with the dragons, were now desperately trying to cling to a large slab of ice rocking ominously in the water. For some reason Bledderag's eyes were drawn to this marooned splinter of his army. It was then he began to notice the clusters of pale skinned figures moving rapidly through the surrounding water. As the milling schools of sea creatures rose and dived beneath the surface, Bledderag caught sight of human-like bodies and upturned fish-finned tails. At first he thought his soldiers were being attacked by a combined army of fish and men, but then he realised that these new sea-enemies were both at once. The sea-creatures were heaving the ice platform up and down with violent thrusts of their powerful tails to try and upset the terrified goblins and trolls into the water. More mer-creatures joined the effort and by concentrating their strength on one end of the ice managed to heave the other end into the air. Most of the ragged enemy battalion tumbled into the water and were quickly dragged under by a forest of grabbing hands. Two of the dark creatures however succeeded in holding on to the upturned edge of the ice and refused to be shaken from their slippery perches. They even found the courage to release one hand and hurl knives, swords and any other weapon they still had about themselves at the mer-folk below. Bledderag could not help a smile emerging on his lips and a slight twinge of pride as his two valiant soldiers made a defiant, albeit pathetic stand against their enemies, but the goblin prince's pleasure was short lived. Two magnificent sea-warriors leapt in unison from the water, rose the full height of the upturned ice slab, seized the two goblins and crashed back into the water and were gone. Countless other winter servants were dispatched in a similar way, whilst even more were being towed out from the edge of the fragile mosaic and drowned.

Ultimately the struggling ceased and a strong, pale skinned body rose from the bloody, pink foam to drag the final black-clad warrior to his doom. The great hole in the ice was choked with floating dead. Those that had stayed back from the battle drew hesitantly away, fearful that the rest of the ice might break beneath them. A large tail fin broke through the crust of bodies in the water, slapped down hard on the surface three times and then slid majestically out of sight. Bledderag turned to address the remnants of his army but they had already begun to disperse in scattered parties back across the bay, unwilling to move in large groups lest they should anger the ice. Bledderag crept as close to the water as he dared, where were the dragons and the chests? Why weren't their great bloated bodies floating in the ice hole with all the rest? Surely they had been drowned! He searched the carpet of bodies before him but there was no trace. He cursed their names aloud and hoped that their blood was now frozen in their veins and that they would drift for eternity through the freezing fathoms of the endless winter sea. The battle was over but to whom did victory belong?

A dull roar approached from behind and Bledderag turned to see a huge flock of snowdragons alight around him. A dragonlord of some importance descended from his fearsome mount and strode purposefully towards the goblin prince, a number of his lieutenants following behind. Bledderag sensed the crowd of generals beside him begin to shrink away and by the time Wargren stood before him the goblin prince was alone. The powerful dragonlord slowly raised his arm and pointed a finger at Bledderag, then his terrible voice broke the silence.

'The Ice Sorcerer will hear of this!' Wargren snarled.

'He will!' Bledderag answered him.

'From you!' Wargren concluded.

Bledderag was placed in the saddle behind one of Wargren's subordinates and the flight of snowdragons took once more to the air, this time to bring the goblin prince before Vrorst himself to explain how the largest army ever assembled beneath the flag of winter had failed to capture the fleeing, half-beaten servants of the Three Wizards.

The stream of white dragons was mirrored in the lifeless eyes of a fallen goblin warrior as it raced across the crystal blue sky. Bledderag stared down at the ruptured battlefield. The bodies of his vanquished army lay upon the frozen bay like an immense, ugly ink blot on the purest white paper. The hand of the goblin prince rested on the hilt of his concealed dagger, a suicide blade steeped in the strongest infusion of deathhemp root. He was not about to let the Lord of Winter laugh over his bones after he had been torn to pieces in the torture chamber of the Throne Citadel. His secret blade at least ensured that Bledderag, son of Hellbender, son of Jemlin, greatest of all goblin kings, had the choice of a different end; one of his own making.

The Southern Ocean

Far beneath the carnage of the frozen battlefield, excited schools of mer-folk converged on three, great writhing forms struggling against, what was to them, a most unnatural environment. The three guardian dragons were almost convulsed with panic. The sea-people had to take care to swim clear of their wildly flailing limbs, lest they be harmed accidentally by a grasping claw or a madly thrashing tail, as the dragons floundered in a blind frenzy. Eventually the terrified monsters were persuaded by the gentle melodic voices of the sea-maidens that they were not in danger and calmed sufficiently to allow the mer-folk to attach giant coiled shells about their heads to provide them with air. Finally, convinced that they were not about to be drowned the three dragons relaxed and were slowly guided through the icy water by a hundred pairs of tiny hands.

Miraculously, Jonquil and Rattajack had also survived their violent entry into the bay. Moments before Arangast had plunged into the very heart of the battle, Snarlgard had instinctively drawn in his wings, thus carefully sandwiching the two companions close to his sides, along with twenty or so bloodthirsty goblins hounding for their blood. The goblins had quickly died in the salt water and when the Autumn dragon eventually opened his wings, Rattajack smartly pulled Jonquil down into the deep water, safely clear of the boiling tumult at the surface. The sea dwellers had quickly distinguished the two companions from the hundreds of other struggling bodies, as they were the only creatures swimming down instead of up, and whisked them away from danger. The sea-people realised that, unlike the three huge dragons, Jonquil and Rattajack would never be able to survive the extreme cold of the icy water and that urgent action was needed to protect them before their blood became frozen.

Suddenly, the two companions were dragged violently downwards by the finned swimmers and Jonquil's blurry eyes slowly focused on the terrifying sight of a huge, dark sea-serpent snaking up towards them out of the thick, vibrant kelp. The great beast rose before them and bared two jagged rows of slime stained daggers, Jonquil almost sucked in a lungful of freezing water in his horror and reached quickly for Rattajack, certain that they were to be sacrificed to this snarling monster. Jaws agape, the giant gargoyle lunged forward and the banf screwed up his eyes and waited for the cruel teeth to close on them.

There was no sudden crushing pain, only a violent spinning sensation and the feeling of being pushed sharply aside. Jonquil half opened his eyes, expecting to see the ghastly contents of the serpent's stomach floating around him. Instead the banf was surrounded by an eternal, pale blue mist and long, elegant fin-tailed figures paler than the mist drifted through it; hundreds, if not thousands of them. They weaved through and around each other in graceful, almost mesmeric formations. As each body turned in the water its silvery scales caught the softly diffused glow from above causing the twisting patterns to shimmer with occasional gentle light.

Jonquil found himself kneeling on a cushion of water with Rattajack beside him. He could breathe quite easily and see with perfect clarity through the miles of crystal water. Somehow he and Rattajack were insulated from the biting cold, although his body still ached from the gnawing effect of the freezing water.

A blur of pale skin and dark scales rushed past his eyes as one of the strange creatures whirled around the two companions in dizzy, playful circles. The figure moved so fast about them that it was impossible to focus on the wondrous being and snatch any detail. Eventually the force of the spinning swimmer surging through the water caused Jonquil and Rattajack to start to rotate themselves in slow, disorientating gyrations. It was as the two companions were being rolled over and over in this fashion that Jonquil discovered that the two of them were surrounded by a springy, transparent skin, which yielded to their weight as they were continuously thrown into it. The mischievous creature finally gave up its game and steadily brought them to a halt. A rather dazed Jonquil carefully shifted himself back on to his knees to inspect their uninvited playmate.

A beautiful face, small and round, with pale, silky skin and long flowing hair that shimmered like silver satin, gazed back at him. The angel smiled and joyously rocked her head from side to side, her hair rippling about her face as if in some strange, wafting breeze. Her eyes were the sharpest, clearest green Jonquil had ever seen and they gripped his heart with their intense beauty. The palms of her delicate hands were white as they pressed against the softly yielding skin that separated her from the banf. Jonquil reached out and covered them with his own and for an instant he fancied he could almost feel the trembling rhythm of her heartbeat. Then she turned and drifted away, a delicately finned fish-tail ending in two silken trailing points, following behind her in graceful rhythmic strokes. She glided towards the crowds of the other finned figures, diving and soaring in the hazy blue veil and at once she was engulfed by them and became a part of them.

Jonquil turned to look at Rattajack and met with a most curious expression. The terragon seemed most perplexed with their spherical surroundings and the strange, new creatures that busied themselves so actively in the waters around them. Jonquil had been more than a little distracted by the pretty young mer-maiden but it did not take long before his explorer's mind returned to its usual inquisitive self and started to investigate the wonderful invisible vehicle in which they were being carried along. It seemed that the terrifying sea-serpent which had risen before them with the blood-curdling smile of death on its face had not been attacking them but rushing to their aid. The ingenious mer-folk had instructed the friendly monster to blow forth a ball of air and envelop the two companions in a giant bubble, thus not only allowing the two of them to breathe and be safe from the cold but also affording them excellent views of the ocean. Now Jonquil had another new world to marvel at but this world of shimmering blues and dancing swimmers called to his very soul. The images of its endless, timeless beauty would stay with him and haunt him forever.

The ice which covered the bay was not just a simple lid on the water as it had seemed from above. From far below Jonquil could see that the frozen crust reached down into the depths with an inverted armoury of diamond spears. Great white columns had grown downwards and here and there actually rooted themselves to the very floor of the bay. The myriad schools of sea-people that had now formed themselves into gently undulating processions slowly weaved to and fro through the crystal forest, retracing their paths to the open sea. Three sea-maidens took hold of the giant bubble and carefully guided it into the nearest migrating stream of their people. Jonquil and Rattajack were taken through deep blue ice tunnels, which sometimes climbed steeply as if they might suddenly break the surface, the light building in their jagged walls until it split into hypnotic segments of shimmering frozen rainbows, then they would curve down again disappearing into cavernous wells of violet emptiness. Jonquil liked to imagine that they were passing through the illustrious corridors and great halls of vast submerged palaces, arches and ceilings lit with an almost dazzling, pristine light that seeped down into their finely chiselled contours, superbly decorated with splendid statues and cascading chandeliers. The only subjects of these frozen kingdoms seemed to be occasional clouds of nervous, silvery fish that dashed in and out of the many yawning windows.

The long, swaying stream of mer-folk gradually began to slope away from the surface. For as far as his eyes could see there were hundreds of finned tails, rising and falling in fluent rhythmic waves that rolled towards him like a thin, graceful tide. In some of the other processions, that had now begun to converge on theirs, Jonquil could make out larger shapes swimming with the sea-people. There were great serpent-like beasts such as the one that he and Rattajack had encountered earlier and there were other more dragon-like creatures, who seemed almost to fly through the water with huge paddle shaped limbs. The sea-people seemed to use these large creatures as beasts of burden for they were harnessed with long, trailing sea-vines to capacious conch chariots piled high with the discarded weapons and armour of the enemy collected from the bed of the bay. Even as Jonquil regarded the slow, majestic creatures, more recovered scimitars, spears and shields were brought to them by individual mer-folk and added to the load.

Suddenly the strangest and yet most wonderful sight greeted Jonquil as he gazed out on to the ocean scene. From the opening of an immense ice cavern, almost directly above them a new train of finned figures emerged and supported through the water by an entourage of sea-serpents the three Guardians of the Vessels came forth into the light. Jonquil and Rattajack were overjoyed to see them and craned their necks to watch the progress of the great dragons as they passed overhead. They looked like three huge decadent kings, happy to be carried about by their dwarfed servants. Each dragon was flanked by load-bearing beasts who carried stores of giant conch shells. Dedicated teams of mer-people ferried the air-shells back and forth from the dragons' heads, replacing those that had been exhausted with new ones, freshly filled with air by the bubble blowing sea-serpents. The dragons' column merged with the two companions' and theirs with another, until all the separate streams of sea-people flowed into each other to form one great river.

The great finned army continued to journey downwards and Jonquil was overwhelmed by the sheer depth of water lying beneath the ice. They had been heading for the bed of the bay for some time and yet still there was no sign of the bottom. However as the grand procession swam lower, so the ice seemed to follow, the volume of water around them growing less rather than more. Immense white fingers reached into the pale blue space to try and block their path, thick mists of floating ice crystals drew gossamer veils across familiar openings. Jonquil saw with horror that the sea was actually freezing around them. The sea-people ushered the larger and more robust serpents and water-dragons to the fore and Jonquil could only imagine that the heavy beasts would be used to smash through frozen walls that had formed since the mer-army entered the bay, sometime before. Although their progress never faltered, their journey was steadily becoming more difficult. A barbed wall of ice now surrounded them, allowing only a narrow tunnel of free water ahead. The mer-maidens that had chosen the task of guiding the giant bubble had to gingerly manoeuvre its vulnerable skin around clusters of cruel spikes that invaded the water on all sides. Jonquil dared not think what would happen if just one of those points ruptured their life-giving globe, for there simply would not be enough room for another sea-serpent to rush to save them. The ice tunnel seemed to go on forever and with every flick of a sea-maiden's tail grow ever smaller. Large chunks of broken ice began to float by, doubtless the results of a furious assault by the sea-monsters up ahead. A flurry of sea-people hastily converged on the bubble to become a living shield, pushing the sharp fragments aside or helping to guide the two companions through this dangerous blizzard.

The sea-people escorting the three dragons behind them were having a much harder time of it. The ice tunnel had grown far too small to get the huge guardians through and teams of 'ice-breakers' were attacking the frozen walls to try and wrench away a forward passage. Just as it was beginning to look hopeless, Jonquil suddenly spotted a light at the end of the tunnel and then the tunnel was gone and they found themselves drifting into a vast, endless blue ocean.

The mouth of the bay had all but frozen solid and had they been only a few hours later, the mer-army would have been trapped beneath the ice with no escape. Waiting for them in the open sea was a welcoming party from the sea-kingdom and there was a great rejoicing when all of the mer-people that had ventured into the labyrinth of ice tunnels leading beneath the frozen bay, were counted safely back out again. A great many curious mer-folk gazed in at Jonquil and Rattajack, eager to see just who it was that they had rescued from the enemy and they spun and shoved the bubble one to another in their playful interest.

When everyone was accounted for the great shoal of mer-people and monsters set off through the water once more. The three dragons and the two companions were to be taken to the secret sea-kingdom of King Olm and Queen Sylphen, far beneath the waves, there to rest awhile and contemplate the next step of their long journey.

As the companions' bubble was gently urged through the water, the indescribable beauty of the ocean opened up before them. To Jonquil's amazement he could see hills and valleys, even mountains and vast rolling plains. The bubble passed over thick forests of kelp and bindweed that swayed hypnotically in some secret breeze. Vast, rocky outcrops rose up like warty, green-clad giants standing sentinel over a forbidden land and innumerable swarms of brightly coloured fish scattered across the shiny surface of the sphere like exploding treasure chests, showering the sea with darting gems at its approach. Jonquil wanted to look in all directions at once for fear of missing some new spectacle. A large turtle wafted past towing a cargo of mer-children clasped to its shell. The creature seemed quite indifferent to its passengers and continued undeterred along its way.

A magnificent sea-dragon moved up along side, a crest of weed-like antlers rising at its head and sweeping down the length of its neck, back and tail. It had similar growths fringing the trailing edges of its large paddles and it was coloured with a blue-stained mosaic of greens and ochres that blended perfectly with the dense rafts of drifting seaweed in which it lived. It was not until Jonquil noticed the pale dancing lines of filtered sunlight glancing along the dragon's flanks, as it slipped effortlessly through the water, that he realised that the sea above them was free of the ice.

The mighty column began to follow the progress of a vast chasm that ploughed its way through the sea floor. Ahead of them loomed a twisted mass of rock that seemed to block the end of the meandering trench but as they drew closer they could see that the chasm continued beneath it as a tunnel, the tower of rock merely bridging the entrance. Out of the corner of his eye Jonquil noticed a strong mer-warrior rising from the depths below them carrying one half of a giant clam shell, another mer-male approached from the other side with what seemed to be the missing half. The banf paid little attention to the two figures at first, as there was so much activity coming and going in the waters about them. Then to his dismay the two warriors closed in on the bubble and entombed it with the two giant shells. Jonquil and Rattajack were plunged into darkness and all knowledge of the route they were about to take denied them. The location of the secret sea-kingdom was jealously guarded by the mer-people and they would suffer no strangers, be they friend or foe, to learn of its whereabouts.

When the shells were finally removed, the two companions discovered that they had travelled through the secret walls of the sea-kingdom and now the hidden realm of the mer-folk lay before them, in all its wondrous splendour. Crowning the centre of the ocean realm was a towering structure that at first sight looked like a hastily assembled mound of thousands of giant shells but on closer inspection began to resemble a rambling city that eventually rose into a palace of astonishing proportions.

The kingdom lay in a vast, shallow bowl, hidden from all sides by a wall of dark mountains standing shoulder to shoulder. Dense groves of thick, feathery weed proliferated on the surrounding slopes and valleys and it was within these dark forests that the dreadful sea-monsters dwelled, the ferocious guardians of the secret kingdom.

The grand procession swept towards the high palace and as it did so, schools of excited mer-people emerged from the wide expanse of the city to join them. As they approached the soaring towers of the central dwelling, the twisting construction, encrusted with shells and coral, suddenly erupted into a chorus of brilliant colours as the sun burst through a blanket of smothering clouds and smiled down with all its power and majesty upon the waves. Sunlight entered the ocean as a cathedral of golden pillars and the whole of the kingdom was bathed in its shimmering glory. The mer-folk rejoiced at the coming of the sun and countless shoals of ecstatic finned figures caught hold of each others tails and formed living chains that ascended the radiant columns of light in slow, twisting spirals. Lofty clusters of silvery fish swimming close to the surface, dazzled like distant stars, disappeared and then dazzled again as they weaved in and out of the spreading beams.

Jonquil and Rattajack were guided into an avenue that was screened on both sides by huge fans of living coral, gentle ripples teasing the fronds in the soft subdued currents. Royal mer-warriors carrying iron-reed lances and lavishly marbled scallop shields appeared on either side of the bubble and the three dragons to form a converging guard of honour. Ahead of them the palace loomed and Jonquil could now see that the main body of the building was actually held aloft upon a ring of mighty coral arches; the returning mer-army entered through these columns and rose up into the heart of the awesome structure. Growing directly beneath the palace was a healthy jungle of curly green weed, reaching upwards into the vast circular mouth, in thick, tangled strands. Every trunk of compact foliage glistened with a cloak of intensely packed air bubbles, each one slowly expanding until it lifted from the leaf to join with thousands of its fellows and float up into the hollow building.

The two companions' somewhat larger bubble also began to slowly ascend the wide shaft after entering through the archways, following the long line of finned figures ahead of them. They found themselves inside an immense vertical passage, its circular walls decorated with huge mosaics depicting ancient, heroic mer-folk deeds. Valiant sea-warriors battled amidst the entangled limbs of ferocious tentacled leviathans, their every detail brought sharply to life by a million skilfully carved fragments of brightly coloured shells and corals. As the bubble rose higher, brilliant shoals of exotic fish portrayed with long, extravagant fins of every shape and hue came into view. Mythical sea-maidens, beautifully crafted in long flowing lines graced the next level of decoration, hand in hand they followed each other like mysterious goddesses twisting and spiralling across the face of the wall. At one point a few of the delicately drawn creatures had broken the circle and were gazing upwards, the tallest of them pointing, high above her head. Jonquil followed their gaze and noticed that the rising column of mer-folk above them had disappeared and that before them was an agitated ceiling of water that flickered with diffused light from beyond. Suddenly two dark shapes closed on the bubble from either side and once again the two companions were blind to the world outside.

In their darkness, Jonquil and Rattajack heard a great commotion of falling water as they were hauled from the surface. They felt a mild bump as the giant shells were gently lowered on to a firm base and then finally a crack of light appeared and the two great clams were parted. For a few moments the two companions could see nothing, for the surface of the bubble had become crazed with a riot of swirling feathery patterns. Then abruptly the bubble burst and the two companions found themselves sitting inside one of the clam shells, a great many pale, inquisitive faces arrayed before them, peering with incredulous wonder.

Jonquil suddenly made the most amazing discovery. They were still under the water but no longer in the water and it was cool, sweet air that greeted Jonquil's nostrils when he and Rattajack finally rose to their feet and took long, deep, thankful breaths.

They were standing inside a vast, 'mer-made' chamber, its curved walls rising into a dazzling, domed ceiling far above their heads. The immense star shaped window was formed by the laying together of beautifully patterned slabs of quartz, amber and other stained fragments, making a fantastic kaleidoscope of multicoloured translucent crystals. The shadows of distant mer-folk, swimming above the outer surface of the fabulous dome, were thrown down on to the rippled surface of the dark pool from which Jonquil and Rattajack had just emerged, then drifted across the curved backdrop of the sun-dappled walls, as the finned figures continued on their way.

Thin white beards of water whispered down the bowed planes of chiselled rock and fell into a network of myriad streams and rockpools that surrounded the central well. They were intentional leaks, gushing from the round walls, purposed to create a soothing hush and a comforting breeze within.

A soft cooing sound followed by the sharp clatter of flapping wings, echoed gently from above and drew Jonquil's attention back to the high dome. A small flock of pure white doves circled beneath the crystal roof, returning briefly to their lofty perches only to take wing once more. The banf was at once amazed and delighted at the spectacle of live birds beneath the waves, but then it seemed that no feat was too astonishing for the ever resourceful race of sea-dwellers.

Jonquil noticed that the wide pool of water beside them, was gently fizzing as the rising mist of air bubbles from the vast bog of oxygenating plants below, floated to the surface. The large volume of air manufactured by the prolific weed was then trapped by the dome, creating a giant air-lock in which to receive non water-breathing visitors.

The wide lip of rock which lay around the deep water, was subdivided into a labyrinth of weaving channels and rockpools. These interlocking ponds and waterways now accommodated a growing population of excited mer-folk, who giggled and whispered with one another, not knowing quite what to make of the large eared elf and his funny green dragon.

Suddenly the calm surface of the deep well erupted into a caldron of white water and a great many mer-folk were forced up from below and washed about like flotsam and jetsam in the surging turmoil. A giant green head rose from the frenzy, streams of water gushing down its emerald scales and its horns adorned with garlands of shiny weed. Gorgoyle blew two long salty jets from his nostrils and roared in joy and relief at finding himself able to climb out of the water and breathe freely. The sound of his great voice shook the walls of the surrounding chamber and its monstrous echo assaulted the high vaults like violent thunder. The sea-people covered their ears and cowered behind their rocks in dismay, never before had such a terrifying noise been heard in the kingdom beneath the sea.

Arangast was the next to surface and clambered breathlessly from the watery chasm to stand next to the spring dragon. A storm of showering droplets fell upon the wary spectators as the Summer Guardian shook the sea from his mighty wings. The mer-folk, seeming to take great delight in this torrential downpour, started to laugh and slap their tails on the water in gleeful appreciation.

After casting a cursory glance at Jonquil and Rattajack and satisfying himself of their well being, Arangast turned anxiously back to the water, to await the arrival of the red dragon. Snarlgard finally emerged aided on both sides by teams of sea-serpents. Carefully, with the other Guardians' help, they eased the exhausted Autumn dragon on to the rocks and there he slumped to rest, not even opening his eyes to take the briefest look at his new surroundings.

A conch horn was blown, followed by another and then another, until a loud fanfare filled the whole chamber. The two companions turned and looked in the direction of the noise and saw three mer-heralds reared up beside two huge spiral shells. The magnificent, white shells had been fashioned into spectacular thrones, their final coils rising into extravagant canopies which overlooked their deep hollowed out interiors. Strong, curved spines protruded in wavy fringes from the edges and backs of the thrones, the downward pointing growths having being utilised as splayed out legs. The capacious, sponge lined insides, were kept filled to the brim by carefully channelled waterfalls, which then escaped over the lip of the wide bowl to continue into the great well, ensuring that the water held inside the shell pools was always fresh.

Two distinguished figures reclined in each shell, their finned halves completely submerged in the deep trough of water, save for their long tail fins which hung casually over the front lip. The male figure on the left had a strong, ageless face with a very long and exuberant growth of white hair spilling over his bare muscular shoulders. A princely collar ornamented with precious shells and pearls looped across his broad chest and on his head rose a crown of glistening, rare marine treasures that made him a king. The female figure had a pale, beautiful face framed with the finest shock of silver hair; tiny shells glistening along its length in delicate clusters. An intricate arrangement of pearl studded strands was woven about her arms and body, making her seem to sparkle with a thousand water droplets.

Jonquil gulped when he realised that he and Rattajack had been unintentionally ignoring these quiet, illustrious beings ever since they had been snatched from the rising tunnel of water and landed on the rocks. The two figures did not seem to mind the lack of recognition or courtesy on their guests part, and smiled warmly at Jonquil and the others, patiently waiting for the two companions and the two able dragons to approach.

"I am King Olm, Lord of the Undersea and Lord of the Sea-Warriors," the male figure said.

"I am Queen Sylphen," continued the female. "Mistress of the Undersea and Mistress of the Sea-Maidens. We give you welcome, young wanderer."

Jonquil took a tentative step forward.

"I am Jonquil, your majesties; and if simple gratitude can be payment for such deeds, I thank you and your people for our deliverance from the enemy."

"We ask for no payment, Jonquil," the queen spoke to him, "At this moment in time your enemies and our enemies are the same. And I fear that it is too soon to speak of deliverance. For the enemy is strong and his power grows. Until He is destroyed, there can be no deliverance, only respite."

"You speak wisely, Lady," Arangast's gravelly tones echoed in the hollow

Olm and Sylphen, Lord and Lady of the Undersea.

chamber. The king and queen both looked up into the noble face of the Summer Guardian.

"That is why we beseech you to aid us further." He continued "We must return to our lords at the Forgotten Island."

"Your plight is well known to us, Guardian of Summer," King Olm replied. "The Wizards of Light have bade us spare no effort in assuring your safe arrival. We shall do so."

"But please," the queen added, "Let us speak no more of leaving, for a while at least. You must rest and your poor compatriot must be carefully nursed, I fear the cold water has done little to ease his wounds. We will talk more of your departure later."

The banf and the terragon were shown to giant oyster shells lying amongst the higher rocks, lined with soft dry sponges that made very welcome beds. After the two companions and the three dragons had been left alone for some time to rest, the mer-folk returned with generous quantities of food sent by the Wizards. Snarlgard had to be fed by a team of solicitous attendants, who tenderly persuaded the injured red dragon to accept the nourishing morsels. The Autumn dragon's wounds however, were unfortunately beyond the healing powers of the dedicated schools of swimmers, and the best they could do was to staunch the worst of the injuries with potent kelp poultices. Arangast and Gorgoyle, themselves the recipients of grievous hurts, were very concerned about the frailty of their brother, both of them doubting if Snarlgard would have the strength to survive the next stretch of the journey beneath the waves. Even though the red dragon, in his feeble tones, was adamant that he was not to be left behind, the Spring and Summer dragons feared the consequences of such an exhausting swim.

For the most part the inhabitants of the undersea city were encouraged to stay away from the five visitors residing in the great dome, to provide the weary travellers with much needed rest and seclusion. Occasionally though, small parties of curious mer-folk would rise into the chamber to peek at the small collection of fantastic beasts to whom they were playing hosts. The boldest of the mer-folk would bring food and tokens, or sing to their guests the strange and haunting ballads of the ocean. Songs that once were heard by lonely fishermen cruising the rich waters of the Bay of Voices on long summer evenings, long ago before the ice came, when the world was at peace. They also sang the lovesongs that beautiful, young mer-maidens would sing from the rocks to dashing, young mer-males leaping and diving through the surf. Songs that would never more be heard in the world above the waves until the snows of Winter had been driven from the land.

Jonquil and Rattajack delighted in the songs of the mer-folk, it seemed such a long time since they had heard light and cheery voices raised in sweet melody. The banf and the terragon were entranced by the life in the ocean and during the few days that they spent in the sea dwellers city, made frequent excursions into the submerged realm to explore their fabulous new environment; courtesy of a series of new giant bubbles and eager mer-folk guides.

To their dismay, however, the banf and the terragon could discover no trace of the

Sacred Vessels. When Jonquil discussed this matter with the Summer dragon, Arangast just hung his head and confessed to fearing the worst. He was sure that the three precious chests had been destroyed along with the raft, under the force of his explosive dive. Either way, the Sacred Vessels were certainly lost to the Three Wizards and they would have to calculate their next endeavours without the power of the seasons.

Eventually the light pouring in through the great window of the dome failed once more and the ocean was cast into the darkness of night. The moment had come to journey on.

Jonquil sat with Rattajack on a rock, overlooking the great black well before them. As they stared down into the bottomless pool, strange, eerie lights began to flicker softly in the far inky depths. Gradually they gained strength until the whole of the pool sparkled with clouds of tiny stars, shooting through the water in glistening, excited showers. The stars turned out to be thousands of small fish, each one glowing with a gentle, iridescent blue light; they surged across the surface in burning shoals and filtered into the rockpools as mingling vibrant sparks.

The King and Queen of the Undersea emerged from the pool with a great entourage. They swam over to the two companions and lifted themselves out of the water on to nearby rocks, the remainder of the emergent gathering following their lead.

"The day is ended, Jonquil, and the dark has come," said Queen Sylphen as her beautifully patterned tail fin played idly in the water. "It is time for you to continue on your journey."

"We are ready, Lady," Jonquil answered her.

"From here you will be guided to the surface," the king told them. "The darkness will shield you from the eyes of the enemy. Then you shall be taken to the Wizards as is our promise. I wish we had rare gifts to give you, that might bestow great magical powers to aid you in your quest. Alas I am no sorcerer, just a simple king. Instead we will give you all that we have; our son Moonfin and our daughter Lyretail. They shall not return to us until you are safely delivered to the agents of the Wizards. Therefore I pray for your safe deliverance."

The banf and the terragon thanked the King, each in his own manner. The king spoke forth again.

"Behold our children, Moonfin and Lyretail."

At his cry, a mer-maiden and a mer-male rose from the water, each graced with the handsome bearing of both their parents. Jonquil gasped in joyous surprise.

"It's you!" he cried, as the same young maiden that had teased their bubble so cruelly, after the two companions had been regurgitated by the friendly sea-monster, coyly lowered her head, her pale, smiling cheeks reddening in the soft light.

"Both of my children chose to guide you on this perilous journey," King Olm continued. "With them I send a hundred of my best swimmers."

"Then we travel in the finest of company, my Lord," Jonquil answered sincerely. And with that the two companions and the dragons prepared to depart.

Snarlgard had rallied a little with the intense nursing of his attendants and announced his intention to make the bold swim to the surface. Jonquil and the other dragons tried desperately to dissuade the Autumn Guardian from attempting such a strenuous ordeal in his greatly weakened state, but Snarlgard simply would not be left behind; despite proclaiming his eternal gratitude to his finned helpers and not wishing to cause them any offence.

The two companions were once again furnished with a spacious air bubble and imprisoned inside two giant clam shells, to prevent their knowledge of the secret entrances. The great dragons were provided with the necessary air shells and the next stage of the journey was begun. A greatly reduced procession of swimmers filed out from under the ring of arches beneath the grand dome of the undersea palace, cocooned by milling shoals of brightly glowing fish, illuminating both the varied shapes and colours of the stream of swimming bodies and the path they endeavoured to follow in the blinding gloom.

When the clam shells were removed some time later, Jonquil and Rattajack discovered that they were part of a long, glittering snake, slowly wending its way up to the surface. The mer-folk and the larger creatures rose away from the bubble as a chain of softly painted shapes, undulating through the deepest blue void. The crowds of living lights that surrounded them, never still for a moment.

Rattajack was fascinated by the sparkling shoals that glimmered over the surface of the shiny sphere and the tiny fish themselves seemed equally interested in the relatively bizarre contents of the bubble. Every time the terragon pressed his nose against the cold skin of the bubble, a score of gleaming blue sparks would rush to investigate the strange impression. Only to explode again into a dazzling fountain of shooting lights when Rattajack nudged his nose out even further at the inquisitive fish.

Above the rising column of mer-folk vague shafts of moonlight tried to pierce the interminable blackness but their reach was poor and they flickered weakly with little effect.

Moonfin and Lyretail had decided not to prolong the tiring journey beneath the waves a moment longer than was necessary. Mainly for Snarlgard's sake they had set a course for the surface, as soon as the long procession had emerged from the dark channels that led through the walls of the hidden realm. Despite the fact that there was real danger waiting for them above the waves, the young prince and princess were resolved that this was the best plan.

Snowdragon patrols hunted by moonlight and their eyesight was keen. Great black galleons also sailed the midnight seas, monstrous warships manned by black-clad mariners that patrolled the unfrozen coastal waters, guarding against the attempted return of the Three Wizards.

The surface of the sea was hardly discernible from the rest of the surrounding darkness. If it had not been for the reflection of the glittering clouds of light-fish mirrored in the rippled roof of the ocean, the two companions would not have realised that they had reached the end of their underwater journey.

A lumbering sea-beast with a scallop saddle approached the companion's bubble from beneath. It was carefully manoeuvred through the water until the skin of the delicate sphere just rested within the ribbed curve of the giant shell. Then with an insistent command from Lyretail and a good deal of prodding and cajoling from the accompanying mer-folk, the powerful sea-beast flicked down hard with its tail flippers and surged upwards through the frothy ceiling. With the force of the motion, the bubble was burst and the two companions were neatly caught inside the large saddle and raised above the waves in an eruption of white foam. So skilful had been the manoeuvre, that, to their amazement and delight, banf and the terragon were hardly even damp as they swiftly embraced the brisk ocean breeze; the scallop saddle required a little bailing out of course, but after this was done the two companions huddled together to face the long swim across the southern sea. Dry blankets were miraculously produced from sealed conch containers by the attendant swimmers and given an eager welcome by the shivering banf. Gradually the remainder of the rising procession of dragons and mer-folk broke the surface and the expedition leaders gathered to survey the night sky.

The clouds that had massed during the day to bully the sun were now thinning out, and Moonfin and Lyretail were dismayed to see that 'silver face' was slowly brightening in the sky. The moon, once revered as a friend and a symbol of purity by the sea dwellers, was now despised and cursed as an instrument of the Ice Lord. Vrorst used it as a great lamp, to shine down on the night-time movements of his enemies and expose them to his sharp-eyed flocks of patrolling snowdragons.

The mer-folk leaders would have preferred not to continue the journey on the surface, under a bright, moonlit sky. They had been praying for a thick covering of cloud to eclipse the great eye in the sky. However, because of Snarlgard the mer-folk had no choice, the procession would have to take their chances on the surface. So reluctantly they moved off towards the South, voices kept low and eyes nervously watching the naked sky.

Moonfin and two of his fellows, Silverfin and Swordfin, swam back from the head of the column to confer with Lyretail and her supporters. Not far ahead of the moving line of swimmers, a vast rolling fog-bank was approaching at some speed. The mer-folk were unsure whether it was wise to enter into it, although by its size and swift progress, it seemed doubtful that they would be able to avoid it. Suddenly, a chilling, high pitched shriek far above them in the black, star-spangled sky, made their minds up for them. The cry was the shrill call of a snowdragon and it was probably one of a hunting flight, scanning the glittering sheet of the ocean from the surging upper draughts. The open water was not the place to be when the moon was full and snowdragons were abroad. The dragonriders had trained their terrible, white mounts to swoop out of the darkness and pluck unsuspecting swimmers from the waves and carry them off alive. Lyretail cast an anxious glance at Jonquil and Rattajack and told them to crouch as low as possible in the shallow shell. Then she swam on ahead with her brother to lead the advance into the looming, milky void.

High above him Jonquil thought he saw clusters of stars being repeatedly extinguished by a succession of dark shapes passing beneath them. The pattern that was formed by the menacing silhouettes was a great wheel rotating across the sky, expanding into wider circles as the bloodthirsty creatures spiralled down for the attack.

Arangast, Guardian of Summer rises to the surface.

A stream of monstrous shadows swept over the moonlit waves, darkening the fleeing convoy of swimming creatures. An ear-splitting cry raced towards the procession, the wind clearly audible as it screamed over the dragon's outspread wings. The lines of mer-folk suddenly up ended and disappeared beneath the surface as the draught of a mighty swoop flattened the water where they had just been. The brave sea-beast carrying the two companions ploughed on ahead regardless of the attack. It knew it may not dive, for fear of losing its charges in the black, icy water. The approaching fog was their only chance, so the mighty animal heaved its way forward through the water, with unwavering determination. Another snowdragon fell into a murderous sweep over the shimmering sheet, its draught lifting the crests from the waves in its wake. In the distance, the large sea-beast bearing down upon the surging fog bank, with the scallop saddle lurching wildly on its back, drew the attention of the white killer's rider and the dragon's hooked talons reached forward to strike.

The approaching roar of the snowdragon's wind-lashed wings made the two companions flatten themselves even further against the bottom of the shell. They pushed their limbs hard against the sloping sides of the scallop until the banf's and the terragon's two bodies were locked tightly back to back. Suddenly the bone-jarring meeting of talons and shell, wrenched the saddle from its sea-vine harness and for a few moments the giant scallop, containing the two companions, was carried off over the waves, clamped in the snowdragon's grip. But the terrifying journey did not last long, for the dragon soon lost its hold on the heavy, slippery shell, and the scallop slapped back down into the sea, skimming across the water in a violent spin. The surrounding waves hissed in protest as the huge wings of the hovering snowdragon beat a hurricane against them. The great white monster hung in the air, poised malevolently over the rotating shell, waiting for the tiny coracle to settle before dropping down to pluck out its prizes and whisk them away.

Fortunately, Lyretail and a team of other quick thinking mer-maidens, launched a strenuous assault on the underside of the floating scallop, and just before the snowdragon could snatch either the banf or the terragon in its claws, the shell was suddenly flipped over and the two companions tipped into the water. The furious white dragon seized the upturned 'boat' and crushed it into a shower of fragments between its four sets of talons, but by then Jonquil and Rattajack had been dragged beneath the safety of the waves and were gone. The snowdragon squealed in rage at its loss and plunged its rear legs deep into the water to try and grasp one of its escaping prey. Then with a tremendous explosion of sea water, the magnificent beast from whose back the companions had been so rudely removed, launched itself from the waves like an erupting tower of rock and fell upon the astonished white creature. The shrieking snowdragon desperately flapped away over the foam to try and escape its fate but the awesome cavernous gape of the sea-monster closed on the snowhawk's neck and with the irresistible force born of its sheer size and strength ploughed the flailing dragon beneath the waves. Neither dragon or dragonrider were to return to the surface.

Gradually the excellent vision of the attacking snowdragons was obscured by the first veils of the spreading blanket of fog. The captain of the dragonflight reluctantly called off the assault and secretly cursed the name of his master for not keeping the ocean free from such battle hindering obstructions. The blood-chilling cry of the snowdragons was not heard again by the fleeing columns of swimmers.

Inside the belly of the fog-bank, all was deathly quiet. Silence oozed from the thick air like slow, black breath. No sounds except the endless slapping of the waves against the flanks of the sea beast came to the sensitive ears of the two companions, who had once again been installed upon the valiant creature's back. It felt as though, once more, they had been cocooned inside a giant bubble and that the walls of the fog were pressing hard against its surface trying to crush them. Occasionally a dull splash would sound nearby as one of the mer-folk dived beneath the surface to escape the blinding mist. At least with the aid of the light-fish the swimmers could keep a check on their bearings from below and stop the procession from drifting too far astray, not that the convoy was moving anywhere at that moment. The sea-beast carrying Jonquil and Rattajack was idly rotating its huge flippers through the water, just to hold its position in the line. Eventually the train of dragons and sea dwellers started off again through the blindness of the fog, the mer-folk having finally decided on the correct course.

After what seemed like hours of aimless drifting, a dull clang sounded out in the black void ahead of them. Jonquil strained his ears in the direction from which he thought it emanated and waited for a repeat. A similar ringing noise sounded elsewhere, although of a slightly deeper tone. The first note came again and this time a little louder. Whatever it was that was making the strange sounds, that seemed to carry with a haunting echo in the thick air, it was moving slowly in their direction. The deeper sound was struck again but this time it seemed fainter, as though the source of the second tone was moving away.

There was renewed excitement in the water. The mer-folk were converging on the sea-beast and urging it forward as though they had all been possessed with a new purpose. The original clanging sound rang out loudly close by and then a chorus of anxious voices tried to raise urgent messages through the gloom, their words marred by a great commotion in the water. As Jonquil squinted ahead, trying to make some sense out of the disembodied voices and sounds filtering through the dark void, a huge black shape suddenly loomed out of the mist before them.

The great shadow towered over the two companions and their sea-monster like a drifting mountain, huge black sails hanging idly from the arms of three masts that soared beyond sight into the fog. The side of the vessel bristled with ranks of long oars pawing gently at the water. Tiny lights shone weakly into the gloom along its length, each one framed with a misty halo. Some of the lamps were held by dark figures moving up and down the deck, occasionally leaning out over the side to try and catch sight of the crowds of bodies swimming around them in the water.

The activity in the waves beside Jonquil and Rattajack had built into a frenzy. There were scores of finned figures leaping and thrashing in the water, diving this way and that in either excitement or panic. Jonquil was not sure whether the mer-folk were trying to swim towards the ship or away from it. The whole scene was boiling with desperate confusion.

The banf stared in awe at the magnificent silhouette of the black galleon as it slowly drifted past. He could see no recognisable insignia flying from its rigging and wondered at the nature of those who sailed it.

The mer-folk were desperately trying to turn the sea monster away from the approaching oars but it seemed unable or unwilling to understand, as if it was being held by some unseen force. At last, in utter bewilderment, it shook itself free from all influences, including those of the shouting mer-folk, arched its long body and dived beneath the surface.

The hasty departure of their great steed resulted in Jonquil and Rattajack being ditched yet again into the cold, black sea. But no sooner had their tumbling bodies splashed into the freezing water than they were scooped up inside a large drag net and hoisted from the violent foam like a prize catch. After they had been landed on the deck of the galleon and the tightly drawn ropes of the net loosened, the banf and the terragon spilled out on to the wooden boards of the dark ship.

The circle of dark mariners that crouched over them were tall, broad shouldered figures, clad entirely in black garments. Even their heads were bound in long lengths of twisted material, only a narrow eye-slit left unmasked. Jonquil and Rattajack were briskly lifted to their feet and turned to face into a lantern held before them. A short distance away along the deck, a tall, cloaked figure stepped out from the shadows into a pool of light cast by a gently swinging lamp, the character's face hidden by a deep cowl. The figure studied the two companions for a few moments and then spoke to the sailors in soft, female tones.

"It is them. Take them below quickly."

The banf and the terragon were grasped firmly by strong, insistent hands and marched hastily but not too roughly towards a small door leading to the lower decks. As he was moved along, Jonquil tried to peer over the side of the ship to look for Lyretail or any of her people, but he could see nothing save twisting plumes of fog drifting through the circles of lamp-light. However, just before the two companions were bungled inside the doorway, the banf thought he heard a plaintive mermaid voice carried high in the still air from somewhere out in the sea.

"May your ocean be kind to you, Jonquil," it cried. "Remember us!"

Then the door was closed behind the two companions and before they started off down a narrow passageway, they heard the ominous sound of a key being turned in the lock. As their burly guards ushered them down a steep flight of oak stairs and along another short, shadow-laden passage, pangs of foreboding stabbed inside Jonquil's stomach and he wondered why he and Rattajack had been delivered into the hands of the enemy.

At last they emerged into a dimly lit but surprisingly warm and spacious cabin. There were no windows or portholes and with a large door reinforced by a heavy iron frame, the room was obviously meant to be secure. The black mariners did not stay to help the two companions admire their new lodgings. As soon as their charges were safely installed they turned and left, locking the door behind them.

In a far corner, they could just make out a squat, pot-bellied shape standing on four shallow legs. It was a small stove grinning at them with glowing red teeth and quietly manufacturing a haze of warmth to heat the room. Standing nearby was a low clothes horse upon which a change of dry clothes had been neatly hung. Jonquil stood shivering in the semi-darkness, dripping into a pool of sea water lying around his feet. The dry clothes were obviously far too small for any of the heavily built mariners that they had seen. It occurred to the banf that the change of garments might have been put there for him, almost as if he had been expected. Rattajack gave his companion a firm nudge in the direction of the stove. The terragon could see no sense in waiting for pneumonia to set in. Jonquil examined the dry garments. They were made of a soft, warm fabric, decorated around the collar and the cuffs with a subtle floral pattern that made his own dishevelled banf clothes seem very crude and rough.

"I'll l'look like a p'prince in these, R'Ratters," he said appreciatively. The terragon answered him with an impatient whine that seemed to say;

"Yes, providing you don't catch your death in those freezing rags first. Get them off!"

Eventually the sodden clothes were discarded and after a brisk rub down and warm by the stove, the new ones were taken from the rail. It seemed unlikely that their mystery captors intended to kill the two of them, after providing the banf with a change of clothes. But who were the black mariners? And where were they taking them?

A loud crunching sound echoed through the bare cabin as the key was turned once more in the lock and the heavy door swung open. Jonquil and Rattajack turned in trepidation to watch the tall, cloaked female enter the dim room.

She carried a large lantern which bestowed considerably more light than the gentle glow from the squatting stove. But despite this improved illumination her face was still shrouded in shadow. She hesitated for a moment in the doorway as if to be sure of the two companions location in the room and then slowly locked the heavy door behind her.

The banf and the terragon shuffled a little closer to one another, hardly daring to think what horror might lurk inside the hooded disguise. The dark shape moved slowly across the room to place the lamp on a solitary table, and then the hole of darkness that masked her face turned to gaze upon the two companions. Despite the generous warmth of the stove at their backs, Jonquil and Rattajack's fear of this unknown person caused a rash of goose pimples to parade across their skin.

Suddenly with a dramatic flurry, the female swept the cloak from her body and threw it to the floor, a shudder of disgust rising within her as the black wrapping slipped through her fingers. The lady's relief at being free from the loathed garment was quite plain.

She stood and faced the two companions and Jonquil was immediately stunned by her loveliness. A most kind and compassionate smile enveloped a fine and graceful countenance, dark hazel eyes searching deeply into theirs. Vibrant coils of auburn hair spilled out over her shoulders, to lie in long, copper ringlets upon a splendid gown that swept down to the floor in luxuriant scarlet folds. The front of the robe was graced with an ornate belt, that dropped almost to the hem, exquisitely embossed with gold scrolls. Sparkling like red fire halfway along its length was a leaf shaped power crystal, sparks of light exploding within it as the lady stepped towards them.

"Be not afraid," she calmed them. "We mean you no harm."
At first Jonquil could barely croak in response but at last a comprehensible string of words formed upon his lips.
"Who..who are you, Lady?" he gasped.
The vision of colour and beauty smiled and slowly lifted her arms in presentation.
"I am Quillion. High Witch of Autumn."

The Haven of the Wizards

Orolan, Lord of Summer, sat within the splendour of his high tower, and smiled warmly at the banf and the terragon.

"So..." The Summer Wizard began. "You come to us at last. When finally you return home, you will have a saga to tell, worthy of many, long, firelit nights."

Jonquil smiled a little uneasily; home seemed very far away, both in time and distance.

Orolan spoke again.

"We cannot tell you, Jonquil, how pleased we are to see you safely here, and you too of course, Rattajack, my friend."

Jonquil reached out to his beloved companion and squeezed his ear. Rattajack's eyes blazed with attentive delight.

"You bring tidings of great sadness," the Summer Wizard continued. "Evil deeds rage unabated in our beloved Enchantica. The hordes of the enemy have grown strong indeed. Fast draws nigh the time when we must show our hand. We have delayed too long as it is.

But there is also a mysterious spark of hope in your words. All that you have said about your homeland, this intriguing Kingdom of the Banfs. We will speak more of this, at length, when you have rested. It interests us greatly."

Jonquil and Rattajack left the illustrious company of the Lord of Summer and were ushered to their quarters by Carobus, one of the high wizards in service to the great lords, who had greeted them as they came ashore at the island harbour. Countless other attendants trotted in and out of their sumptuous lodgings, feverishly attending to their every need; indeed, it seemed to Jonquil that the servants outnumbered the tasks they sought to carry out by at least ten to one. Whenever one of the witches, fairies, elves, lesser wizards, ladies or gentlemen managed to prise a request out of the banf, for either himself or for Rattajack, five or six of them would almost race each other to try and fulfil it, but the competition was at all times good natured and Jonquil was amused at how gracious and polite the servants were to each other, for even the slightest accident or trespass.

The room that had been prepared for them afforded much comfort. It was situated in one of the many towers that crowned the breathtaking spread of the Wizards' palace. Instead of windows, all of the round tower rooms had open archways that led out on to wide balconies, providing wondrous views of the whole island.

As Jonquil lay down to rest upon a soft bed of cushions, his mind recounted the excitement of the last few hours. He was tired but the endless array of bright images that flickered against his closed eyelids, prohibited sleep. His tree-clogged mind needed time to digest this latest new world, the world that he had tried to imagine when his innocent, woodland eyes had first fallen on the fabulous spectacle of the Summer Vessel.

Now he was here, residing in the home of the mighty Wizards, amongst the architects of that miracle. The banf was sharing the island with people that could build huge galleons to sail across the oceans, create vast cities that rose like pillared mountains into the sky. Even the clothes they wore escaped his comprehension; they were so beautiful, so finely made. Not the brightest woodland flowers or berries could match their intensity. The skilfully sculptured folds and drapes would shame the plumage of the proudest forest pheasant, prancing through the bracken in his breeding finery. Jonquil's drifting thoughts began to relive his arrival at the fabulous island.

The Autumn Witch and the two companions had stood together in the bows of the black galleon, as it finally reached safe waters and broke free of the clinging grey mantle that had shrouded them for so long. They had looked out onto a wide open sea that rolled out to meet the horizon beneath a clear sapphire sky. Jonquil turned to watch the other ships of their small fleet, previously unknown to him, emerge from the drifting cocoon and greet the glorious sun.

The water was alive with mer-folk, revelling in the sunlit waves, shoals of them leaping and diving through the plumes of spray thrown up by the ship's bows as it sliced through the crystal waters.

Jonquil looked for Lyretail or Moonfin but the finned figures were moving too swiftly for recognition; he hoped they were safe.

The banf's ship let off a rocket that screamed far into the sky above them, drawing a thin white line on the air. Eventually it reached its zenith and with a loud crack became a bright star that curved lazily towards the water. The banf could not be sure, but he fancied he saw a tiny spark far away on the horizon follow a similar path. The captain of the ship, at least, seemed satisfied that their signal had been approved and that it was safe to continue.

As the galleons drew near to the island, the mariners hurled lengthy tow ropes out to a fleet of longboats, bristling with teams of oarsmen who waited to heave the large ships to the quayside. The harbour was situated inside a wide, cliff lined bay, whose twin promontories seemed to reach out into the water with a deep, scooping embrace. At its heart, nestling precariously amongst the sloping rock was an intense cluster of white walled houses, climbing up and over each other in a not unattractive crooked manner. The small harbour settlement reminded Jonquil of some of the mushroom villages in his homeland, the fungal houses seeming to almost fight each other for space as they rose through the twisted aerial roots of an ancient Green oak. A small crowd had gathered on the quayside to welcome the new visitors. The Autumn Witch led the banf and the terragon from the black galleon and presented them to Carobus, High Wizard of Summer. He then formally welcomed them in the name of the Three Lords of the Seasons and escorted them to a gaily-coloured open carriage.

With a rapturous cheer from the collection of islanders, Carobus drove the two companions and Quillion away from the harbour and across the sun-drenched island to the City of the Wizards. As they journeyed from the bay, Jonquil and Rattajack could hardly believe the sweeping landscape of lush vegetation that passed by them.

Exquisite fauna and flora proliferated in the wooded glades and emerald plains. The air was thick with honey-seeking insects and sweet throated birds, all enjoying the full unspoiled splendour of the Summer sunshine.

The City of the Wizards was dominated by the great palace itself, towering over the surrounding architecture like a jostling collection of vast cathedrals. Brightly coloured domes, spires and minarets shone with unequalled brilliance in the radiant light. Great rashes of verdant forest flourished within the fabric of the city, climbing over the peaks and ridges of the walls and buildings; providing natural homes for the many races of tree-dwellers who were counted amongst the Wizards' faithful.

The horse-drawn carriage drove through the main gates, which had been skilfully wrought into the shape of a giant Enchantica Rose, and along miles of twisting roads and tree lined avenues that eventually led to the main structure of the palace. Jonquil and Rattajack delighted in observing that in every possible nook or cranny, along the way, a tree or shrub had either been planted or allowed to grow. Every wall and building of the city dripped with thick beards of foliage or flowers. Every road or concourse ran beneath a tunnel of arched tree canopies. The spread of rising architecture was swathed in a living green mantle, making the mountain of spectacular buildings appear to have grown from the soil of the island, rather than having been purposely built upon it.

Passing through a heavily carved archway, the carriage entered a wide courtyard, bathed in the full glory of the sun. A thickly grown assortment of exotic fruit trees bordered the walls, all in various stages of their cycles, some in spring blossom, some in full summer foliage and others borne down with the weight of heavy fruit.

High wooden doors opened at their approach from another archway leading from the square and in front of this entrance the horses were brought to a halt.

"Come, my friends." Quillion spoke to the banf and the terragon. "The Lord Waxifrade awaits us."

Jonquil and Rattajack stepped down from the carriage in silent compliance, not quite knowing whether to be honoured or fearful of such a high meeting.

A short, open corridor led to another arched doorway, that opened into the main building. Then followed a series of long passageways and brightly tiled cloisters which worked their way into the very heart of the palace. The inner chambers and walkways bustled with the activities of the Wizards supporters. Groups of lesser wizards strolled by, discussing the finer points of some magical theorem. Parties of elves walked beside Lords of Men, or lesser witches, each brightly clothed individual busy with his or her own vital purpose. All of the inhabitants broke from their private thoughts to acknowledge the Autumn Witch and to greet the two companions. Quillion returned their greetings and seemed to know every one of them by name.

At last they arrived at the tower of the Autumn Wizard. A spiral stairway led to an oak door emblazoned with gold, bronze and copper leaves, sweeping across the grain in a tumbling, wind-blown design. This entrance opened into a large ante-room which took them to the mighty threshold of the Wizard's chamber itself. Extravagant mosaics of bloodstars, rubies, topazes and sun-diamonds, glittered in a chorus of Autumn shades as the jewel encrusted doors silently swung inwards at their approach. Seated on a huge throne of gnarled, twisted trunks that might have grown from the centre of a huge leaf design, fashioned in coloured tiles on the floor, was a kindly, white haired old man. He was dressed in breathtaking robes of scarlet, gold and purple, that spilled on to the floor before him in luxuriant shimmering folds. It was Waxifrade, Lord of Autumn.

He gestured for them to enter and the High Witch and the two companions stepped into the spacious, circular chamber that opened onto a wide balcony through a ring of splendid arches.

Quillion placed a gentle hand on Jonquil's shoulder and guided the banf and the terragon forward; the Autumn Wizard smiled as his two visitors drew nearer.

"Welcome," he said softly to them. "And thankyou."

Following the impressive architecture, the inspiring galleons and the enchanted climate, Jonquil had expected the great overlord of Autumn to be both spectacular and terrible. A magnificent but fearful figure that raged like an angry god, forcing his minions to their knees by the sheer radiance of his presence. Much to the banf's relief however, Waxifrade was none of these. He sat, slightly hunched, perceptive hazel eyes peering out from beneath the shaggiest white eyebrows, the remainder of his face obscured by a full, snowy beard, simply smiling at them.

His disposition appeared to be one of gentleness not importance, kindness not splendour. Like a friendly old grandfather on a rather good pension.

Jonquil's former trepidation dissolved and he smiled back at the wizard.

Waxifrade rose from his throne and turned to lead the two companions out on to the wide balcony that ringed the tower. As he walked away, Jonquil was amazed at the length of the Autumn Wizard's hair, which snaked down the back of his exquisitely embroidered robe in a long extravagant plait. The Wizard looked back to see if the banf and the terragon were following, and smiled at the expression of wonder that had been permanently fixed to Jonquil's face ever since he had first stepped on to the fantastic island. The first question that Waxifrade put to the banf caused his eyes to grow even wider.

"Tell me, Jonquil," the Autumn Wizard began. "Whatever happened to your wings?"

Before long the banf and the Wizard were engaged in a passionate discourse on the finer qualities of life in the Green Sky Forest; a subject with which Waxifrade seemed to have a particular sympathy. Jonquil discovered that the Autumn Wizard knew nothing of his people, and had thought the banf to be an entirely different being altogether. The Autumn Wizard had been both alarmed and intrigued to discover that an entire race of people had been overlooked by the old lists and begged Jonquil to tell him all about the remarkable mushroom dwellers and their hitherto unknown kingdom within the Great Forest.

After Waxifrade came an audience with Fantazar, Lord of Spring. This meeting was frank and exciting. The Spring Wizard, though not unkindly, dispensed with the more gentle niceties of his Autumn brother and quizzed Jonquil relentlessly about his adventure since leaving his home. The Spring Wizard had a boisterous sense of humour and made Jonquil laugh more heartily than he had done for a very long time, but always the conversation returned to the Kingdom of the Banfs. All three wizards simply could not hear enough about this newly discovered people. However, Jonquil was to find that one question haunted him wherever he went;

"Where are your wings?"

Jonquil came before Orolan, Lord of Summer last of all. Clothed in shimmering robes of gold and staring authoritatively at the banf from a living throne of wild flowers. The Summer Wizard exuded an aura of quiet strength, an air of authority, not higher but a little more commanding than that of his brothers. He greeted Jonquil warmly and asked him many questions. He seemed to learn far more from the banf's answers than the vague fragments of information they appeared to contain. The Summer Wizard also took a great deal of interest in Rattajack, regarding him as something of a phenomenon.

"But you have dragons here," Jonquil told him. "I have seen them."

"Not like Rattajack, my friend," Orolan answered him. "His like we have known only from drawings and vague descriptions, contained in the oldest manuscripts. You call this fine fellow a terragon; in our ancient writings, they are known as 'arven'."

"Arven," echoed Jonquil and the name teased his thoughts until a beam of recognition flashed across his face.

"Arvana!" the banf exclaimed.

"This name is familiar to you?" Orolan asked him.

"Arvana, the mother of all terragons. It is one of the oldest stories in the Banf Kingdom. How Arvana, mother of all terragons, came to the Green Sky forest to live with the mushroom dwellers. I thought it was just an old banf's tale."

The Summer Wizard made no reply but smiled thoughtfully at Jonquil for a few long moments. Jonquil was amazed at the degree of interest he and Rattajack had created amongst such illustrious beings. He had always thought the banf kingdom and its inhabitants to be such an ordinary, even boring place. Jonquil would never look upon it in the same light again. That is if he ever managed to return there.

Jonquil also learned from the Lord of Summer, much to his relief, that Snarlgard and the other two Guardians had arrived safely at the Island, and were now being attended to by the Wizards' healers. Orolan regretted that for the time being, a visit was out of the question. All three dragons had been seriously maimed by the enemy and needed absolute rest and quiet in the ensuing weeks, in order to achieve a complete recovery. The Autumn dragon had been close to death, when he had been reverently lifted from the black galleon, that had rescued him. The banf resolved that as soon as they were allowed, he and Rattajack would pay their respects to the three noble dragon princes.

Orolan told the banf that they would speak again, in more detail, of the fate of the world, after he and Rattajack had rested and so they bowed respectfully and took their leave.

Jonquil lay fully stretched on the soft cushions, having brought his thoughts fully up to date. His whole body was bathed in a warm beam of afternoon sunlight, that

Waxifrade, Lord of Autumn and the Lady Quillion.

seeped into the banf's bones and wrapped him in a delicious sleeve of warmth. A chorus of small finches chirruped and squabbled with each other as a piece of bread was chased relentlessly between the pillars of the room, then away across the rooftops.

Of all three seasons, it was Summer that ruled over the Forgotten Island and the air smelt warm and alive. Muted voices from far below mingled with the gentle hum of insects attending to the blooms of the immense cascades of flowering vines that thrived in the tropical climate. The endless throb of the hypnotic sounds conspired to lull all the strength from the banf's sun-drenched body, until it drowned in sleep.

Jonquil finally conceded and when his eyes opened again the city was in darkness.

Diligent attendants had noiselessly brought oil lamps to light the room, whilst the two companions slept. Rattajack had awakened of course but not revealed it to their hosts, lest they should accuse themselves unnecessarily of clumsiness or ineptitude.

Jonquil strolled lethargically out on to the balcony, wrestling with an all encompassing yawn. Rattajack trotted out after him. The two of them stood side by side surveying the darkened city. Clusters of lights spotted the great pool of blackness below them. Music, bursts of laughter, songs and merry voices echoed inside unseen courtyards, streets and avenues. Lights burned in the other towers around them and shadowy figures could be seen on the balconies, promenading in the warm evening air. Above it all, the great cloudless dome of the heavens shone with a full compliment of starlight; clear and proud.

The banf turned to look at his companion. Even in the subdued light from the oil lamps, the terragon's eyes shone with a brilliant intensity. Jonquil stroked his chin and stared deep into the iridescent orbs.

"Home, Ratters," he whispered. "I never thought I would miss it so much."

The terragon bowed his head as if to sympathise.

"The Wizards' Palace. This great city. It is better than I ever dreamed it would be. But all that talk of the White Ring and our people, has made me very homesick. Right now, I would give anything to walk under a roof of Green oak branches and feel the crunch of forest leaves beneath my feet."

Rattajack's head tilted to one side and a large amber eye fixed him with its full gaze.

"I wonder how Snarlgard is?" the banf mused, suddenly a mischievous smile broke across his face.

"Come on," he laughed. "Let's explore!"

The corridors and courtyards through which the two companions meandered, after descending from their tower, were all but deserted. Eventually they found themselves in a long, dimly lit passage, containing many doors that disappeared into darkness ahead of them. Suddenly, a heavy oak door flew open and a short, fat, grey haired old character, dressed in extravagant costume, stomped out into the corridor. He wore a belted coat of brilliant green and gold, green pantaloons and knee length hose of the brightest purple. His balding, white haired, head was framed by a wide collar of rich lace. He was clearly in far too much of a hurry to notice the two companions, and stumbled blindly on in front of them.

His arms were heavily laden with bundles of material, paper scrolls, reels of thread, yardsticks, dividers, half-made garments and a variety of other encumbrances; all balanced on top of each other and anchored beneath his chin. The little old man growled and cursed as he staggered along the corridor, not at all in keeping with the gracious disposition of the rest of the population. Or at least, he would have cursed, if his jaws had not been jammed shut with the volume of items crammed underneath them.

Ribbons and brocades flowed out behind him like streamers in the draught he made, and bobbins and thread reels clattered to the tiles as he charged on ahead regardless. A yardstick dropped awkwardly between his knees almost legging him over, but ever onward he blustered, spitting yet more curses through clenched teeth as another pile of objects tumbled to the floor.

Jonquil called after him, hardly able to stifle his amusement at this hilarious spectacle. And the two companions followed in the short character's wake, retrieving all the debris that he had furiously abandoned.

Four doors further on, the funny old man came to a halt and tried to lift the heavy catch with his nearest elbow. Jonquil could see that the little man's wobbling load was liable to topple to the floor at any moment, so immediately leapt to his rescue.

"Allow me," he offered to the old man and swiftly pushed the door open.

The little old man squinted at Jonquil for a few moments, a twinge of puzzlement furrowing his brow, then he muttered a hasty 'thankyou' and plodded into a small candlelit room. Jonquil and Rattajack followed him a little way in, deposited the various items they had rescued and turned to leave. A chirpy voice stopped them in their tracks.

"Don't go!" the old man cried. "I am just about to take supper. Share some with me. You are the ones from the black galleons, aren't you? Yes, yes I thought you were. Come in! Come in!"

Jonquil peered in at the old man from the doorway; Rattajack peering around Jonquil.

"How do you know about us?" the banf asked.

"How do I know?" the old man repeated. "I have ears, haven't I? The whole city is talking about you. What news! What news! The windsprite who's lost his wings. What news!"

Suddenly curiosity got the better of the banf and he hurried into the room.

"What did you call me?" he cried.

The old man squinted at him once again and then repeated, quite matter of factly. "A windsprite, isn't it?"

"What's a windsprite?" Jonquil asked in wonder.

"Search me," the old man replied. "I'm just repeating what I've heard. I wouldn't know a windsprite from a windmill! But then, I don't get out all that much, do I? Not with the amount of work that's piled on to me, day in, day out!"

For a moment, the old man's expression returned to the one that had been perched on top of his bundle in the corridor, but then a lighter face replaced it.

"Sit down," he urged. "Both of you. By the globe. I'll fetch some 'swill'."

The old man disappeared through a small archway leading to another room, shrouded in darkness. The chink of stoneware flagons and the swish of liquids could be heard and the old man, after groping about in the other chamber, stubbing his toes at least twice and cursing about it profoundly, assured his guests that his return was imminent.

Jonquil and Rattajack did as they were bid and settled themselves by a large glass globe, mounted on an ornate bronze stand. A marbled whirlpool of amber light, wheeled within it, in twisting mesmeric circles.

The room itself appeared to be a workshop of some kind, all the available space on the walls having been consumed by a riot of shelves and cupboards, from floor to ceiling. The shelves bowed visibly with the weight of the items they contained and scraps of material and paper poked out of drawers that were clearly stuffed too full to close. Unravelled ribbons dripped down the shelves in colourful coils and rolls of brightly dyed fabric, poised precariously on climbing stacks of badly placed boxes; only dusty cobwebs to hold them in place. The two companions cowered beneath this sleeping avalanche and Jonquil could not help thinking that one good sneeze in the right place would bring the whole inventory crashing down upon their heads.

Next to the far wall there was a long table, with strange shapes cut from yellowed paper, pinned to a wide length of shimmering verdant cloth. Beyond that there was what looked like a window, but there were so many thick, dust-laden books piled up in front of it, that it was hard to tell.

With a clunk and a stumble, the old man reappeared in the archway. He dragged a padded-backed stool close to the two companions with his toe and dumped two large stoneware bottles in front of the globe. With a cheeky smile he turned to them and chuckled;

"My supper!"

To Jonquil's horror the little old man then began to rummage through one of the cupboards supporting a wall full of daringly stacked heavy boxes, heaving large books aside with never a care. The precarious loads shook ominously as the frantic search continued, tiny waterfalls of dust cascading from above. Naturally a volley of frustrated curses accompanied the old man's quest.

"Where are they?" he grumbled. "I don't know! After 'she' has tidied up in here, even a simple drinking cup is harder to find than the Cloak of Xanthia!"

Suddenly something substantial dropped from on high and clattered at the old man's feet.

"Ah, there's one of them," he sighed. Picking up the small wooden bowl from the floor. "How in the Wizards' names did that get up there? Humph! I expect 'she' put it away! Ah! And there are the other two."

In a trice the three bowls had been filled to the brim, with the ale that the little old man affectionately called 'swill' and swiftly offered to his two guests.

"Bottoms up!" he hailed and before the banf and the terragon had even had time to sniff their helping, the old man was already pouring out his second.

"Yim!" he cried and up went the bowl again.

"Yim!" Jonquil repeated, assuming it to be some form of drinking salute, and took his first sip of ale.

The old man stared at him, his expression a little perplexed.

"No, that's me," he said "I am Yim."

Jonquil smiled weakly in apology, not yet having summoned the courage to swallow. Then finally the foul brew slipped home.

"My name is Jooooossshhaaa!!" Jonquil gasped and proceeded to have a near convulsion as the vile liquid assaulted his throat.

Yim chuckled a little, with a knowing grin playing on his lips.

"Yes. It does have a bit of a slap to it when you're not looking. You'll soon get the hang of it. Have no fear." And another bowlful spilled from the bottle.

Jonquil felt a desperate need to change the subject. He was sure his stomach would turn inside out if he subjected it to another dose of Yim's swill. The banf could not remember ever tasting anything so bitter or grim. He was sure that stagnant ditchwater must have a kinder flavour. Mercifully, the old man seemed far more interested in the contents of his own bowl than the contents of Jonquil's, and was quite conscientious in the task of keeping it full.

The banf stole a glance at Rattajack. The terragon had proceeded no further than a sniff at the foul brew and gave Jonquil a look as if to say, "You ought to know better!"

Jonquil turned back to Yim.

"What is that?" the banf asked, referring to the glowing orb.

"Eh?" Yim grunted "Oh that! The globe. A gift from the Wizards themselves, no less. A mere token of their esteem," he preened, wafting his fingers through the air in a nonchalant, almost dismissive gesture.

"Have you ever seen one before?" Yim inquired of the banf.

"No, never." Jonquil replied.

"Well," the little old man began. "It's a mood-globe. Its colours respond to my feelings. It's a wonderful thing. Better than a log-fire for day-dreaming into. When I'm happy, it glows yellow and if I'm feeling absolutely over the moon, it erupts into fountains of white stars! Needless to say that doesn't happen very often.

When I'm angry, it's red. When I'm sad, it's blue. When I need to think, to meditate, it flows with peaceful waves of green."

Yim paused to give a short mime of what he looked like when in peaceful thought. His hands spoke volumes. Then his attention returned to the globe.

"I appear to be orange at the moment," he observed. "Well, there's a thing!"

Jonquil's eyes eagerly scanned the room.

"What do you make in here?" He asked the old man.

"Humph! A royal mess according to some, if you would listen!" the old man giggled. Then he straightened himself somewhat and pushed his nose into the air.

"I am the official robe designer to the Wizards, my dear Josha."

"Pardon?"

"Designer! Yes! Exclusive costumier to the High Lords of the Seasons! And try saying that when you've had four bowls of swill and are about to sink your fifth."

And true to his word, he did.

"You make the Wizards' robes?" Jonquil asked in astonishment.

"Every stitch!"

"But they are wonderful!" the banf exclaimed.

"Thankyou." Yim smiled, a little too widely. "Do you know, I spent four months on the Lord of Summer's robes. Four months!"

Jonquil was suitably impressed.

"I sewed over three hundred flagondries on it!" the old man declared.

The banf bravely suppressed a snigger.

"You are very clever, Yim." he said.

The old man boldly thanked Jonquil again.

"It is nice to know that someone appreciates my art," he began "Oh, don't misunderstand me. I will say nothing against the Wizards. They are most gracious towards me, most kind. But there are others, Josha. Or rather one in particular; a whip-cracking harpy with a tongue like a dragon's tail, who answers to the name of Viéja! She believes it is her task to stand over me and work me until I drop! I am an artist! I am sensitive and impressionable. I need understanding! I can't be expected to deploy my genius like a machine. It's absurd! And yet that is exactly what I am expected to do. Humph! And they wonder why I'm so miserable."

"What are you making at the moment?" Jonquil asked, indicating the cloth laid out on the table.

"That is a celebration robe for the Lord Fantazar," Yim proclaimed, rising from his seat, wavering a little and tottering over to the table. He lifted one end of the fabric and twisted it until its shiny surface caught the light.

"Well it would have to be really, wouldn't it," Yim concluded. " As it's green!"

"What celebration?" Jonquil asked.

"Not the most adventurous of clients," the old man continued, not having heard the banf. "They are sticklers for their colours. Green for Spring. Gold for Summer. And red for Autumn. But never black! The Wizards of Light do not wear the colour of darkness!"

Jonquil tried again.

"What celebration, Yim?"

The old man did not answer, he was far too busy reciting the creed of the Three Wizards with a booming, theatrical voice.

"The three Lords of the Brotherhood, and their supporters, do not wear furs, or feathers, or any material that an animal has had to die to provide! This is their creed!"

Yim carefully spread the cloth back on to the table, ran his fingers lightly along the edge of one of the paper cut-outs, satisfied himself that all was in order, and then fell back into his seat by the globe.

"What is the celebration?" The banf patiently repeated.

Yim stared at him, his eyes wide with incredulity.

"Why, victory celebration of course!" he cried.

"What victory?"

"Victory over V'Vr!.. VVV'Vor!.. Vrs!.. ..the Unmentionable One! All of the great lords have ordered new robes. For the day when they take back what is rightfully theirs."

"But how can you be so sure that they will win?" Jonquil pursued.

Yim looked horrified. It was obvious that such a question had never even entered his head.

"Of course they'll win!" he assured the banf. "How can you doubt it? Why, there's three of them. There's only one of him. He's outnumbered..er..three to one! Of course they'll win!"

Yim suddenly leant towards Jonquil in a dramatically conspiratorial manner, as if he was about to impart a grave secret, his voice dropping almost to a whisper.

"Don't be deceived by how they seem. I know, they look so kind, so gentle, so solici..ci..citous! But they are very, very, powerful beings. Well! They control the seasons, don't they? How much more power do you want?"

Yim broke away from the banf, eased back in to his chair and stared almost hypnotically into the swirling globe. His voice grew strange as his mood became stern and contemplative. His eyes were wide, almost vacant.

"We will win, my friend. Have no fear. The only question is, will it be in time to save Enchantica?"

Jonquil's eyes followed Yim's into the globe, which was now a turquoise orb, slowly spinning in rolling waves of blue and green. The glowing sphere seemed to bestow an inner peace on the watcher, and Jonquil felt himself drawn ever deeper into it's core, the soothing lights melting into his mind.

Suddenly the silence was shattered by a sheer explosion of uproarious laughter, from the little old man. His body shook so much with the strength of it, he could hardly form words to explain. At once, the mood globe was transformed from slow, pensive patterns into a burning ball of yellow light. Yim's trembling hand fell heavily on to Jonquil's shoulder as he tried to steady himself to speak and after several abandoned attempts that ended in volatile bursts of giggles, the little old man eventually succeeded in executing a sentence.

"Have you heard the song about the Cowman's wife?" he sniggered.

"No," Jonquil chuckled.

Yim wobbled with mirth.

"I'll sing it!" He quivered.

Jonquil and Rattajack listened for a while, and then concluded that the first verse of 'The Cowman's Wife' consisted of a long spell of uncontrollable laughter, and a string of incomprehensible words and noises. Yim was clearly determined to enjoy his rendition of the song, every bit as much as his two rather bemused guests.

The second verse was a little clearer, and the rosy nosed old man sang it with great gusto.

"Dum diddy hee! Dum diddy hey!
I bet you'd like a pot of gold to carry it away!

The tale of the Cowman's wife,
She was the bane of his life,
Not very pretty,
A face like a dragon.
It was such a pity,
She had to wear a bag on!
A shame for the Cowman's wife!"

As soon as the last word left his mouth, Yim dissolved once again into a quake of belly shaking laughter. Jonquil couldn't help a burst of giggles himself. The little old man's uncontrollable fits of mirth were quite infectious. Yim only just managed to restrain himself sufficiently to carry on with the third and fourth verses, both of which were punctuated by regular interruptions of prolonged sniggering.

"Dum diddy hee! Dum diddy hey!
I bet you'd like a keg of ale to carry it away!

Beware of the Cowman's wife,
Her tongue was as sharp as a knife,
She'd pin back his ears,
And deafen him with naggin'.
He'd try to get a word in,
But her tongue would keep a waggin'.
Relentless was the Cowman's wife!

Dum diddy hee! Dum diddy hey!
I bet you'd like another keg to carry it away!

Hooray for the Cowman's wife,
A cart load of trouble and strife.
To say that she was chesty,
Would never be a lie.
If she turned around too hasty,
She could black you in the eye!
Buxom was the Cowman's wife!

Dum diddy hee! Dum diddy hey!
I bet you'd like a girl like her and have her winched
away!

This time Yim could hold back the floodgates no longer, and laughed himself right off his chair. Jonquil found the bizarre spectacle of Yim's short, upturned legs kicking against the air in both pain and ecstasy far funnier than his song, and laughed heartily along with him. The two of them filled the little workshop with the raucous noise of merriment, the sound carrying far along the quiet corridor.

Rattajack was unconcerned with the precise details of the joke, it didn't really matter to him. He just loved to hear laughter, especially Jonquil's. The terragon's ears sprang forward, he piped a joyous rhythm to coincide with their guffaws and slapped his tail hard on the tiles.

Even the mood-globe seemed to quiver with delight, flashing and shimmering in rashes of lemon and white. Shocks of light shards were thrown out into the room, and raced in swirling reflections across the over stocked shelves, and the faces of the three figures that sat around it.

Suddenly there was a presence at the door, large and menacing. Yim's roaring stopped abruptly and he snapped bolt upright from the floor. The little old man's face dropped almost to his knees and his eyes grew round and sheepish. The room instantly became dark as the vibrant glow died from the mood-globe.

Jonquil twisted around on his stool to see who it was who had caused such a dramatic change of atmosphere. The heavy form of Viéja stomped into the candlelight.

On seeing the now empty ale bottles and Yim seated on the floor, her eyes narrowed and her mouth tightened into a thin, dark line. This expression made her wide face seem even wider. She immediately glanced over to the making table and judging from the distinct lack of improvement in her expression, found the Spring Wizard's celebration robe, to be at exactly the same stage of development, as when she last saw it. Viéja's eyes slowly made their way back to Yim.

"Isn't she a bruiser?" the old man muttered under his breath. Luckily only the two companion's large ears caught it.

Viéja was draped in a long, voluminous gown, that shook rather than swayed as she moved within it. Her hair sprang from her head in spiky, rag-tied tufts, a few escaped ringlets dancing before her sullen eyes. The lady had evidently retired for the evening some time ago, as her eyes still blinked with sleep. Two puffy hands clapped together and her whole body bounced twice on its heels.

"So!" She said finally. "This is how you work late, is it, Master Robe Designer?"

"Viéja, my dear...," Yim ventured, but to no avail.

"Out of my sight for only the shortest time and this is what becomes of you. Drinking ale and drunken songs!" she bawled.

Yim pouted outrageously.

"I am nots drink, drunk!" he slurred. "And mind your manners, will you. I have guezts."

For the first time since she entered the room, Viéja, acknowledged the presence of the banf and the terragon. She even blushed a little and fumbled with her fastenings and hair, in a superficial attempt to smarten her appearance. A sort of smile happened briefly on her lower face and a softer, uncharacteristic tone diluted her voice.

"Please forgive any rudeness, but we labour under the cruellest of schedules. We can't have the great lords postponing taking over the world, just because their robes aren't ready, now can we?"

Viéja made to go but then turned sharply on the visibly wilting designer.

"I will need the embroidery sketches for the Lord of Autumn's new robe tomorrow." She snapped. "Early!"

And with that the storm abated and the three revellers were alone again.

"That was Viéja," Yim apologised. "She is my..er..foreman...woman!"

A blur in the doorway.

"Don't you listen to him, young Sir,"

She was back.

"I am his fiance!"

The two companions left shortly after the little old man fainted. Viéja simply marched over to Yim's collapsed form, scooped him up in her thick arms and deposited him in the darkened room next door. As the burly lady was showing Jonquil and Rattajack out of the workshop, she asked if they would not repeat any of what they had seen to the great lords, as they might not see the humour in it. Jonquil felt certain that the Lord Fantazar, at least, would see the funny side, but the fearful expression haunting Viéja's face made him promise that he would say nothing. She bade them goodnight.

Jonquil and Rattajack returned to Yim's workshop late the next morning, to make sure that he was alright. They found that the spritely little craftsman, had been up for hours and was busily attending to a richly decorated border on the hem of Fantazar's new robe. The little old man was dressed in a startling outfit of red and gold, with a luxurious purple bow tied at his throat. Yim explained that he had earlier enjoyed the august presence of the Spring Wizard himself, when he had arrived at the 'studio' for a final fitting.

Yim had entertained the great lord in the other chamber, which had been shrouded in darkness the previous night, and was, the two companions discovered, ten times larger than the cramped, over-burdened workshop. A screened alcove concealed the little designer's bed, but apart from that and one or two chairs, some robe-making dummies and a long table, the spacious room was bare. The floor of the chamber had to be kept clear of furniture and other obstructions, Yim told them, to facilitate the spreading out and cutting, of the huge lengths of material required to create the Wizards' long, extravagant robes. Leading off from the room was a small, circular side-tower, illuminated by a ring of generously sized arched windows. Hanging within, on two carefully padded stands, and bathed in a flood of sunlight, were the half finished robes of Summer and Autumn. The richness of the material and the intensity of the colours, took Jonquil's breath away. But it was the supreme craftmanship and quality of design, that made the banf look at the funny little character, fussing about his workshop, with renewed admiration.

The two companions made frequent visits to their new found friend, during their long stay on the island, and were always given a hearty welcome. Especially if they happened to go at night, round about suppertime!

Relaxing days turned into blissful weeks, which slowly became golden months. The banf and the terragon found the Wizards' island to be a treasure trove of interests. Apart from their repeated visits to Yim, there was a whole world of cultures and customs condensed into the island's richly varied population. Jonquil found his innate senses of curiosity and fascination, soaring ever upwards to unknown heights. However, as time marched on, the two companions became more and more anxious about their home, and despite the delightful life they were enjoying on the enchanted island, wished that the great lords would give them leave to move on.

Late one evening, as they returned to their lodgings, the banf and the terragon found Carobus waiting for them. The Three Wizards had requested Jonquil and

Rattajack's presence at a High Council in the Tower of the Stars.

The wizard brought Jonquil and Rattajack to the entrance of a large chamber, open to the outside by means of a wide archway. Beyond the opening there was a deep wooden platform, reaching out into the air. Perched on the very lip of the projection were two waiting carrier-dragons.

Jonquil stopped dead in his tracks. Carobus placed a reassuring hand on his shoulder and confessed to the banf that the only alternative to a shattering climb up a winding staircase, thousands of steps strong, ascending the highest spire in the palace, was a brief dragon-flight over the towertops.

The sight of the two readily harnessed dragons, attended by their grooms, evoked grim memories of Jonquil's terrifying flight over the Green Sky Forest on the back of the Summer dragon. His head started to swim with the mere thought of flying again.

Carobus led them on towards the platform. As they passed through the large chamber, Jonquil noticed that on either side the walls were partitioned into open boxes. Some of these compartments contained other carrier-dragons that were curled up asleep, uninterested in the activity around them.

Rattajack noted with relief, that none of the stables were barred or sealed by doors, and his keen woodland eyes, accustomed to life in semi-darkness, observed that the carrier-dragons were not shackled to their wooden homes, or restrained in any way. They were clearly free to come and go as they pleased. Choosing to stay and serve the Wizards and their followers, rather than being forced to. Indeed, Rattajack could sense only waves of contentment and peace flowing from the recumbent beasts, the same attitude he felt from all of the Wizards followers and attendants.

Jonquil learned from Carobus that this was only one of many dragonports located in the palace, and that a regular traffic of carriers flew to and from the island, to secret locations on the mainland, and other islands, conveying special messages to and from the Lords of the Seasons. It was one of the few voices the Wizards had left, to communicate with their supporters, besieged in their respective kingdoms within Enchantica.

One of the dragon-grooms held a looped harness in front of Jonquil and bade him kindly step into it. The belt was then pulled tight at his waist and he was invited to climb astride the crouching dragon. Rattajack, after a little hasty improvisation by the grooms, who had been unprepared for the terragon, but seemed singularly thrilled to meet him, was fitted with a similar device. Eventually, both companions were tightly buckled and secured to the endlessly patient carrier. Carobus mounted the second carrier, with considerably less fuss it must be noted, and the two dragons called Samphire and Furza, leapt into the air.

The banf had intended to keep his eyes tightly shut until he felt their steed's feet land firmly at the high tower, but his explorer's soul forbad it and his eyelids sprang open to witness the spectacle.

The two carriers wheeled twice around the dragonport turret in wide circles, searching for an up draught. As soon as the warm rush of wind, channelled skywards by the high walls of the palace, tugged at the taught membranes, the dragons banked into the thermal and sped like rockets across the vast expanse of the Wizards' residence.

Yim enjoyed the August presence of the Spring Wizard himself.

Clusters of conical roofs and needlepoint spires filed past them. Bulbous domes delicately washed with starlight loomed ahead and then swept by underneath. Pale blue roads wriggled their way past rashes of houses, through courtyards and gardens, skirted lakes and copses and then finally converged with their fellows.

The sea blazed with moonlight on every horizon, calm and pristine against the dark silhouette of the island. The moon itself, had ignited a whole bank of attendant clouds, spilling a reservoir of silver across the star-laden sky.

Ahead of them, rising from the furthest corner of the palace, a thin, black rapier invaded the midnight sky; a long, dark finger accusing the heavens. Jonquil could now see how impossible climbing the great tower would have been, it rose up forever, stabbing the clouds at its pinnacle. Even the carrier-dragons had to find fresh thermals to lift them to the top, no ordinary breeze would take them. Gradually the two dragon-steeds ascended the tower's height in slow spirals, its high chamber still a good distance aloft. The round stone walls yielded not a single window and, like the trunk of a giant tree, it seemed solid and eternal.

Eventually the two carriers arrived at the summit of the Tower of Stars. The high chamber was open to the sky and the dragons hovered for an instant above its tooth-edged walls and then flapped inside.

The Tower of Stars

Four magnificent marble thrones faced each other across a wide stone table. The Lords of the Seasons occupied three of them, the fourth was left empty. Sitting between the thrones were the High Wizards of Spring and Autumn: Perslane and Hoolock respectively. Carobus motioned for Jonquil and Rattajack to approach the circular table, showing the banf to a chair and then finally seating himself in another. Rattajack was more than content to rest at Jonquil's side.

The Summer Wizard was the first to speak.

"Thankyou for coming, my friends," he commenced. "I welcome you to this high tower of council. The ancient place of deliberation, where grave issues have been raised and resolved beneath the gentle gaze of the stars, for many centuries."

Jonquil looked upwards into the circle of open sky. The primitive, austere rooftop did seem to be infiltrated by the quiet, soothing influence of the starscape. There was peace and stillness to be found up here, relief for the soul. The banf was surprised to feel quite untroubled at being held so far from the ground, with only a high toothed wall to save them all from being blown into oblivion, by the upper draughts. The cloud-scraping tower was well named, Jonquil decided. From up there, the stars looked very close indeed.

Samphire and Furza joined their brothers and sisters, who had ferried the Great Wizards and their attendant wizards to the lofty gathering. Sorren, Breen and Helia were amongst the flight of carriers who had effaced themselves from their lords' presence and perched on the ruined teeth of the surrounding wall. They allowed the strong winds to play beneath their outstretched wings and were eventually lifted into the darkness to soar about the lonely needle, until their services were recalled.

The High Council first heard the voices of the three attendant wizards. Of Perslane, High Wizard of Spring, resplendent in long, gilt-edged, emerald robes.

"The work of Yim?" Jonquil pondered to himself. The wizard's garments had certainly been crafted by a fine hand.

Perslane gave word of the plight of the Eastern Realms; traditional friends and allies of the Lords of the Brotherhood. The kings had gathered their people inside their huge fortified cities, as they were wont to do when the scourge of Winter threatened from the North. Vast snowdrifts, twenty men high and fifty men deep, had been formed against the gates and the outer walls of the fortresses; treacherous snow that belied substance but would bury any that tried to walk upon it. The Lord of Winter hurled mighty storms of ice-hammers, balls of ice as big as a fist, down from the skies. They pounded the roofs and turrets of the Eastern cities, creating an unbearable, incessant thunder. Screaming gales tore through the deserted streets, beating at doors and windows, and clawing at roof-tiles and chimney stacks. Heavy snowfalls were transformed into terrifying blizzards, intended to further intimidate

The Tower of Stars

the innocent city dwellers, cowering in fear within their homes.

All of the Eastern Kingdoms were in some way vulnerable to the ravages of Vrorst's power; lying either on exposed mountain sides or sweeping across open valleys. They were easy targets for his malice.

Therefore it was with great regret that the armies of the Eastern Kings could offer no assistance to the Wizards. The five brother-monarchs added that they feared for their own survival, if the wrath of Winter did not lessen in the long days ahead.

This was grim news for the Lords of the Seasons. The Kings of the Eastern realms had long been their staunchest supporters, never failing to answer the call for help. They had rallied their powers and risen to any challenge laid down against the forces of Light. And of course Vrorst knew this and had consequently turned his full fury against them, to prevent the Eastern Kings from aiding the Wizards' cause.

Hoolock, High Wizard of Autumn spoke next, clothed in robes of deep scarlet.

Waxifrade's attendant wizard brought news of the woodlands. Especially the enchanted folk that dwelled in secret dells and forgotten glades, that contained the hidden kingdoms of the fairies and the elves.

Hoolock had received messages through the Autumn fairy, Fossfex, that certain factions of the secret people had turned their backs on their fellow Enchanticans, and refused to take any further part in the struggle against Vrorst. Henceforth, the fairies and the elves of the Great Forest would use their magic only to strengthen their concealment, and fiercely defend their borders against all comers, be they the servants of Winter or not.

Even King Trillil, whose fairy realm deep within the southern reaches of the Great Forest, had always extended the warmest and most loyal salutations to the Lords of the Seasons, was becoming increasingly disillusioned with the violent excesses of the Ice Sorcerer, and the apparent apathy of the Three Wizards towards them.

Queen Trinia in the neighbouring realm, a long time advocate of estrangement and exclusion from none enchanted races, declared the Wizards of Light to be her enemies. She had branded them traitors and deceivers, for abandoning the noble races of Enchantica to face the wrath of the Ice Sorcerer alone. She had called upon her fellow kings and queens of the Enchanted Folk to form an alliance outside that of the Wizards. A coalition, dedicated to serve and protect only the interests and ambitions of the fairies and elves. Even to sue for peace with the Lord of Winter, if he could be persuaded to give cast-iron assurances that their desired isolation from the world, would be respected and endured for the length of his reign.

The Wizards assembled around the stone table, did not seriously believe that any of the forest monarchs, including Trinia, would ever consider entering into any agreement or pact with Vrorst. Threats of such action were meant to serve as a spur, to force the Wizards to move against the enemy. The Enchanted Folk had always favoured an insular existence, but deep in their hearts they knew that an Enchantica ruled unchallenged by Vrorst, would soon sound the death knell for their own smaller worlds.

The last of the attendant wizards now gave his news, Carobus; High Wizard of Summer.

The tidings that he had to share with the Council were by far the most disturbing.

The wizard held a map, which he proceeded to roll out before the members of the council, his fellow attendant wizards helping to hold it flat to the table. It was a new map of Enchantica. A copy of an original drawn up by Vrorst; his new vision of the world. Apart from the Secret Kingdoms, which were painted green, the whole of the chart was coloured white.

Carobus began to describe the intentions behind the map and what they meant for the free peoples of Enchantica.

Vrorst had claimed Enchantica for his own. This was hardly news. The three Lords of the Seasons forced to live in exile on the Forgotten Island, were only too aware of that fact. However, the Lord of Winter was not so far consumed by his evil insanity, that he could not see that a world ruled solely by Winter, would never survive. He had finally recognised the need for the other three seasons. How else would the fruits of the land grow to feed the people who fed his people?

And so, he had devised what he called his master plan. Transform the former Secret Kingdoms of his enemies into immense flourishing gardens. In that way he could keep the remainder of his realm frozen beneath a desert of snow and ice and yet still have the means to sustain the lives of his minions.

The Lord of Summer noted that to achieve his ends, Vrorst would first have to gain dominion over the Seasons of Light. As controlling the Spring, Summer and Autumn Fire Orbs himself was impossible, this meant that the Lord of Ice would have to make the Three Wizards his slaves, and bend their influence to his will.

The Autumn Wizard also solemnly observed, that if by some catastrophe, the Ice Lord's ambitions should be realised. It would no doubt mean that only those Enchanticans who abandoned their allegiance to the Brotherhood of Light, and swore a new oath of loyalty to the Lord of Ice, would be eligible to participate in this exclusive bounty. Those noble races who had, over generations, built up strong defences against the murderous servants of Winter, would be forced to tear them down and place themselves at the mercy of Vrorst's dreaded legions.

Jonquil suddenly had a terrible vision of teams of starving banfs marching with heavy axes towards the stems of the White Ring. Hordes of grinning goblins and trolls, gathering in slavering anticipation outside, waiting for the moment to rush in. The banf offered a silent prayer to the stars that this would never be allowed to come to pass.

Orolan told Jonquil and Rattajack not to lose heart. The enemy was mighty indeed and the task that lay ahead of the Forces of Light was truly formidable. However, the Three Wizards had discovered the weapon of knowledge, which would provide them with the final victory over He that relied solely on the blood of his mortal armies to secure his crown.

The Summer Wizard reminded his brothers, of the fateful day when Vrorst committed his Grand Betrayal. The Wizards had decided not to send forth a great host to pursue the robbers, as the Ice Lord would have expected, but to seek the ancient wisdom of the Great Spirit. The Three Lords had finally found the precious parchments that made up the Old Rules, buried beneath the foundations of the Wizards' Palace on the Forgotten Island. The prehistoric writings spoke of the creator's laws and creed, and also included a vast biography of ancient Enchantica.

Within these great lists and histories, the Three Brothers had re-discovered an age-long mystery.

"Which brings us," the Summer Wizard continued. "At last, to you, my friends. Let us talk of a very special place, that before your coming, existed beyond our knowledge. Let us talk of the Banf Kingdom."

Jonquil's eyes immediately brightened. This was a subject that he loved to talk about, even if it did make him sick with longing to return there.

The Summer Wizard leaned forward, and pivoting on his elbows, laid his interlocked hands on the table before him. Orolan fixed Jonquil with an inquisitive stare.

"What do you know of Old Magic?" he asked the banf.

Jonquil looked in vain at Rattajack, but the terragon simply returned his vacant expression. They had never heard of it.

"Old Magic," the Summer Wizard told Jonquil. "Is the very essence of goodness and truth. It is the antithesis of evil, and the one element that evil cannot wield, withstand or destroy.

Veins of this powerful force rise from the core of the world like the inverted roots of a tree. Whenever one of these potent capillaries breaks through the soil, a visible manifestation grows from the ground. We call them agamid. You call them mushrooms. You know yourself, Jonquil, that mushrooms contain enchantment. As you have described to us, your people have used that gift to protect themselves from their enemies for generations. Have you never wondered why it is that evil creatures cannot bear to approach the mushrooms of the forest? It is because they shine with the blinding intensity of Old Magic. Only creatures of a good heart can stand to go near them."

"Like the White Ring!" Jonquil exclaimed.

"Exactly like the White Ring," the Lord of Summer concurred. "It is written in the ancient scrolls, that there are three 'havens' in Enchantica. Three places where Old Magic springs from the soil in a veritable torrent. These sites are known as the Wells of Hope. They are sanctuaries, Jonquil, immune to the attacks of evil forces.

Two of the havens are known to us. One, as you may already have guessed, is here on the Forgotten Island. The other lies far beneath the peaks of the Marble Fortress. It is many days march below the roots of the mountains, through a treacherous labyrinth of endless tunnels and caverns. Not even the most skilled dwarf explorer would live to see his journey's end, if he should ever choose to attempt that quest, without a guide.

We Three know the way. Perhaps one day we will make that journey, for the Well of Hope beneath the Marble Fortress is said to be a sight beyond imagination."

The other two Lords of the seasons concurred in muted tones.

"But what of the third haven?" Orolan asked, gazing deeply into Jonquil's green eyes, and making the banf feel more than a little uncomfortable.

"For many long years the mystery has remained unsolved. We had already guessed that it waited to be found in a place far from the prying eyes of the world. In a dark corner of the Great Forest, perhaps? In an unlooked for locality where the visible presence of Old Magic was so prolific that its identity would be unmistakable."

A most unpleasant shiver began to play up and down Jonquil's spine, as a chilling realisation slowly dawned on him. He had the dreadful feeling, he knew what the Summer Wizard was going to say next.

"I think, Jonquil," Orolan began. "After what you have just heard, that it will come as no surprise to you, when I say that we believe the Banf Kingdom to be the third Well of Hope."

Jonquil's brain refused to believe what his large ears were hearing. The Banf Kingdom was the Third Haven. One of the three most important places in the known world. It was incredible. How could it be true?

"But it has to be true!" Fantazar argued. "Do you have any idea how much Old Magic would be required to sustain a wall of mushrooms as large and as powerful as the White Ring? Only a Well of Hope could possibly contain the amount of enchantment necessary, to produce such a indomitable shield. There can be no doubt, my friend!"

Jonquil was stunned. He turned to look at his companion. Rattajack seemed totally calm and unmoved by the exciting news. If Jonquil did not think that he knew better, he might have interpreted the terragon's expression to mean that Rattajack had known of the significance of the Banf Kingdom all along. But that was impossible, wasn't it? Jonquil thought that he would have the shocking statement confirmed just one more time.

"Are you absolutely sure that this is true?" he asked the Wizards.

"If there was any need for further proof," Orolan commenced his reply. "Then he is sitting at your elbow!"

An even deeper expression of bewilderment rose into Jonquil's already heavily furrowed brow.

"The arven are mentioned in the writings of the ancient articles," the Summer Wizard continued.

"They are?" Jonquil gasped.

"In detail," Orolan replied.

Jonquil's natural curiosity once again took command of his tongue.

"What do they say?" the banf urged.

"Many things," Orolan answered him. "That they are the most remarkable of creatures."

"Ho, ho! I knew that already!" Jonquil laughed, hugging his companion warmly around the neck.

"Did you also know," Waxifrade inquired, "that it was Rattajack who heard our words after the Battle of the Green Oak? Vrorst tried to distort our messages with clouds of confusion, but Rattajack, with the aid of his higher senses, pierced through the fog and heard our voices. Through him, we were able to guide the Three Guardians, and yourself of course, to the Bay of Voices."

"It is also written that the arven are the first born," Fantazar added. "The first born of all dragons."

Jonquil's mouth almost dropped to his knees.

"Indeed," the Summer Wizard smiled. "If your old banf's tale is true, and Arvana really was the mother of all terragons, then she was also the mother of all dragons!"

The banf stared at Rattajack with eyes like saucers. The terragon playfully nipped at his nose and nuzzled his neck, as if to say.

"It's alright, I always knew I was special, but I still love you!"

Jonquil turned back to face the Three Wizards.

"But what have Ratters' special powers got to do with the Banf Kingdom being the third haven?" He asked them.

Orolan then told Jonquil, that it was written in the Old Scrolls, that wheresoever the third Well of Hope was found, there also would be found the last family of the arven. The Summer Wizard sadly summised, that over the centuries, the sensitive and harmless terragons had disappeared from every corner of Enchantica, except the Banf Kingdom. Only the White Ring had saved the noble creatures from total extinction.

"You have a very rare and precious companion there, my friend," Orolan told the banf. "You should treasure him."

Jonquil looked deeply into the amber depths of Rattajack's eyes, and suddenly felt very humble and privileged.

"I do," he answered softly.

The Summer Wizard decided it was time to move towards a conclusion, and changed the subject slightly.

"Tell me, Jonquil," Orolan inquired. "Does the kingdom of the banfs have a king?"

"Yes, of course." Jonquil replied. "King Merlion. He lives in the big city, where the four giant Green Oaks grow. In the very heart of the kingdom."

"Is he wise?" Orolan asked.

"I don't know, Lord. I have never seen him." Jonquil confessed. "Although I am sure he is. I mean, they usually are, aren't they?"

All of the wizards seated around the table exchanged a series of ironic looks and discreet chuckles.

"Usually, Jonquil," the Summer Wizard smiled, "although, unfortunately, not always!"

"Do you wish the King to come here too?" The banf asked.

"No, my friend," Orolan began, "quite the reverse. I think we should go to him."

Jonquil leapt from his seat.

"Really!" he cried.

"Please ..." Orolan tried to calm him. "Please listen carefully to my words...."

The Lord of Summer paused to allow Jonquil to resume his seat. The banf sat back down again his eyes bursting with childlike excitement, at the thought of the great Wizards of Light arriving at the gates of the White Ring. The banf could not wait to see the look of total disbelief explode across Old Yargle's face. It would be worth all of the hardship and danger just to see that.

"We have no need to leave this place," the Summer Wizard told Jonquil. "The Forgotten Island is a Well of Hope, and as such cannot be harmed by Vrorst. We could remain here in blissful isolation, simply turn our backs on the noble peoples of Enchantica. After all, is that not what most believe we have done anyway? The Ice Sorcerer could never hope to capture this island, but by freezing the sea and laying siege to us, he could turn it into a gilded cage.

The truth is, of course, we have no intention of staying here to await the Ice Lord's coming. Every day we delay returning to Enchantica, our people take a step nearer towards disaster. We have let them fight alone for too long.

It is true that some have turned from us. The Kings of the Western Shores have accepted Vrorst's bribes and submitted to his will. They have built great galleons for him, in which to terrorise the open seas. Indeed, the danger is now so great, that even our own fair ships and mariners have to don the black garb of the enemy, lest they be attacked by Vrorst's fleet. In truth, we cannot blame the Western Kings for their misguided alliance with the Ice Lord. What ruler when faced with an impossible choice, will knowingly lead his people along the path to suffering and death?

One thing is certain, as Vrorst's prisoners we can achieve nothing. Therefore, we must travel secretly to the mainland, to a place where we know we can be safe. The kingdom of your people, Jonquil, is now the only place on the whole of the mainland, that can afford us such protection. We must go there!"

Suddenly a dreadful thought struck Jonquil and for a terrible moment he re-lived Arangast's devastating plunge through the frozen roof of the Bay of Voices.

"What about the Sacred Vessels?" Jonquil cried. "How can you retake Enchantica without them?"

The Wizards exchanged grave looks with one another, and for a moment the banf wished he had kept his insensitive outburst to himself. Eventually Orolan turned with a heavy sadness to Jonquil.

"The chapter of the three Chests of Power has been closed, forever," the Summer Wizard sighed. "We must devise new methods to defeat the Ice Lord. We must fight on without their aid."

Orolan smiled ironically at the banf.

"We have no choice!"

With that, the high council was concluded. Before climbing back on to Samphire's back, Jonquil politely asked if he and Rattajack might pay a visit to the injured Autumn dragon. Waxifrade seemed delighted that they should think to make such a request, and gladly gave them leave to do so. Hoolock, the High Wizard of Autumn, was only too pleased to offer himself as a guide, whenever the banf and the terragon should decide to go. Not surprisingly, Jonquil asked if they might go to Snarlgard right away. With a smile, Waxifrade gave his consent, and the three great lords bade the two companions goodnight.

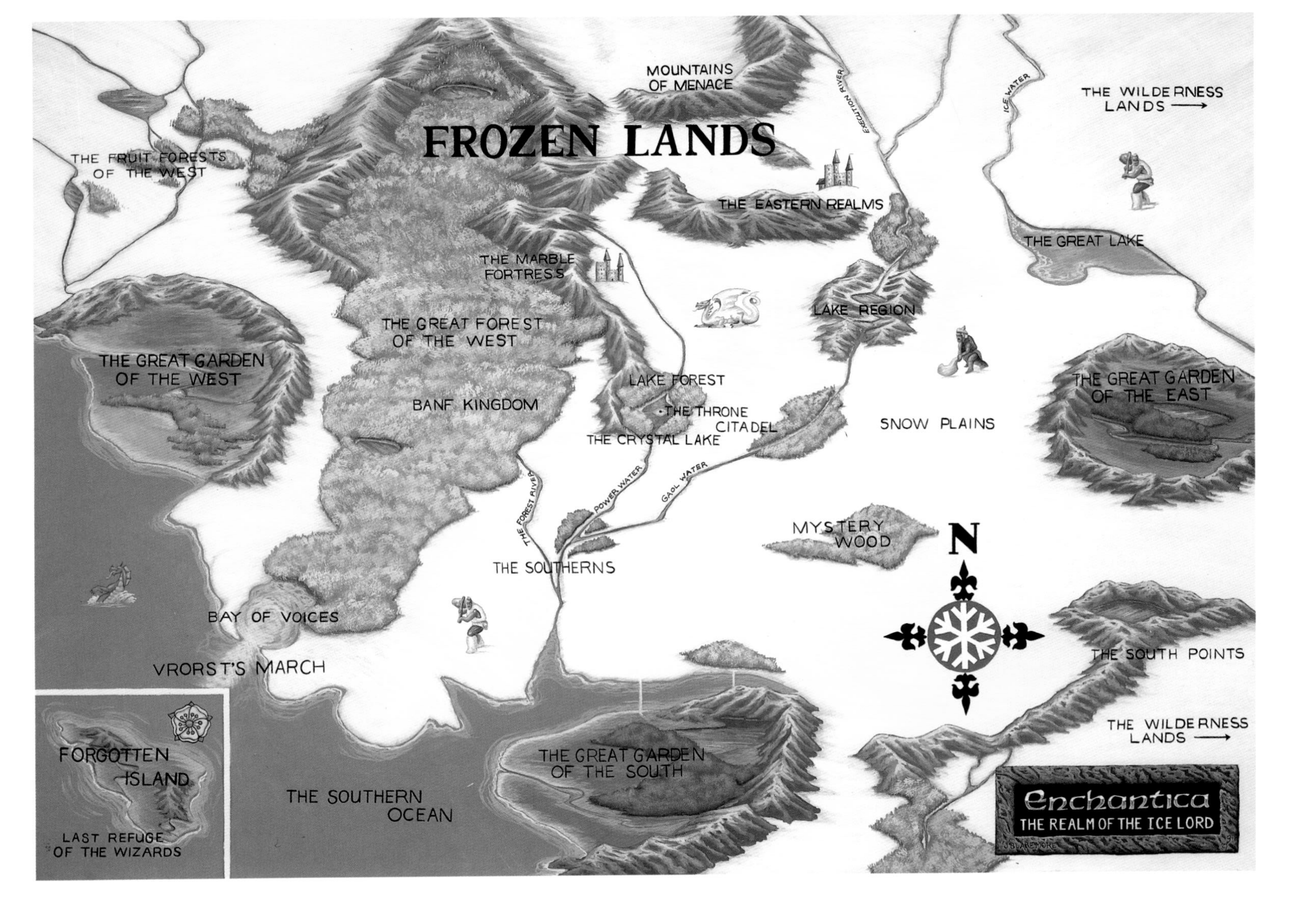
FROZEN LANDS
MOUNTAINS OF MENACE
THE FRUIT FORESTS OF THE WEST
EXECUTION RIVER
ICE WATER
THE WILDERNESS LANDS
THE EASTERN REALMS
THE GREAT LAKE
THE MARBLE FORTRESS
LAKE REGION
THE GREAT FOREST OF THE WEST
THE GREAT GARDEN OF THE WEST
LAKE FOREST
THE GREAT GARDEN OF THE EAST
BANF KINGDOM
THE THRONE CITADEL
SNOW PLAINS
THE CRYSTAL LAKE
THE FOREST RIVER
POWER WATER
GAOL WATER
MYSTERY WOOD
N
THE SOUTHERNS
BAY OF VOICES
THE SOUTH POINTS
VRORST'S MARCH
THE WILDERNESS LANDS
FORGOTTEN ISLAND
THE GREAT GARDEN OF THE SOUTH
THE SOUTHERN OCEAN
LAST REFUGE OF THE WIZARDS
Enchantica
THE REALM OF THE ICE LORD

A Parting of Beloved Friends

The full tropical splendour of the Forgotten Island entertained the two companions for a few more long, sun-drenched days following the High Council. They spent most of that time on the golden beaches. Exploring, playing, relaxing and of course, swimming. Jonquil and especially Rattajack, continued their recent love-affair with the ocean. The warm, jewel-like waters teemed with playmates; mer-folk, dolphins, clouds of darting fish and even small sea serpents, the offspring of the larger, fearsome specimens, that guarded the deep water approaches to the island. The banf and the terragon's high spirits were made even more buoyant, when the Wizards told them, that they were to return to the Banf Kingdom, ahead of the great lords themselves. The two companions were to appear before King Merlion, as envoys, and prepare their fellow banfs for the Wizards' arrival.

On the very day, that Jonquil and Rattajack were to leave the paradise that had been their home, for many exquisite months, they lay on the warm sand and reflected on the wonderful things that they had done, since they had arrived there. And wondered if they would ever do any of them again.

They had swum with shoals of fish, that filled the waters like living rainbows. Rode on the back of dolphins, that sliced through the crystal surf. Galloped through the foamy waves, at sunrise, on silver-white ponies. Dozed in the gentle heat beneath the shade of an exotic fruit tree, listening to the rhythmic hum of the attending insects. They had chased butterflies through the swirling meadows, cloaking the rolling downs. Quenched their thirst from the sparkling springs that gurgled happily in the forest clearings. And stood on the highest hill and surveyed the radiant jewel that was the Forgotten Island.

The haven of the Wizards was truly a place of deep enchantment, Jonquil and Rattajack could breath it in the air and feel its soft caress on their skin. The haven did not contain as many mushrooms as the Banf Kingdom, although the two companions had found a fair number, whilst exploring in the thick, city forests. Jonquil could only guess that the reason for this, was that the Wizards did not encourage the mushrooms like the banfs did. One thing that did flourish on the island, however, or rather around it, in the sea shallows, was the Enchantica Rose. The delicate white blooms, that were the emblems of the Brotherhood, lifted their heads above the gentle waves, like a carpet of scattered blossom.

Finally, evening arrived, and the two companions prepared to depart from the island. Yim had somehow found the time, within his busy schedule, to make Jonquil a set of fleece lined Winter clothes, to guard against the freezing Enchantica gales. Luckily, Rattajack, did not feel the cold, so needed no such protective cladding. The terragon looked on with some amusement, as the banf dressed himself in his new garments and finally pulled the snug fitting cap over his large ears; a cap that Yim had copied exactly from Jonquil's description of a banf's Winter hat.

It was with mixed feelings that they approached a last meeting with Orolan, Lord of Summer, before commencing the long dragonflight home.

The Summer Wizard was waiting for them in the dragonport from which they were due to leave. The same platform from which they had flown to the High Council, a few happy days before. A smile exploded across Jonquil's face, as he recognised a short fat figure, dwarfed by the tall frame of the Wizard, standing next to him. Yim had come to see them off. The banf and the terragon warmly greeted the wizened old robe designer.

"Can't stay really," he confessed. "Viéja is on the warpath! Just thought I would come and see you off the premises. Take care and keep safe, won't you. 'She who must be obeyed' says the same!"

Yim clasped Jonquil's hands tightly inside his own and shook them firmly. He then seized the terragons front two limbs and made a similar gesture.

"Well," he fumbled, suddenly a little embarrassed and searching for words. "W'We'll meet again I am sure. M'Must go. Far too much to do, in far too little time, as usual. Hope the clothes fit?"

"They are perfect. I am sweating in this heat!" Jonquil assured the little old man.

"Well, you will soon feel the difference, once you have crossed the ocean," Yim continued. "Keep safe, both of you!"

With that the little old man bade them farewell and hastily trotted away into the palace, pausing for a brief wave before disappearing through the large archway.

Jonquil felt the firm hand of Orolan on his shoulder. The Summer Wizard turned the banf and the terragon to face him, his eyes were strong and reassuring.

"Jonquil, the Wanderer," the Wizard began, speaking in soft, thoughtful tones. "There is a certain air about you that defies description. A gift of good fortune, that keeps you safe. Perhaps the amount of mushrooms that you have consumed in your lifetime, has left a residue of Old Magic in the fabric of your being, which protects you from evil doers. I pray that in the days to follow, that charm does not desert you.

Do not abandon hope, my friends. I know the odds against us seem overpowering. I will not deny that the enemy is very strong. However, we three Lords of the Brotherhood are not totally powerless. We still have a sting left in our tail. For in the camp of the Ice Sorcerer, we have a spy! An eye at his shoulder! I tell you this only in the hope that it may bring you some small comfort. For whether or not, our spy will prove effective for us, in the end, I cannot foretell. For your own protection, I will give you no further details.

Now, without further fuss, allow me to introduce you to a great friend."

Orolan held out his hand and a handsome, russet coloured Carrier-dragon, who had been patiently standing nearby, approached them.

"This is Charlock," the Summer Wizard told them. "He is very special to me."

The dragon allowed the Wizard to stroke his forehead and pat him lovingly under his chin.

"Charlock," the Wizard said to the dragon. "Meet Jonquil the banf and Rattajack, the arven — or should I say terragon."

The carrier-dragon bowed its head respectfully to the two companions and they both returned the gesture.

"I have asked Charlock if he will carry you to the Banf Kingdom. He has agreed to do this. My friends, you could search the length and breadth of Enchantica, and find no worthier beast to bear you on this trip. He will be your trusty steed and your best friend. I have always found it so."

The dragon nudged the Wizard affectionately with his snout, Orolan held Charlock's face in his hands and stared deeply into his eyes.

"May only the fairest winds fill your wings, till we meet again, Lord of Dragons." the Summer Wizard spoke softly to him.

"Come now!" Orolan turned to the banf and the terragon. "All the farewells have been said. It is time to fly. Already the sun is melting into the sea. By the time you are clear of the island, dark will be upon us. Fly fast and fly straight. One small dragon flying alone will stand a better chance of slipping through Vrorst's net. Good fortune go with you!"

Jonquil and Rattajack were securely buckled into their harnesses, by the attendant grooms. They nervously said their final farewells to the Summer Wizard and the island, and then Charlock spread his wings, launched himself into the air and they were gone.

As the light gradually failed, the island raced away beneath them and was replaced by the dark expanse of the ocean. Eventually, a white border on the horizon, heralded the approach of land. Even though it was practically dark, the dragon and the companions could clearly see the frozen wastes of Enchantica, glowing against the shadows, in a deep cloak of snow and ice. The air temperature suddenly dropped, as Charlock flew out of the influence of the enchanted island, and Jonquil immediately thanked Yim, for the skill he had imparted into the banf's warm Winter clothing.

As they approached the pale shores of Enchantica, the dragon and the companions noticed a long arm of ice, directly beneath them, reaching far out into the sea from the Bay of Voices. It was, as the Wizards had feared, a bridge, thrust out from the mainland by Vrorst, to carry his first black legions across the sea, to assail the Forgotten Island. The Ice Lord clearly intended to tighten his grip on the Southern Ocean, and attempt to restrict the Three Wizards' freedom even further.

Charlock had been instructed to follow the course of the Forest River, upstream, to the point where it emerged from the eaves of the Green Sky Forest. The banf kingdom was believed to lie somewhere within a large area, approximately due west from there. This meant flying eastwards along the coastline, for some miles, and eventually crossing over the gates of the Summer Moat.

To his great embarrassment, Jonquil had not been much help to the Wizards in locating his homeland. As, before his encounter with the Three Guardians, he had never stepped beyond the vast expanse of the Green Sky Forest. And consequently could not say with any confidence, exactly where within the great spread of the forest, the Banf Kingdom lay.

Trying to find the mouth of a frozen river, in a snow-swept landscape, would have been difficult enough in the daylight. In the dark it was nigh on impossible. Luckily for Jonquil and Rattajack, carrier-dragons have an excellent, innate navigation system, that enables them to negotiate their way through the most difficult of terrain, even on pitch-black, starless nights. A skill which they would often put to good use, when transporting the power crystals from the heart of the Marble Fortress, to the dragonports of the Throne Citadel; during all seasons and all weathers.

Charlock knew that the Forest River took a course that ran, for the most part, due south, once it was free of the Great Forest. Therefore, a flight due north ought to keep him on more or less the right track, until they reached the walls of the Green Sky. Somehow the dragon knew that he would be able to feel when the snow-laden land, beneath them, finally gave way to the trees. Even though the black void which covered the world, would show no perceptible change. Just as he instinctively knew if he was flying over water or mountains, forests or valleys. All natural things emitted energy waves, which could be read from the air, like the lines on an invisible map. The darkness and the heavy covering of snow was no real obstacle to a perceptive carrier-dragon. Charlock's senses were so keen, he could actually feel the current of the Forest River, flowing beneath its frozen lid.

A boisterous wind began to build in a slow but steady acceleration. Charlock found himself drifting incessantly to the east and having to struggle to maintain his desired course. He tried climbing or dropping to different heights but the battle against the growing gale continued, and the dragon found himself straying far from the river and their northward path.

The Carrier dragon was faced with a dilemma. Should he try to find a place of safety, where they could land and wait for the storm to abate? Or should he struggle on and risk being blown a long distance out of their way. Naturally they were carrying only the smallest amount of food necessary to last them until they reached the Kingdom of the Banfs. If the dragon and the companions drifted too great a distance, and the food was exhausted, Charlock might not have the strength to finish the journey. The carrier-dragon had just decided that the risk was too great, and they should put down in the first patch of forest they encountered, when a bolt of wind like a hammer blow, punched them high into the void. Suddenly, they were seized by the jaws of a titanic whirlwind, that raged above the coastline, and spirited them away into its catastrophic embrace.

Jonquil lost track of time and space as the twisting wind tunnel sucked them ever deeper into itself. Invisible demons, pushed and pulled them, hurling them from one to another, as though the dragon and the companions were small children trapped inside a wicked game. The banf felt a constant pressure pushing from beneath him, as though the wind was trying to prise him from his saddle. But the buckles that held Jonquil were well made and strong, and refused to fail.

Charlock tried to hold his wings closed, to make himself harder to lift, but the force of the maelstrom wrenched them open again, and filled them with cold breath, to worsen the turmoil. The carrier-dragon had been robbed of his navigational senses by the intense energies of the storm, and had no idea how far they had been blown from their course.

At last, the cyclone grew tired of them and spat them out into the night. It was only then, as the battered dragon managed to regain control of his wings and beat them hard to fly out of the influence of the attacking winds, that Charlock and Jonquil discovered their terrible loss. Rattajack had been stolen by the storm.

Charlock resolved to locate a convenient copse of trees nearby and shelter until morning. Jonquil independently reached a similar conclusion and reluctantly accepted that this was sensible.

The carrier-dragon found a suitable outcrop of evergreens and swooped beneath their bushy canopies, coming to rest amongst the feathery upper branches of the largest of the trees. Jonquil then waited with growing apprehension, for the coming of the dawn.

By the time the long hours of darkness had finally skulked by and a thin greyness appeared on the horizon, Jonquil was frantic. The wind storm could have carried the terragon for hours before letting him go. Even though their chances of finding Rattajack amongst the endless snow plains were slight, Jonquil longed to get up there and try for his beloved friend. Charlock, although as eager as Jonquil to recover the terragon, was mindful that the Wizards had expressly advised against flying over snow in daylight. The keen eyes of the snowdragon patrols, could spot a rabbit in the mouth of its burrow from beyond the clouds.

A little of the food rations was hastily broken out, Jonquil insisting that Charlock have the larger share. Then the carrier-dragon lifted from the roof of the small copse.

Wind storms were clearly regular visitors to the Southern Plains, for the snow fields had been sculpted into a rippled texture of waves and ridges. Vast, curling crests and precipices, provided a thousand hiding places, in which a frightened terragon might take refuge for the night, safe from the eyes in the air. The dragon flew over numerous bushy copses and sporadic bursts of woodland, all capable of affording excellent concealed shelter to a hiding terragon. It was hopeless, Rattajack could be in one of a million places. Even without the threat of discovery by the enemy, they could never hope to search every crevice and tunnel in the snow, every canopy of every tree. The terrain was simply too wide and difficult.

"It would be easier," Charlock thought to himself. "To find the Cloak of Xanthia, than a tiny dragon lost in a thousand square miles of featureless snow desert."

The banf felt as though half of his soul had been torn from him, now Rattajack was gone. Jonquil would rather have leapt from Charlock's back and thrashed aimlessly through the snow until he froze to death, than let the terragon think he had abandoned him. Part of Jonquil would die if he had to leave his beloved companion behind. Rattajack was a part of him, separation was unbearable.

The carrier-dragon was sad for Jonquil, and wished they might search longer for his lost friend. But they had already allowed the morning to grow too bright before finding their way back to the course of the Forest River. Soon the eyes of the enemy would be upon them.

Charlock knew that Jonquil would never willingly call off their search, so the carrier-dragon reluctantly made the dreadful decision himself and slowly turned into the west, to try to locate the frozen river.

Jonquil comforted himself a little, however, with the knowledge that Rattajack was an arven. A creature of legendry abilities. He would probably survive his ordeal, despite the odds, better than Charlock or Jonquil, and emerge from it, triumphant.

Little did the banf know, how prophetic his private thoughts would turn out to be.

Following a good deal of frantic reconnoitring over the featureless snowscape, Charlock discovered that they had been blown almost a day's flight out of their way, in a mainly north easterly direction. The small copse that had sheltered them during the night, was probably one of the many outlying clumps of trees which preceded the great expanse of the Mystery Wood.

It was now mid-morning and the sun rose unhindered against a flawless blue backcloth. The wind storm appeared to have sucked every cloud from the sky, during the course of its night time ravages.

Charlock was uneasy. He hated having to fly against a stark white groundscape in such unbridled sunshine. It was a bold risk, and he feared discovery. Their only chance would be to keep to every patch of woodland they could find, and pray that his prominent silhouette, would be swallowed up by the treetops.

It was the banf, ironically, that first raised the alarm, on spotting a white speck high in the blue void behind them. Jonquil had been as silent as the grave since they had abandoned the search for Rattajack. He had become withdrawn and disinterested in their quest. Perhaps the fearful sight of the snowdragon, far in the east had jolted his senses, for now their adventure had his renewed, earnest attention.

Charlock remained calm and kept stoically to their present flight pattern, not wanting to relay the impression of panic or an attempt to escape, to their distant observer. Jonquil kept him informed of the white dragon's movements. As far as the banf could tell, it did not appear to be gaining or losing ground, but simply hanging in the air, following at its leisure.

The carrier-dragon knew this tactic well. He and the banf were being observed. The enemy not yet sure if they were friend or foe.

In the days when Vrorst still trusted the carrier-dragons to transport his crystals, from the Marble Fortress to his new Ice Palace on the sight of the former Throne Citadel, Charlock and his brothers would often find themselves being tracked by relaying teams of high flying snowdragons. At the first sign of deviance or deception by the carriers, the snowdragons would dive out of the sun and stoop mercilessly to strike at them. The Ice Lord still used captive carrier-dragons for selective tasks, usually long distance flights. Mezereon, Vrorst's hench-wizard had not yet turned his hand to creating a snow beast that could fulfil that specific need. He was more interested in breeding aggressive, even swifter snowdragons; that were ideal for war, but were built for speed, strength and agility, rather than endurance.

Charlock clung to the vain hope that their watcher would assume him to be a slave carrier-dragon, on the Ice Lord's business, even though he had no escort. Charlock had no choice but to bluff it out and pray that the dragonrider's indecision, would carry him beyond the snowdragon's striking range and force him to turn back.

Charlock spread his wings and they were gone.

Disaster! Jonquil located a second white flier, low to the south and moving at great speed. Its flight path rapidly converging with their own. They were discovered!

Charlock knew from bitter experience that attempting to out fly the snowdragons was futile, for they could fly like the wind. The dragon and the banf's only chance was to drop from the sky and hope to be lost amongst the sculptured landscape of the snow plains. Charlock snapped shut his wings and tipped them into a sharp dive; the white desert racing towards them at horrifying speed.

A tall crest appeared to the left, its crusty overhang forming a long, half covered tunnel, that after meandering wildly beneath the surface of the plain, finally divided into a tangled honeycomb of smaller trenches and burrows. The dragon picked his spot, checked his speed, and boldly ploughed, feet first, through the roof of the tunnel; the hard, frost bitten snow exploding before them like a surging white surf.

Suddenly a rush of wind roared overhead as one of the snowdragons skimmed low over the ridges above them; waves of snow dust whispered along the walls of the tunnel in its wake. More powerful white dragons bore down on the place where Charlock had broken the snow crust, four of them wheeling in tightening spirals, to cover any sudden flight by the carrier-dragon.

Jonquil quickly picked himself up out of the deep powder snow, leapt ahead of Charlock and led the dragon into the maze of holes and banks that opened up before them. The banf and the carrier-dragon scrambled this way and that through the network of twisting furrows, now and then wasting valuable time by following the course of a covered ridge that either abruptly ended in a solid wall, or opened up to the sky, forcing them to hastily retrace their steps.

The pounding of heavy, clawed feet echoed in the tunnels behind them; one of the snowdragons had landed, and taken up the chase. It did not seem to matter how fast Jonquil and Charlock ran, the enemy always seemed to be just around the last corner.

The banf suddenly halted in his tracks, the breath bursting from his stooped body in long plumes of steam. Jonquil seemed to be listening for something. One of his long ears lifted to the sky, and his eyes, strained with concentration, were fixed on the ceiling of the tunnel.

Dark voices approached from behind and soon the enemy would be upon them. Charlock was about to urge Jonquil forward when suddenly he heard it too; a growing, high pitched scream, splitting the air, like the fast approach of a giant arrow. Jonquil hurled himself at the carrier-dragon, pushing him bodily back down the passage. Moments later, the roof of the tunnel, over where they had been standing, burst inwards, showering the banf and the dragon with a deluge of hurtling snow.

A broad beam of light spilled on to the floor of the shadowy tunnel, through the new vent in its covering. The air was thick with disturbed snow particles, and through the milky haze a deep growl bellowed forth. Then a monstrous shape rose from the pile of snow brought down from above, silhouetted against the strong flood of light. Muscular limbs and folded wings, shook the frozen debris from its long body as it crawled towards the banf and the carrier-dragon. The snowdragon's snaking tail flashed white in the daylight, as its menacing, pointed face led it forward.

A white-clad form slid down from the snowdragon's back, and drew a long scimitar from its sheath. The dragonrider cautiously crept forward with the dragon, a leering snarl fixed on both their faces.

Jonquil and Charlock scrambled to their feet and tried to escape back along the tunnel, only to be met by a wall of dragonriders blocking their retreat; scimitars held purposefully before them.

The dragonriders, clothed in armoured robes of silver and white, appeared almost ghostly as the snow dust reluctantly settled about them. Their grim faces were made more fearsome, by the helms that sat proudly on their heads; fashioned in the shape of a snarling dragon.

The enemy began to close in on the banf and the carrier, and the two noble creatures braced themselves for the inevitable rush and the sharp thrusts of the scimitars.

Suddenly, a clear voice from the rear cried, "Wait!"

The eyes of the enemy turned as one to watch the tall, elegant figure, stride majestically to the fore. Her long, white robe edged with a wide border of blue ermine.

The dragonriders shrank away as she passed between them. Even the snowdragons seemed to quake at her approach. She fixed the banf with a steely stare, sharp-blue eyes burning into his own. Her pale, strangely haunting face was framed in a turban of white fur, and crowned with a jewelled silver star; an opulent stole of blue ermine was wrapped tightly about her shoulders.

The Lady's interest in the carrier-dragon and the banf had been, at first, only casual. She had intended to suspend their slaughter; only long enough to be sure that they were not beings of any importance. But perhaps it was as the Lord Orolan had told him, there was an air about the banf; an aura that refused to be ignored. A lesser being might have dismissed the strange light glowing in Jonquil's startled eyes, and condemned him to be slain, but she was Tuatara, High Witch of Winter, and was possessed of much greater perception than the common herd. An inner voice suggested that her prisoners might prove worthy of further investigation, so she turned to the armed riders about her and snapped;

"Bring them!" And before she strode out of earshot added;

"Alive!"

Nine snowdragons and three captive carrier-dragons made up the Ice Witch's flight; the latter looking on with surprise and sadness, as Jonquil and Charlock were bound and brought up to the surface. The carrier-dragons were poor, dispirited beasts; pale reflections of their free brethren that soared on the thermals rising from the Forgotten Island. Charlock was visibly dismayed to look upon them.

Tuatara and her party had been returning from a new garrison in the Mystery Wood (a vast fortress that had recently been constructed to guard the great plains), when her out fliers had spotted the lone carrier-dragon. They were now due to make the long flight to the Mountains of Menace, where the diplomatic skills of the Ice Witch were required to avert a near revolution.

Jonquil was placed on to the back of one of the snowdragons, and shackled behind its dragonrider. Charlock was tethered about his neck with strong chains, and forced to fly in tow, from another of the swift, white beasts; at a cruel, relentless pace.

When Hawkhood, one of Tuatara's lieutenants, asked her if their party would now divert from their errand, and return to the Throne Citadel with their newly acquired prisoners, he met with a surly, negative response. The Ice Witch's presence was urgently required at the court of Hellbender in the Mountains of Menace and that was the route they would take. The prisoners would have to suffer the journey with them, there was no alternative. Tuatara would deliver the banf and the carrier-dragon to Vrorst personally, after her business with the Goblin King was done.

With that, the Ice Witch and her entourage, including the unfortunate Jonquil and Charlock, left the low wastes of the Southern Plains and flew for the High peaks of the Mountains of Menace.

It was a long, arduous journey that took them from the deep south, to the far north of Enchantica. Jonquil, who in his short experience of it, had never grown to love dragonflight, found his time, chained to the rear of the snowdragon's saddle, a slow, tortuous nightmare.

The snowdragons, Jonquil wearily observed, seemed incapable of flying straight or level. They loved to weave about the sky, banking and swooping from one rising gust to the next; soaring and stooping like great hawks commanding the wind. The carriers, who were being employed as beasts of burden, slowed them down (much to the faster dragons' frustration.) After racing on ahead and piercing the clouds like white arrows, the snowdragons would have to break into wide circles to allow the slower dragons to catch up.

To make the trip even more protracted and unbearable, the lengthy expedition was flown in separate stages. The dragonflight alighting at various garrisons and dragon stables strategically founded along the route; to acquire fresh steeds to complete the next section of the journey. The enduring carriers, however, were not changed; being possessed of great stamina, and wisely abstaining from the energy wasting aerobatics of the enemy's white flocks.

At the changeovers, Jonquil was yanked out of his seat by the rider charged with guarding him and thrown into a covered corral with Charlock and the other carriers. In their company, he was fed and watered. An unidentifiable, steaming slop sitting heavily in a wooden bowl; which was thrust into his chest, was the only nourishment he was offered. It was probably intended to be oatmeal, though it tasted like gravel. However, following Charlock's example, he accepted the food, such as it was, for he was sure to need his strength and courage to face whatever trials lay ahead of him.

As the riders re-emerged from their lodgings the next morning (or whenever the Ice Witch decided it was time to continue) the banf was plucked from his resting place (and if still asleep, given a good kick first) and tightly bound on to the back of a new white dragon, ready for the next flight. And so the dreadful journey continued.

Tuatara was lost in her own thoughts. The wide formation of snowdragons that flew about her, disappeared from sight as the Ice Witch's mind kept returning to her last audience with Vrorst.

She had spent a good deal of time with the Ice Sorcerer, in the days leading up to his ascension. Vrorst had welcomed her counsel, and listened intently to her plans and ideas, many of which he had decided to adopt, or adapt to his own needs. The Ice Lord had made her feel high and worthy, and he had asked her to sit beside him in his snow chariot, at his right hand, when they had marched down from the Frozen Kingdom. Vrorst had made Tuatara feel like a queen; not just a queen of witches, but a queen...of the world?

All the high captains of Winter had told her that it was only a matter of time before Vrorst took a consort; a queen to share in all the wonders of the new world he was creating. The most forthright consensus of opinion, indicated that Tuatara was considered to be the Ice Sorcerer's first and only choice.

The Ice Witch coyly denied that she was held in such high favour, but secretly waited for the day when Vrorst called her to him and asked for her hand.

An involuntary smile played across Tuatara's lips, as she recalled the final words Vrorst had spoken to her, before sending the Ice Witch on the vital mission to the goblins; a task the great sorcerer would entrust to no other.

"You wear a good deal of silver on your robes, Tuatara," he told her. "You dress like a queen!"

The Ice Witch soon recognised that there was no malice in his voice, and that it was safe to flirt.

"Does it offend you, Lord," she pouted.

"Not at all," he answered, thrilling her with a well crafted smile. "If you dress like a queen, I shall have to make you a queen...."

Tuatara's heart almost burst in her chest, at Vrorst's words, her pale face visibly flushed with feigned demureness and surprise. Was this the beginning of a proposal?

Vrorst would have had to have been blind not to have seen the question deeply inscribed across the Ice Witch's reddened features. As he was a being of infinitely superior perceptive powers, the Sorcerer was already leagues ahead of her, and knew exactly what the Ice Witch wanted to hear.

Instead, Vrorst bestowed another rare smile upon Tuatara, and softly told her that the matter would be discussed further; on her return from the Dark Mountains.

"For I have a grave errand for you, Queen of Witches," he announced. "Hellbender is sitting atop a volcano of revolution and is coping with it badly. As you know, the King of the Goblins, is not well acquainted with Tact and Diplomacy; the twin brothers of Reconciliation. If he is allowed to continue with his ill-advised summary executions of high goblins, the imbecile will incite all of the goblin races to rise up in mindless civil war. And that is a gift to the Wizards of Light, I do not intend to make. As the highest symbol of my power, I send you to Hellbender. Persuade him to resolve his little domestic difficulties and bend once again to my will!"

Tuatara bowed low before the Lord of Winter;

"I will do so," she answered.

The Ice Witch repeated the words aloud to herself, seated in the richly adorned saddle of her snowdragon mount.

“I will!” She crooned. But there seemed to be a new connotation to her words, and the dreamy smile which accompanied them, lasted until the dragonflight had passed over the first foothills of the Mountains of Menace.

At the Court of the Goblin King

A sullen cluster of snow-capped peaks, rising to a flat-topped colossus of jagged rock, heralded the end of an interminable journey for the flight of the Ice Witch and her prisoners. The Dark Mountains, blushed with deep shades of amber, the reflected glory of a dramatic sunset dying in the west, marched on from this fortress of granite, ever northwards to join the mighty ramparts of Vrorst's old frozen refuge.

The skein of snowdragons closed into a tight, arrow shaped formation for the approach to the Great Gates; Hawkhood and another rider having already flown ahead to secure a safe landing with the goblin sentries.

At almost two thirds of the towering column's height, a narrow tongue of rock protruded from the base of a roughly hewn, enlarged cave entrance. Twin spikes of rock, embellished with carved insignia, forked the end of the thin promontory, its edges bristling with two walls of barbed iron pales. As the descending lines of white dragons stepped down on to the stone platform, Jonquil looked up into the faces of two giant goblin figures carved from the body of the mountain, standing guard either side of the cave entrance. They wore fierce expressions, their thick hands clasping the hilt of long spiked war clubs; the heads of which lay at rest between their taloned feet. Both characters, who were slightly different, were portrayed in grandiose armour and costume, crowns fashioned from the horned skulls of some fearsome animal, sat proudly on their heads.

Before Jonquil and Charlock were roughly herded inside the open gates of the goblin city, along with the other carriers, the banf noticed that a third statue had been started at the elbow of one of the others, its head and body just discernible from the rough face of the mountain.

Heavily armed goblins from Hellbender's personal militia, the elite of his warriors, escorted the procession of snowdragons and riders (headed by the Ice Witch) through the long, torchlit hallway that led to the throne room of the goblin king. The curved walls of the corridor were lined with doubled ranks of soldiers, each bearing large, oval shields and tall, hooked halberds.

Judging by the apparent uneasiness of the dragonriders, who glanced nervously from side to side as they passed between the rows of goblin pikemen, and whose gauntleted hands never strayed too far from the hilts of their scimitars, the banf assumed that the guard of honour, assembled to welcome Tuatara's party, was unusually large and threatening.

Waiting to greet the Ice Witch at the head of a short flight of steps that led to the threshold of an enormous, square entrance, barred by two solid iron doors, was Mummichog. He was the bent, wily, elder statesman, who served as court advisor to Hellbender, and who, through his extreme shrewdness and sharp wits had survived the reigns of three goblin kings; an admirable achievement in the face of ruthless court politics.

The wise old goblin was the only resident of the Dark Mountains that the Queen of Witches came even close to respecting. His was the calming voice of reason that quietly argued against the goblin king's wild demands and ideas, daring only to suggest (in the most respectful of tones), that perhaps an alternative course of action might prove more effective and less offensive.

Without the wise, old goblin to act as peacemaker, during Tuatara's previous infrequent encounters with Hellbender, the goblin king might easily have found himself shrivelled by a bolt of blue fire for his bold insolence.

Mummichog wore the straight, simple robes of an 'Invisible'; a curious, self-effacing caste of goblin society that reputedly abstained from the usual aggressive, depraved, murderous activities enjoyed by the rest of the population. He wore a close-fitting head mask, that covered the top half of his face, only narrow slits allowed for his eyes, that supposedly represented anonymity and selflessness; but Tuatara knew better than to think that this seemingly, unassuming individual was no more than a humble, priestly creature. The real mask that Mummichog wore covered more than just his face. He was a consummate deceiver and a silver tongued beguiler; whose ruthless ambition had spelled disaster for many a younger courtier; foolish enough to try for a share of the king's favour. Mummichog's vast experience enabled him to skip, light-footed across the stormy moods of his violent masters, and emerge at the end even deeper entrenched in his king's affections than before.

Infact, he displayed much of the skill and legerdemain that the Ice Witch practised so artfully herself; perhaps that was why Tuatara almost liked Mummichog.

Though his dark robes were meant to suggest the old goblin was a shadowy, peaceful creature of harmless ways and meditation, he appeared to Jonquil to look more like a short, malevolent executioner.

At Tuatara's approach, Mummichog motioned to one of a crowd of subordinates, all similarly clad in simple robes, who lifted a heavy, iron-topped staff and hammered twice on the great doors, the sound echoing in some vast chamber beyond. The old goblin then took a solitary step forwards and bowed respectfully to the Ice Witch, Tuatara responding with the slightest of head movements. Suddenly with a groan, the two mighty doors parted, and the host of Hellbender was revealed inside.

An immense cavern, dripping with stalactites from a high, domed ceiling, in places fusing with their upward growing brothers to form trunks of rock, opened out before them, as Mummichog led Tuatara and her dragonflight forward.

A great mass of armed goblins, in full battle dress and bristling with a variety of effective looking weapons, filled the main part of the chamber. Even Tuatara seemed a little surprised to see such a show of strength, paraded for her benefit. Was Hellbender trying to impress her with the power of his army? Or was this mustering of forces a sign of a king under siege?

In the centre of the chamber, four grotesque, horned icons, representing a powerful, demonic, goblin deity, faced outwards from a wide, circular dais. Each statue squatted before a huge caldron of fire, their evil faces made even more sinister, by being lit from below by a dancing, orange light.

The grisly spectacle of a ring of blood stained pikes, each bearing the grimacing, severed head of a goblin, rose from the base of the stone platform. Ugly trophies of some recent skirmish.

Rising prominently from the centre of the round platform itself, was a pale throne, of a curious construction. From where he was standing, Jonquil could not quite see what the throne was made of. The pile of pale objects might have been conch shells, but the banf could not be sure. Seated within it, was a slouched, fat goblin, yellow fangs gleaming in a smug, arrogant grin, his mostly bare, olive-green skin, stained with an orange glow.

Tuatara, Hawkhood and two other dragonriders, separated from the rest of the party and walked through a corridor, that had just opened in the thick crowd of Hellbender's guards, leading to his throne.

The Princess Okra, who had been standing at her father's side, stepped down to greet the Ice Witch, and having done so, removed herself, thus leaving only the great goblin king himself, Hellbender, son of Jemlin, ruler of his people for over eighty years, and until recently, undisputed king of all the tribes of the Dark Mountains, to give his welcome to the Queen of Witches.

The king and the sorceress stared deeply into each others eyes. Hellbender made no effort to rise from his sagging position. He simply remained slumped in his large throne, specially designed to lounge in, audaciously showing the soles of his bare feet to the Ice Witch, his gold mace reclining casually in his arms.

In the spirit of diplomacy, and so as to aid expediency in her quest, Tuatara chose to ignore this gross insult that the King of the Goblins was deliberately showing to her. She had better ways of occupying her time than teaching imperious goblin scum how to behave in the presence of high beings.

The briefest salutations were briskly exchanged.

The Queen of Witches could see that Hellbender's languid attitude was nothing more than a thin facade. It was a performance, a superficial affectation designed to convince the surrounding faithful, that their king, despite the threat of massive insurrection from his people, was unperturbed by it all; fearless and nonchalant. Even the arrival of the highest captain of the Ice Lord, sent especially to reimpose the authority of Winter and take control of his crown, Hellbender pretended to treat as a minor inconvenience, a mere trifle he was quite ready to accept with a bouquet of geniality.

Tuatara knew only too well that the supercilious smile, fixed a little too rigidly on the king goblin's face, hid an inner expression, festering with hate and humiliation, outraged at the interference of an outsider in his affairs, especially a female.

"There is much to discuss, Hellbender, King," Tuatara coolly announced. "We should talk without delay."

Hellbender's eyes narrowed a little, betraying a tiny portion of the bile seething within him. He had wanted to take the initiative with the Ice Witch, make it appear as if her intervention was his idea. However, not wanting to risk further loss of face, he resisted the temptation to rebuke his 'guest'. The Goblin King silently motioned to Mummichog, who in turn gave a prearranged signal to another minor, and somewhere the strangled wail of a goblin horn lifted above the crowd.

The multitude, gathered about their king, obediently answered the call of the horn and began to file out of the throne chamber, filtering slowly through a ring of gated openings built into the curved walls of the great cavern.

The remainder of the Ice Witch's party were shown to their quarters. The fearsome snowdragons were led away by their riders to specially prepared stables, none of the goblin attendants daring to approach them. The prisoners, which included the captive carrier-dragons, were incarcerated in nearby cells. Tuatara made it clear to Hawkhood and his deputies, as they took their leave of the throne room, that all of the prisoners were to be carefully watched, each cell having a dragonrider guard as well as a goblin one. The Ice Witch had lost more than one prisoner, in the past, to the guardhouse dining table, on her previous stays in the Dark Mountains. She did not intend to lose any on this occasion. Hellbender gazed innocently on as Tuatara warned her subordinates to be wary of raids in the night, and then dismissed them from her side.

Soon the Queen of Witches was alone with the Goblin King and Mummichog.

"Perhaps you would be good enough, your majesty," Tuatara began, her voice dripping with false politeness. "To furnish me with an account of the fantastic events that have happened in recent days, here in the Ice Lord's realm of the Dark Mountains.

I have to tell you, great king, that rumours abound within the hallowed halls of the Throne Citadel, that your people have chosen a new leader, and now they are in revolt."

Hellbender's eyes flashed a brighter shade of red as he suddenly straightened himself and took on a much more interested posture.

"My people are not revolting!" he growled in response.

The obvious flippant retort leapt mischievously into Tuatara's mind, but she strongly resisted the urge to voice it.

"There may have been a few.....incidents," the king continued.

"A few incidents?" Tuatara exclaimed, staring at the ring of severed heads surrounding the throne dais. "You have executed eight tribal chiefs! Hardly the actions of a king courting the good will of his subjects."

"They deserved it! Treacherous scumbags!" Hellbender roared. "And I will kill eight more if I have to."

The sorceress raised an eyebrow and gave the goblin a half smile;

"That is if they don't kill you first," she said.

"What?" Hellbender leapt from the throne and padded angrily up to the Ice Witch. Tuatara stiffened a little at his approach, and the goblin king suddenly checked his advance as if a weapon had been drawn against him, although the sorceress had done nothing more than simply flex her fingers. This slight movement, however, was clearly sufficient to remind the goblin of some former confrontation.

"W'What do you mean?" the king asked, a little more softly.

"Is it not true that there have been attempts on your life?" Tuatara responded.

Hellbender's eyes almost burst from his skull with rage, he ground one of his heels into the face of the stone and his fists thumped hard against his naked thighs in fury.

"Who spreads such lies about me?" he demanded. "Is it someone close to me?"

He turned swiftly on the attending Mummichog, daggers leaping from his eyes at the elder goblin. Mummichog remained silent and still, his masked eyes never straying from a small patch of ground located between his feet. Hellbender dared him with unspoken threats to make some defence, but the wise old goblin knew from experience to seek the sanctuary of silence. The Ice Witch decided to divert Hellbender's malice. She needed Mummichog's influence over the king to prevail, and so could not afford to let the old advisor be forced to forfeit his good position.

"The source of the rumours is irrelevant," Tuatara told the goblin king. "The important thing is are they true? You must know, Hellbender, that the Lord of Ice will not support a king who cannot control his people. I could prevent you from being overthrown, but if the goblin tribes will not follow you, what is the purpose of it?"

The king goblin glared at Tuatara, frustration and despair coursing through his body in tremulous spasms. His fists clenched and unclenched, his fangs ground savagely against each other. At one point, he even seized the shaft of his gold club and whacked the fragile frame of his pale throne, splintering one of its components. Hellbender began to look more and more like a wicked pupil, sulking outrageously and desperately trying to string together the threads of an excuse. Eventually he turned and slumped into his throne, an enormous pout protruding from his face.

"Insults and lies," he whimpered, almost to himself. "And not even a gift."

The Ice Witch gave Hellbender a look which only half betrayed the impatience building within her.

"What did you say?" she asked shortly.

"A gift," Hellbender repeated. "It is customary when one visits the court of a great king to bring a gift. I want my gift!"

Tuatara could hardly believe her ears. She might have guessed that the goblin king would use some abstract tactic to try and change the subject, and divert the focus of undesirable attention away from himself, but this tiresome portrayal of a spoilt child was not even mildly effective.

"Your majesty!" Tuatara sneered. "I have not come here to this accursed place on a social visit! I have been sent here to prevent a disastrous civil war, the blame for which lies squarely on your shoulders. If you manage to remain alive, for the duration of my stay here, you may count your life a gift!"

Hellbender made a rapid decision to abandon his former ploy and returned passionately to the matter at hand.

"Gremba!" he cried. "Self-appointed Lord of the Northern Goblins. He is the cause of all this unrest!"

"Strange," Tuatara calmly answered him. "I was led to believe it was due to your incompetence as a ruler."

The king goblin landed a crashing blow on his throne with a tightly clenched fist and his eyes burned with red fire.

"I have been king of all the goblin tribes for eighty long years. I have lost count of the number of challengers skulls I have crushed with my royal mace. I have gnawed my teeth to stubs on their bloody bones."

If this impassioned statement was intended to impress the Ice Witch, it failed. She had long since ceased to be moved by the murderous, depraved behaviour she had witnessed over the years carried out by the goblin hordes. Eating their enemies, impressed her least of all. Hellbender seemed to have caught his second wind and arrogantly continued.

"I know," he said. "That every king's reign must come to an end, one day, but I will not stand down from my throne until my skull has been cleaved by a worthy successor; and Gremba of the north is not that goblin!"

Hellbender's expression darkened a little, and he submitted to a brief twinge of sadness, or the nearest thing a goblin can feel to it.

"I had hoped that one of my sons would have come for my crown," he reflected. "But they tell me that they are both dead. And I tell you, my Lady. I would rather leave my crown to my daughter than name that scumrat Gremba as my heir; as I have been advised!"

A fresh volley of daggers winged their way over to the shadowy Mummichog, standing silently nearby.

Tuatara wondered if she ought to tell the goblin king that Bledderag, his son, had not died at the Battle of the Bay of Voices, as had been reported by the few wretched individuals, who had survived that conflict. Deceitful goblin warriors, who, not wanting to incur the wrath of their vicious king by telling him that his son was cast in chains, and taken from the battlefield in shame and dishonour, had created an heroic scenario for the ending of Bledderag. They claimed that he had fallen like a mighty warrior, safe in the knowledge that the goblin twin would certainly meet his death in the torture chambers of the Throne Citadel; and therefore not be in a position to contradict their tale.

In truth, neither of these supposed endings was true. Only Tuatara herself amongst those present at Hellbender's court knew what really happened to the king's son.

Bledderag had been taken prisoner by Wargren after the ill-fated battle, but whilst the dragon party had been flying over the wide expanse of the Great Forest, the goblin prince had broken free of his bonds, inflicted a fatal knife-wound to his accompanying dragonrider and leapt from the snowdragon's back. He had plummeted like a stone through the low lying banks of cloud and disappeared forever into oblivion.

Wargren had not bothered to instigate a search, he had been satisfied that from such a height, no living creature would survive the fall. Bledderag was probably spread rather thinly over a wide area of the forest floor.

Tuatara resolved to keep her knowledge to herself. Hellbender believed his son was dead, that was enough.

The Goblin King drew his feet up on to the seat of the throne and started toying, coyly with his toes. The almost boyish expression that never really succeeded on his face, warned the Ice Witch that a proposition was on its way.

"If," Hellbender began. "Gremba was out of the way. I believe all would be well."

Tuatara breathed an inward sigh of relief. At last they were approaching the solution that she herself had considered before leaving the company of the Ice Lord, although for political reasons the suggestion had to come from Hellbender himself.

"Without Gremba to lead them," the goblin king continued. "The Northern tribes would be thrown into confusion, running about their rabbit holes like headless chickens! Then I would stand before them, mighty and irresistible, an inspiring figure, much like my new statue by the great gates...."

"I noticed that you had started it," Tuatara interrupted him. "I am sure your forefathers can hardly contain the honour they must feel at having your majestic figure join them at such an appropriate time. You are the the longest ever reigning monarch of the Dark Mountains, since the tribes were united, and as such more than entitled to be carved into immortality by your goblin craftsmen. But if they do not hurry up with your likeness, they might not get the chance to finish it."

Hellbender coughed uneasily and tried to dismiss the dark insinuation;

"As I was saying," he hissed. "Without a leader, the Northern Goblins would flock to my banner and proclaim me once again rightful king of the Dark Mountains, king of all goblins!"

He threw a sly glance at the Ice Witch, an artful glint sparkling in his scarlet eyes.

"Wouldn't that please the Lord of Ice?" Hellbender teased.

Tuatara refused to play.

"Not the deepest, darkest pit in the whole of these mountains, could hide Gremba from your magic," the king continued. "Is it not so that with the merest flick of your little finger, Gremba would cease to breathe?"

Tuatara decided to play a little game of her own;

"You are a resourceful king," she evaded. "Why not send assassins of your own?"

"I have done!" Hellbender protested. "And they have all been returned to me....in bits!"

The king suddenly cast his eyes upon the ground as if he burdened a great shame.

"I even sent my daughter to that scragging scumbag. To marry him, on this old crone's advice. A blessed union between our two great peoples! Bah! He kept her for three months; had his way with her no doubt, and then sent her packing! Not to his taste, he dared to inform me. Bowelrat! By the bones of my fathers, I swear I shall feast on his brains!"

Tuatara abruptly turned from the stone dais and started down the few steps leading to the main floor of the cavern.

"There is much to consider," The Ice Witch left him with. "I shall deliver my decision in good time. After all, I have to be sure that Gremba would not make a better king of the goblins than you!"

Hellbender lay back into the cradle of his throne and followed the sorceress with his eyes. He allowed her to almost reach the opening that led to her apartments before delivering his final word.

"Half a million goblin warriors I could send into battle with the Lord of Ice, if all the tribes of the mountains were united beneath me. If, however, Gremba is allowed to continue living, I promise you that the whole of these mountains will rise up in a war the like of which has never been told.

Have no doubt, my Lady, that I would be victorious. At the end of it, I would still emerge as undisputed king. But who can say how many brave warriors would perish in such a conflict, thousands upon thousands perhaps; a sorry and greatly weakened ruler would I be then, a poor ally to the great lord of Winter."

Tuatara disliked intensely the supercilious smirk that accompanied the final words of the goblin king's short speech; even though she was some distance from the throne now, she could still see his large fangs gleaming in the firelight.

"You will have my decision in due course," she told him and swiftly withdrew.

Hellbender grunted dismissively as the sleek form of the Ice Witch was swallowed by the dark mouth of the doorway. A lascivious smile grew on his lips when he thought of just what he would like to do to the Lady Tuatara, if she was his for the taking. But that was a dream, and dreams were a waste of brain space.

Eventually the king slowly turned his attention to his elderly advisor, who had stood as silent as stone, throughout the whole council with the Ice Witch. Hellbender was in no mood to be charitable, and for some reason the black robed figure hunched beside him, trying to look as humble and as unassuming as possible, annoyed Hellbender beyond reason. Mummichog instinctively sensed that the king was about to enter a violent rage. He debated with himself what his chances would be, of calming Hellbender down, with a few well chosen compliments and sympathies, now that the Ice Witch had cast him into such a fury. Should he stay and comfort his king when the storm broke, or sprint out of clubshot?

"And as for you!" Hellbender roared. "You scragging lump of dragon dumping! Get out of my sight before I raise your voice an octave!"

In less time than it takes to sigh, Hellbender was alone.

Tuatara had not progressed far along the poorly lit corridor on her way to her quarters, when the dark form of Okra suddenly stepped out of the shadows. As the goblin princess was dressed almost entirely in a full length black robe, apart from a circle of silver draped around her muscular olive-green shoulders, the Ice Witch did not really see the princess until she was almost upon her. Tuatara just managed to stop herself crying out in surprise, and rebuked the she-goblin severely for approaching the Ice Witch in such a clandestine manner. The Sorceress sharply asked Okra what she wanted.

"Only to ask, Lady," The goblin princess nervously began. "If you intend to grant my father's request and kill the Lord Gremba."

Tuatara, who by this time had suffered more than enough royal goblins and their infantile games, turned her full fury on the young princess.

"You may be the daughter of the King, Princess Okra, but that does not entitle you to eavesdrop like a common spy, on a highly secret council. Count yourself very lucky that I do not inform your father of this outrage!"

And with that Tuatara stormed off down the corridor, but the princess was not about to give up so easily and ran after her.

"I must know! Please tell me!" Okra pleaded.

The Ice Witch stopped and looked suspiciously at the young she-goblin;

"How does this lofty matter concern you?" Tuatara demanded.

Okra's face was racked with a terribly overplayed look of entreaty; she wrung her hands dramatically and tried her very best to sound sincere and convincing; she failed completely.

"I only want what is best for my people," Okra lied. "I love my father and I want everything to be alright."

Despite the great weariness that the goblins inspired in the Ice Witch, she could not help but smile at the very concept of a goblin professing to love anything, especially another goblin. Love was an emotion that occurred in the hearts of the inhabitants of the Mountains of Menace, about as often as thoughts of vegetarianism occurred to lions, or advanced mathematics to forest trolls.

Okra was lying through her fangs and Tuatara simply refused to waste her time searching for the truth.

"Either tell me what all this is about, or take your leave," the Ice Witch snapped.

Okra had the eyes of her father, red and deceitful, and a mouth that was incapable of saying what was on its owner's mind.

"I know Gremba has been very wicked," she began to say, and Tuatara thought she saw a slight grin break across the princess's face, at the memory of it. "But I am sure that this horrid situation can be solved without anyone having to die."

"I would have thought that you of all people would have wished him dead, after he humiliated you." The Ice Witch responded.

"Perhaps I should," Okra answered demurely. "But I don't see why it is necessary for him to die, to gain our revenge."

"Well, your father is of a different opinion," Tuatara told the she-goblin. "And for once I find myself in the unique position of agreeing with him!"

The Ice Witch dismissed the goblin princess with a waft of her hand and strode out determinedly for the sanctuary of her private rooms.

A flash of red fire flickered in Okra's eyes as she stared transfixed into the burning head of a torch, dark thoughts boiling in her brain. Eventually she stiffened and her eyes narrowed as if a huge conclusion had been reached within the turmoil of her mind. She had her decision, now she must act on it, speed was of the essence. With a steely expression cast on her face, the goblin princess hurried away purposefully into a connecting corridor that would take her to her bed-chamber. As she hastened through the dim passage, Okra wondered if the King would care for a goblet of her special wine before retiring.

Huddled in the darkest corner of a bare stone cell, sealed by a bolted iron door, and separated from Charlock and the other carriers, sat a cold and miserable Jonquil. He sat on the floor, his knees tucked firmly under his chin, his arms wrapped tightly around him. He had been saved from the freezing, hard stone, by a small, moth-eaten fur blanket, that smelled of stale goblins, graciously provided by one of his dragonrider guards. The goblins guards had been quite happy to let him freeze.

A solitary oil lamp, of minute proportions, produced the tiniest flame to combat the permanent darkness filling the cell. It barely created enough light to illuminate itself, let alone anything else. Never-the-less, it was the only focal point that offered an alternative to Jonquil's otherwise black environment, so his eyes stared vacantly into it.

The eye in the banf's mind, however, was cast upon an entirely different scene; the deep snowfields of the Southern Plains, where his beloved green companion had fallen out of his life.

Ever since Jonquil had been frog-marched away from the great gathering in Hellbender's throne room, and thrown bodily into the cell, where he still languished in roughly the same foetal position that he had first assumed, the banf had relived over and over again the sequence of events leading to Rattajack's disappearance. Indeed, from that day forward Jonquil's thoughts never strayed far from his lost friend, and he made a silent vow, never to allow his wanderer's feet to rest, until he had found his beloved Rattajack and they were together again once more.

Jonquil cleared a thin procession of tears from his cheeks, mopping them with his sleeve. The smiling vision of Rattajack that he had painted on the blackness, slowly began to fade, until all that survived was two sparkling amber orbs, glowing with a soft inner light; then finally they too were gone.

Suddenly the bolts on the heavy door squealed in protest as they were wrenched back, and two goblin guards carrying torches entered the small cell. They stood for a few moments, the firelight playing across their grisly features, as they looked for the banf.

"Look lively, scum!" the first goblin spat into the darkness, as his eyes scanned the floor. "His majesty wants you!"

The second goblin finally located Jonquil, burrowed into the furthest corner from the door, and growled a lungful of obscenities at him, whilst clamping two pincer-like fingers on to the lobe of one of the banf's large ears. Jonquil winced in pain as he was dragged into the outside passage, his two abductors joking with each other in their own raucous tongue, occasionally squeezing one of his arms or legs and sniggering derisively at the size of them. Jonquil had the uneasiest feeling that main topic of discussion between the two goblins, was his meat content; and he prayed that they would decide he was too skinny.

Suddenly a tall figure stepped into the passageway from a side room, ahead of the two goblins. It was one of Hawkhood's guards. The goblins stopped in their tracks, when the dragonrider demanded to know what they were doing with the Lady Tuatara's prisoner.

Jonquil saw shadows of stooped figures creeping up behind the tall guard, but before a cry of warning could escape him, a cold, sweaty palm slapped over his mouth. The two goblins smiled innocently at the rider, and explained that they only wanted to exercise the prisoner, to ward off the cramp; they intended no harm. The dragonrider drew his scimitar half out of its scabbard and suggested that the two goblins put Jonquil back where they had found him, but before he received an answer, a heavy wooden cudgel struck him soundly from behind.

The banf was bungled on through the passage as the unconscious guard was bound, gagged and dragged out of sight. The pressure on Jonquil's ear did not ease until he was wrestled into the throne room and hurled to the foot of the stone platform before the waiting Hellbender.

The goblin king dismissed the guards and surprisingly descended the short flight of steps and helped the slightly dazed Jonquil to his feet. A cry of horror burst from the banf's mouth, as his fearful eyes met with the disembodied stare of one of the mounted heads.

Hellbender chuckled, and slowly ran his burning eyes over every inch of the banf's body. Jonquil could feel the king testing the muscle on his arm as he lifted him up, his fingers probing through the thick fabric to measure the layers of sinew beneath. The glistening grin that sat uncomfortably on the goblin's face, did little to ease the banf's apprehension.

"Forgive my guards," Hellbender said softly into Jonquil's ear, breathing a cloud of sickening odour over him. "They are peasants! Brutality is all they know. Come!"

Jonquil's skin shivered in protest as Hellbender pawed at him with his clammy touch; stroking his bruised earlobe and caressing his neck. The goblin king wrapped a comradely arm around the banf's shoulders and gently turned him to face the throne. Suddenly Jonquil let out another cry of alarm as his eyes at last recognised the pale objects from which the great chair had been made. Hellbender's throne was constructed from a towering pile of boiled skulls.

"Do not be afraid, my friend," Hellbender told him. "They cannot harm you now. They might have tried to do you hurt, whilst they were alive; treacherous dogs! But I paid them for their ambition. As I will all those who dare stand against me."

Fire from the surrounding cauldrons was mirrored in the goblin king's mouth ivory, as his lips glazed them with fresh saliva. Hellbender's fat tongue caressed the roots of his sharpened incisors, deploying yet more drool, until tiny waterfalls were born at the corners of his mouth. Hot, musty breath repeatedly blew into the banf's nose and throat, threatening to choke him. Eventually his lungs commanded him to turn away and search for some unfouled air. Even with his back to the king, Jonquil could still feel the intensity of his terrible eyes; they bored into his skull like burning red pokers, and singed his brains.

Hellbender led the banf forward, closer to the throne, his heavy hand squeezing inquisitively at Jonquil's shoulders and neck.

"Would you like to hear how I came to acquire this unique piece of furniture?" the goblin asked.

Jonquil told his mouth to say no, but he distinctly heard the word, 'Yes!' leave his lips.

The banf consoled himself with the thought that at least whilst the goblin king was preoccupied with the telling of his tale, Jonquil would have time to think of a way to escape. After all, the banf imagined that he could easily outrun the fat goblin and disappear into the network of tunnels and passages that no doubt riddled the city. Who knows where he might eventually emerge? Hopefully somewhere, where neither the goblins or the Ice Witch could find him.

Hellbender propelled Jonquil gently but with an irresistible firmness towards the great chair, and to the banf's disgust, he had to seize hold of the two uppermost heads to stop himself from toppling headfirst into it. The skulls were icy cold to the touch, and Jonquil recoiled in horror when he realised his fingers had strayed into the damp eye socket of one of them. He snatched them back again, fearful that something awful might be living inside the empty cranium.

"Go on," Hellbender urged him. "Sit! You could not refuse such a rare honour."

Jonquil interpreted "could not," as "dare not!" and dutifully perched on the very edge of the throne, careful to let as little of his body come into contact with the stacked heads as possible.

Hellbender stalked up and down the dais in front of the banf. The two lengths of black material that hung from a gold waistband, hidden by the overhang of his large belly (his sole apparel apart from his skull crown and few items of jewelry), swung rhythmically, between his bowed legs, as he walked.

The goblin king's story commenced with a lengthy preamble, setting the scene and providing what Hellbender considered vital background information. Jonquil could not concentrate on any of it. All he could focus on was the interminable stomping of the goblin's bare feet on the hard stone.

"Then," Hellbender cried, raising the excitement in his voice. "When they knew I was alone in here, with only my gold battle club between me and certain slaughter, all thirty five of them burst in upon me, screaming for my blood!

What happened next is the stuff of legend and song, my wingless friend. Needless to say by the time I had finished with them, not one was left standing. I single-handedly clubbed every one of them to death."

The king swung his mace dramatically through the air, as if fending off many attackers, chopping and parrying, leaping and ducking; Hellbender trying to re-enact in mime, that which he had just told in words. Finally he ceased and held his mace triumphantly above his head, waving in acknowledgement to an uproarious ovation from his imaginary subjects.

"As an example to the rest of my..er.. adoring followers," the goblin continued; "I commissioned the building of this throne; to serve as a reminder of my invincible power. It was only poetic justice really. These scumrats refused to support me in life, so I decided to make them support me in death!"

Jonquil might have expected a megalomaniac of Hellbender's proportions, to have exploded into peals of hysterical laughter at his clever pun, hold his sides in mock agony and congratulate himself a thousands times on his sharp wit, but the goblin king barely even chuckled. Instead he leaned over the banf, his sickening grin growing even wider, and fixed Jonquil with a stare so potent, it threatened to turn him to stone.

The banf tried valiantly not to return Hellbender's gaze, but the goblin's blood red orbs, wrenched Jonquil's eyes back to them, and held them with a grip like iron. Hellbender's teeth parted as his head moved nearer, his grimace growing into a widening gape.

Jonquil could feel himself seeping through the back of the throne, melting under the glare of the goblin's red torches, dripping through the gaps in the bones and drowning in a seething whirlpool of boiling blood. But even this was no escape, for the eyes were following, now disembodied from their head, filling his sight with a sea of red. Hellbender's pupils - narrowed into black stripes - slowly became the two statues, standing sentry at the great gates, towering over the formless banf before a furious scarlet inferno. The heat was blistering, Jonquil could feel his skin splitting with the intensity of it, his own blood spilling into the wild ocean in steaming rivulets. A terrible smell assaulted the banf's lungs; musty and acrid, it emanated from an approaching white cage that opened to claim him, and all through this searing torture Jonquil could hear a distant voice, whispering like a howling gale, endlessly repeating to itself; "My gift! My gift! My gift.......!" Suddenly a brilliant blue dragon dived into the seething red fire, and the brightest white light pierced the turmoil, dousing the flames as if the floodgates of a mighty dam had been wrenched asunder. Jonquil's liquefied body shuddered back to solidity as the word 'No!' stabbed through his ears like a rapier.

The banf's mind tore itself from Hellbender's trance, just as the points of the goblin's fangs were closing on his throat.

Hellbender turned in a blaze of fury and scowled at the Ice Witch, his eyes dripping with menace.

"Do not interfere!" he snarled. "This prize is mine!"

Tuatara swept across the floor of the cavern like a blue haze, the walls of the chamber shaking with her anger. Loose stalactites dropped from the ceiling and shattered in crashing explosions of sound, about the throne platform. Hellbender suddenly forgot his hunger and became very afraid.

"You may not have him!" Tuatara roared. "He is the prisoner of the Lord of Ice. If he is harmed in any way, King of Scum! I shall see to it that you answer personally to the Ice Sorcerer himself!"

Even in the subdued light of the throne room, the colour could be plainly observed draining from Hellbender's face. With eyes as wide as goblin shields, he stepped away from the quaking banf.

Without another word being spoken, the two dragonriders that accompanied the Ice Witch, rushed forward to seize the banf and with all haste whisked him away to safety.

Tuatara allowed the goblin king to suffer for a few more moments under her furious gaze and then confidently strode away.

Hellbender crawled into the cradle of his throne after the Ice Witch had departed, and trembling like a child, curled into a foetal ball. The king did not notice his daughter move silently over the chamber floor, a goblet of her special wine, held reverently in her hands. When she arrived at the throne, Hellbender did not wait for her loyal greeting, he just snatched the gold vessel from her, and drained it in one gulp. Okra was not even given the chance to inquire if the King liked her wine, he just bawled for more. The princess was only too happy to oblige.

The next few hours of the night strolled by without incident, almost peacefully, Tuatara mused, or at least as peaceful as a night in the Mountains of Menace possibly could be. There was the usual catalogue of mysterious disembodied screams or howls that periodically permeated through the honeycomb of hollow passages, from somewhere deep within the restless, hidden city, that always accompanied the darkness hours.

Hellbender's people, although by nature mainly nocturnal creatures (like any other cave dwellers), tended to practice an uneasy diurnal existence, so as to make themselves more useful to the Ice Lord's needs. This meant, however, that they had to try and sleep during the night, some of the goblins finding it more difficult than others. The result of this unnatural lifestyle was frequent violent skirmishes between roaming insomniac goblins, irritable through lack of sleep, which nearly always ended in a death or two, or at best a spell of casual torturing, to help pass the time.

The lights which softly played inside Tuatara's crystal orb, had a wonderful soothing effect on her tired eyes. By placing her fingertips lightly on the skin of the glowing sphere, her whole body was filled with a cool ecstasy, that drained all the sloth and fatigue from her bones and left the Ice Witch feeling rested and renewed. The frustrating antics of the goblins never failed to make Tuatara weary; not weary for sleep, but for peace of mind; for sanity; the orb made all this possible. It was only a globe of dwarf crystal, not particularly unique; but the colours the Ice Witch discovered in the heart of it, eased her spirit.

The lake people believed that crystals were tears from the stars, and as such had powerful healing properties. Tuatara had often employed various types of crystal, to enact changes of mood or personality on herself, to suit the contrasting needs of different occasions. Indeed all of the higher races of Enchantica placed great value on crystals, including them in jewelry or as precious decorations on robes and garments. Their presence was always associated with change and replenishment; and so perhaps it was not surprising that the most profound metamorphoses of all to occur in the world, the changes of the seasons, were also achieved by precious stones: the great Power Crystals of the Wizards.

Jonquil had been furnished with a small gemstone to calm him, after he had been rescued from the jaws of Hellbender. Tuatara's handmaidens had carefully laid the banf down on one of their beds, within the suite of chambers that had been laid aside by the goblins as the Ice Witch's apartments.

When the banf had been carried in by one of the dragonriders, he had been shaking uncontrollably. His eyes had been rolling aimlessly into his skull and streams of gibberish spouted from his mouth. For a short while Tuatara had thought Jonquil beyond rescue, but the banf had proved to be made of sterner stuff than she had assumed, and gradually his condition had stabilized. The Ice Witch had known fearless warriors, giants of brawn and muscle, crumble under the potency of Hellbender's evil eyes, and succumb to the will of the goblin king, like willing lambs to the slaughter. Luckily for Jonquil, Hellbender had been too hungry to bother using his devastating hypnosis to its fullest effect. The banf might have felt as though his brain was being boiled in its skull, but in reality the power behind the trance had been relatively light.

Sleep, Tuatara knew, was the best and only way to properly heal Jonquil's violated soul, and the only way to induce such deep and reparative rest, was to charm him into unconsciousness with a slumber chant. After she had done this, one of the Ice Witch's handmaidens was charged with watching over the banf whilst he slept, and allowing no-one other than Tuatara herself to disturb him.

The Ice Witch had a feeling that Jonquil would prove to be an important prisoner. She wanted to make sure that he was in a reasonably good state of health, before presenting the banf to her master. What happened to him after that, was none of her concern.

The Ice Witch sat back from the table which held the orb, allowing her head to recline far over the back of the high wooden chair in which she was seated. The carved edge of the wood was cool in the nape of her neck and slowly her eyelids fell, as she drifted into meditation.

She thought of her Lord, the empty throne beside him, and her future.

Suddenly there was a loud hammering on her doors, raised voices pleading for attention. The thunderous sound shattered her elusive karma and the Ice Witch's eyes flew open into wide, violent circles. Tension resurged into her body and Tuatara's fingers flexed stiffly from the arms of the chair, blue sparks spitting at her nail-tips.

Sleepy handmaidens stumbled to the door in a state of great agitation and annoyance. The bolts on the frame were furiously drawn back and as they did so, the door burst inwards and the distraught form of Mummichog fell over the threshold.

Tuatara, now standing and with her back to the gibbering elder goblin, raised her eyes to the ceiling and wailed inwardly (to no-one in particular);

"Will this night ever end?"

Mummichog half crawled over to the Ice Witch, his old body so gripped by trauma, that he could hardly muster the breath to make any sounds of explanation.

Animosity sharpened Tuatara's voice to such a degree that those around her took a step backwards, anticipating the onset of her wrath.

"What is it?" she demanded, without turning to look at him.

"The King!" Mummichog gasped. "The King!" Shock would allow him to speak no more.

"What about him?" the Ice Witch snapped. "What has he done now?"

The elder goblin wailed in despair;

"He's dead! The King is dead!"

Tuatara spun around like a whirlwind, seized Mummichog's robes at his throat, and snatched him to his feet with one hand.

"Dead!" she roared. "But how? By whose hand?"

The old goblin pawed imploringly at the Ice Witch's hand, still tightly clenched at his throat. His eyes were grief-stricken and fearful, with the look of one who had just seen his every wish or dream dashed into a thousand pieces. Years of effort and intrigue invested in Hellbender, now come to nothing. It was for his own future that Mummichog grieved, for the death of his vehicle to power over the goblins, not the death of his king.

"You must come!" he gasped.

Tuatara threw him bodily towards the door;

"Lead the way!" she commanded.

The Ice Witch swept out of the room like a sudden blizzard, close on the heels of

Mummichog who scurried along the twisting corridors before her shadow like a beaten dog. They soon arrived at the entrance to the great chamber and upon entering the room that dripped with pillars of rock, they found Okra, seated casually in her father's throne, a ring of burly warriors standing guard about her. The body of the king still lay where it had fallen, sprawled unceremoniously at the base of the steps leading down from the stone dais, an empty wine goblet gripped firmly in his fist.

One look at the grotesquely twisted features of the victim, his body arched into a tortured pose, a final scream of stomach-tearing agony carved indelibly into his face, revealed to Tuatara the unmistakable cause of the goblin king's demise: deathhemp poisoning. The Ice Witch recognised it at once. It was a device of murder that she was more than familiar with, having employed it herself to devastating effect on numerous occasions.

Hellbender's lifeless eyes, now devoid of all their dark power, stared pitifully from the floor of the cavern. Combined with the infuriating grin on Okra's supercilious face, (which was far too reminiscent of her father) they threw the Ice Witch into an uncontrollable rage.

She flew up the short flight of stone steps, smartly knocked two of the princess's body guards aside and rose, tall and terrible before the trembling Okra, her face glowing with fury.

The hands of Tuatara's outstretched arms, hooked into claws and turned inwards to one another. Veins of blue lightning crackled between them, and the murderous eyes of the Ice Witch sparkled in the flickering light, like twin flames of death.

The large goblin warriors, who had earlier been prepared to take on all comers, and had threatened even Mummichog when he had tried to get close to the princess, suddenly looked pale and uncertain as they stood around the throne. Two loud sparks spat towards them from Tuatara's fingers, and by the time the second one had arced to the floor, the dais was guardless.

A long, pale finger stabbed the air and an ear-splitting sound like the shearing of rock, reverberated around the jagged walls of the domed cavern, as a streak of blue fire leapt from Tuatara's finger at the head of the goblin princess. Okra's arms instinctively flew across her face in a hopeless attempt to shield herself from the Ice Witch's attack. The vacant eye cavities of the topmost skull on Hellbender's throne shone with a radiant blue light and then the whole head exploded in a shower of white stars.

Smouldering dust and bone debris littered the hair and shoulders of the goblin princess, when she finally peered out from behind her raised arms. Tuatara's finger was still pointed ominously at Okra's head, but somehow the Ice Witch managed to resist the temptation to atomise the goblin princess in a blue starburst, and stain the walls of the cavern with her blood.

"What have you done, you little fool?" Tuatara screamed.

Okra twisted fistfuls of her black robe into a winding knot, as she cowered like a terrified child before the Ice Witch. She was too traumatised to speak.

Suddenly a host of jubilant voices rose into the silence from beyond the great chamber. The dark hole of a doorway slowly began to glow, the light steadily building within it, as a large torch bearing crowd rapidly approached from inside the long passage.

Tuatara could only stare with incredulity into the mouth of the entrance, a brief question dropping from her lips;

"What now?" she breathed.

An exultant mob burst into the throne room, horns wailing, drums pounding, voices raised into a dreadful chorus of joy. It seemed as though half of the goblin city had contracted some great madness and had spilled out into the night, for some unknown celebration.

Okra forgot her fear of the Ice Witch almost at once and was gripped by an urgent curiosity. Mummichog gazed at the crowd an expression of great confusion lining his face; the explanation for this bizarre revelry seemed beyond them both.

As the first of the multitude approached the flickering pool of orange light thrown out by the four towering demons, and their gleeful eyes fell on to the stricken form of their dead king, cries of joy became moans of despair and then wails of grief. The news of what they had discovered at the throne, travelled back through the ranks of goblins in waves of dismay, until all of the singing and noise from the instruments had been silenced.

The crowd slowly edged forward, spreading like an approaching sea before the raised dais, those creatures further back craning to try and see the body of the king; a look of fearful disbelief haunting their faces, matching the expressions of those watching them from the throne platform.

A sudden resurgence of excitement emanated from the rear of the gathering, as if something or someone of significance had just entered the cavern. A nucleus of heavily armed protective goblins pushed and jostled their way forward through the crowd, surrounding one unseen individual. A strange look leapt into Okra's eyes as the small group drew nearer and her fingers dug into the eye holes of the skulls in the sides of the throne, as if someone was about to take it from her.

Mummichog's perplexed expression was abruptly lightened by a knowing smile, as his old eyes recognised the self-important figure striding arrogantly inside his ring of supporters. The elder goblin cast a triumphant glance at the goblin princess, renewed confidence in his future flooding back to him. Okra returned his look with a stony stare, her mouth tightening into a thin line of defiance.

Tuatara did little more than raise a superior eyebrow as the jaunty individual bowed in respect before her. Then he mounted the first step of the platform, turned to face the steadily increasing sea of heads staring expectantly at him, and raised both his twin battle clubs high above his head.

"Hellbender the Great, King of all Goblins is dead!" he cried. "I, Bledderag, his son and heir, have returned to claim the throne of my father! Long live the King!"

"Long live the King!" the cry was echoed by Mummichog, much to Okra's disfavour, and gradually a similar chant swept through the gathering, each goblin in turn adding their voice to the general uproar.

"I have returned from the grave, dear sister," Bledderag shouted to Okra. "Thankyou for keeping my throne warm for me, since our father's sudden departure from it!"

A rash of sniggers broke out amongst the nearest goblins in the crowd, Mummichog also was anxious to be seen, publicly sharing the joke. The goblin princess, however, retained her sullen attitude and made not even the smallest attempt to move.

"The son of Hellbender lives," Bledderag grinned. "You have to step down now. You have no claim here."

Mummichog decided that now was the moment to attempt to regain his former authority as elder statesman of the goblins, and in his most diplomatic voice he gently approached the goblin princess and tried to persuade her to vacate the throne for her brother. He used every ploy and lever his silvery tongue would allow, finally pleading with Okra for the sake of the goblin peoples to stand down; but the goblin princess would have none of it.

"Never!" She screamed. "I killed my father, not Bledderag; therefore this throne belongs to me. I have earned the right to rule!"

Bledderag erupted into a storm of hysterical laughter, he could hardly believe his ears, and though he roared with amusement, his eyes were cold and hateful.

"There has never been a Queen of the Goblins! Never! It's unheard of!" he laughed. "Are you mad?"

Another volley of loud sniggers rippled through the mob and this time Okra rose proudly to her feet.

"I am not mad, brother!" she said with remarkable calmness. "I am your queen."

Bledderag tried to laugh at her again but there was a steely glint in his sister's eyes that slightly unnerved him, and his laughter ran dry. Okra seemed totally unafraid and wholly determined not to yield; this was something that the goblin prince had not expected.

"If you wish to be king, brother," Okra continued. "You will have to kill me first, as I killed our father. That is our law!"

Bledderag's mouth gaped in astonishment, for a moment he was speechless but then he managed to voice a reply.

"Are you serious?" he gasped. "You want me to challenge you?"

"I am deadly serious," Okra answered him. "It is the only way."

Bledderag's perplexed expression lived on his face for only a few seconds more. He rolled his eyes to the ceiling, raised his arms in concession and slowly turned back to his sister.

"Then I shall just have to kill you, sister dear," he said with comic lovingness. "No hard feelings, you understand."

The muscles in Okra's cheeks tightened as a fresh uproar lifted into her face from the crowd. Bledderag began to grin again, his eyes hungry for the battle, and his war clubs tapping impatiently against his shin plates.

Mummichog made a new attempt to rescue the situation by appealing once more to the goblin princess to submit, thus hoping to establish himself further in the role of peacemaker. However, his efforts were predictably to no avail, and secretly the old goblin was relieved. Okra enjoyed a great deal of personal popularity amongst the rank and file of the goblin city; the present drunken rabble being only one body of opinion. It would be in the best interests of future stability, Mummichog reflected, if the goblin princess was no longer around.

The Ice Witch had silently observed this remarkable confrontation with cool interest. Like the goblin prince, Tuatara had fully expected Okra to stamp her feet in a petulant show of frustration, and then obediently offer the throne to its rightful heir. This surprising stand of defiance from the goblin princess had gone a long way towards impressing the Ice Witch. Not least because Okra was a female and Tuatara herself was a female, battling for position in a world dominated by male beings; and if only in a very small way, Tuatara found herself admiring Okra for her courage, albeit the bravado of the insane.

It was indeed ironic that a race of creatures who indulged in murder and corruption so enthusiasticly, should observe the ancient laws of their people so diligently. It seemed to be the one thread of civilisation that bound all the evil, ferocious tribes together; and therefore, Tuatara decided that it was best not to jeopardise what little respect the goblins possessed for law and order, by overruling this challenge.

To the surprise of both protagonists and all those present, the Ice Witch gave them leave to carry on and smartly removed herself from the arena, announcing before her departure that the duel to the death would take place at dawn, and that she, as envoy of the Lord of Ice would officiate as a witness.

The challenge having being made, the two royal combatants withdrew along with their respective supporters to prepare for the battle to come: single combat to the death. Everyone in the goblin city, including Okra's own supporters convinced that the result was a foregone conclusion. Only the goblin princess herself, glowed with an inner smile, and thought differently.

With the grand distraction of the ensuing death duel to occupy them, Hellbender's former subjects almost forgot that the late king's remains were still littering the floor of the throne room. Supervised by Mummichog, the dead king's body was less than respectfully dragged down to the incineration fires and casually offered to the flames, with hardly a kind word being spoken. As Hellbender was consumed by the fire, the elder goblin did tarry, for a moment, to wonder if life in the Mountains of Menace would ever be the same again.

Of one thing Mummichog was certain. If by some accursed miracle Okra should win the death duel between her and Bledderag; the old goblin's life, as Hellbender himself would have put it; "Would not be worth a dragon's fart!"

A Duel to the Royal Death

During the last hour before dawn, news came to the goblin city that a great host had marched forth from the northern strongholds led by Gremba. The age long feud between the north and south goblins was about to reach its climax; the Dark Mountains staring inevitably into the face of civil war.

Tuatara still hoped for reconciliation, but the grim expression of determination fixed on the face of Gremba, as he strode confidently over the peaks leading to Hellbender's city, ahead of a vast army of bitter warriors, made the prospect of peace seem remote.

Jonquil awoke with a body-wrenching scream. He leapt out of bed cringing in pain and desperately trying to brush some imaginary attackers from his hair and clothes. His attendants attempted to calm him but their approach only made his agitated condition even worse; the banf could not bare anyone to touch him. Eventually, when Jonquil's tortured mind accepted that he was in no danger, he slowly sat back down on the bed and tried to convince his trembling body, that the terrifying episode he had just experienced had been only a dream, and that now it was gone.

The vivid nightmare had recurred continuously since the Ice Witch had cast her deep spell of sleep over him, some hours before. Each time it returned with greater vigour, the horror more intense, the pain more real.

Jonquil dreamt that he was roused from a deep sleep and found himself alone in the great chamber, curled up on the seat of the skull throne. The fires in the four statues' cauldrons had long died and the whole cavern was in darkness. There was a faint glow emanating from somewhere about the banf because he could see the outline of his folded body against the smooth tops of the stacked heads.

Then a horrible realisation crept over him. The soft light was emerging from the eye sockets of the skulls themselves, tiny pockets of red fire, burning in the empty cavities, spilling their evil glow over the banf. Jonquil had the uneasiest feeling that the crowd of heads surrounding him were no longer dead. Perhaps it was only a trick of the poor light, but the bony faces seemed to have developed snarls and scowls, their teeth sharpened into rows of spiny fangs, their eyes narrowed into menacing stares.

Jonquil wanted desperately to climb out of the loathsome chair but his strength had deserted him. His arms and legs were suddenly limp and useless as if his whole body was floundering in a tub of thick mud. The banf cried out in frustration, franticly trying to heave himself on to the shallow sides of the throne and topple over to freedom, but the more he strained and wriggled the further he sank into the pit of the throne.

Dark voices began to murmur about his head, terrible, hollow moans that rose into high wailing echoes. It was the most dreadful sound that Jonquil had ever heard, a chorus of tortured screams; the spirits of the thirty five traitors shrieking in unison at the pain of their murder. The howling durge grew ever louder, the noise vibrating inside the banf's ears, threatening to burst into his brain. Just at the point when Jonquil was sure he could stand no more of the strangled squeals, the skulls fell silent.

The sudden peace should have brought relief, but somehow the abrupt silence was more terrible. Jonquil glanced nervously from side to side, the eyeholes were still shining, numerous beams of red light piercing the blackness. Then, in one movement, the glowing heads began to rotate inwards, each malignant face turning its attention on the banf, until Jonquil was bathed in a shimmering red pool. As they moved, the skulls dragged their broken, yellowed teeth over the bony crowns of the heads below, the sound screeching through Jonquil's body in a nerve-jarring symphony, setting his jaws on edge and forcing the hairs to rise in shivering waves at the back of his neck.

A rush of dull whispers crept into the banf's ears; at first an inaudible breeze of lost words, but then steadily gaining in intensity until a single clear chant united all the occupants of the throne community into one voice. Two words were breathed over and over again at the banf, as the first of the sharp teeth stabbed into his skin;

"Our gift...our gift...our gift......!"

The throne of skulls enveloped the banf, sucking him into its throat, smothering him with biting heads. Clothes and hair were snagged on broken fangs as the darkness, filled with burning eyes, closed on him.

It was always at the point where the tightening wall of snapping teeth began to tear the flesh from his bones that Jonquil screamed into consciousness, his shaking body glistening with a sheen of sweat.

It would take a long time after his departure from the Mountains of Menace before the curse of Hellbender's trance would finally cease to invade Jonquil's restless sleep.

Sentinels posted on the high ramparts of the flat mountain announced the arrival of the dawn; a pale blue wash bleeding into the dark fabric of the night.

Fresh fires were laid at the feet of the four icons, and hundreds of torches were hung on the walls of the chamber and along the many connecting passages. In addition to which, almost every goblin, male or female, young or old, carried torches with them as the whole of the goblin city poured into the huge throne room through the gaping square entrances.

By the time the two opposing parties had arrived at the scene, a glittering sea of light filled the floor of the cavern, its spined dome awash with a bright yellow glow.

Okra and Bledderag came together at the stone platform, Mummichog standing between them as self-appointed keeper of the gold mace, that had previously belonged to Hellbender, and guardian of fair play. Bledderag was required to repeat his challenge and name his weapons. Predictably he chose to fight with the twin battle clubs, now synonymous with his name. His armour consisted of a breastplate, shoulder guards and leg shields. A ring of his enemies' teeth crowned his helmet, long plumes of bushy hair falling on to his back.

Okra, to the astonishment of those that looked upon her, was wearing no armour of any description, and caused an uproar when she mounted the stone steps and revealed herself to the multitude. She had changed from the rather drab, straight robes of a goblin princess, to the sensual and provocative gold and silver adorned attire of a queen.

An opulent necklace of platemail, crafted from solid gold pieces, rose into the she-goblin's hair behind her heavily adorned ears. Her purple-lined black robe, that left half of her body naked, was gathered into a kilted skirt at her waist, two trailing lengths hanging between her exposed, muscular legs. Okra's left breast was encapsulated in a silver, spiralled cone; a more obvious covering could not have been conceived. A mantle of purple fabric swept across her shoulders and a cluster of shrunken heads stared out from her right hip. Her head was embellished with a shallow golden crown, a small skull, at its head, sitting snugly between her bulbous eyebrows.

It soon became clear to everyone that Okra had not dressed to fight, she had dressed to captivate and arouse, and indeed the eyes of every male goblin close enough to see her were transfixed by her seductively draped body. The silver cone that just concealed Okra's breast, glinted tantalisingly in the torchlight as it pointed up and down with the overplayed motion of her breathing.

The goblin princess had always been regarded as a beauty, an object of desire, but the almost obscene way she had adorned herself and paraded across the platform had nearly driven the mostly male crowd into a frenzy, their mouths drooling as their eyes dripped down her ample green curves. If Okra had wanted any of those assembled before her to fight in her place, at that moment, she could have had the choice of hundreds.

Mummichog tried to regain some sort of control over the proceedings and pressed the princess to state her terms for the duel, namely what she was intending to fight with; the elder goblin trying valiantly to avert his eyes from the bobbing silver cone as he did so. Okra answered him with just one word.

"Thrace!" she announced.

The old goblin's brows knitted into a frown;

"What is a thrace?" he asked the she-goblin. "I have never heard of such a weapon."

"Then allow me to show you, old crone," Okra haughtily replied. "As ruler of the Dark Mountains, I am entitled to a champion, to fight in my name. This is our law, is it not, Mummichog?"

The elder goblin grudgingly agreed.

"I might have guessed you would try to wriggle out of this somehow," Bledderag sneered.

"Do you object to me choosing a champion?" Okra casually inquired, knowing full well that if Bledderag should publicly refuse, it might be interpreted as a sign of weakness.

"Naturally, I would much prefer to have the pleasure of bashing your skull instead, dear sister," the goblin prince snarled. "But there is no warrior in the whole of the Dark Mountains that could beat me in single combat! So show me your champion, and I will show you his brains!"

"You accept my terms then?" Okra asked.

"Of course!" Bledderag roared.

The goblin princess allowed a brief smirk of satisfaction to crease her face, then turned towards the doorway from which she had arrived and gave a signal to some of her supporters who waited there. The goblins momentarily disappeared inside the tunnel and then returned with a tall figure, covered for the most part by a long black veil, held in place by those that guided the figure towards their mistress.

Okra stepped back as the long shape climbed the platform and then the she-goblin strode purposefully forward and quickly divested the figure of his loose wrapping with a dramatic flurry.

As the dark blanket fell to the ground, a hiss of disgust rose up from the assembled ranks of goblins, for standing next to the goblin princess, dwarfing her with his height and muscle was a man; a gladiator stolen from Fforl, the northernmost realm of the five eastern kings.

"Thrace!" Okra announced; her eyes gleaming with delight at the look of surprise striking the face of her brother and Mummichog.

The gladiator stood tall and broad; his hard-trained body rippling in the pale wash of torchlight. Apart from a loin cloth, and a long cloak falling diagonally from one shoulder, he wore only the barest of covering. Shoulder plates, leg-guards and one arm of platemail were his only armour; a small, round shield emblazoned with the eagle of Xanthia was held in his left hand, a short broadsword, he brandished in his right. A visored helm concealed his features but longs plaits of blond hair escaped to fall in twists along the crease of his back. His eyes were lost in darkness, two angry, black slits in a polished metal mask, was the only face he revealed to his enemies.

"What is this?" Bledderag screamed. "I challenged you, Okra. Not your pretty troll! Dismiss this ogre and lets get on with it."

"But this is my champion," the she-goblin cried.

"It is not legal!" Bledderag bellowed.

Mummichog tried to intervene but before the elder goblin could say anything that might spoil her plan, Okra shouted him down.

"This is my champion!" She repeated. "And if you refuse to fight him after accepting my terms, the duel is void, and you forfit your claim and your right to challenge. This is our law!"

A troubled murmur buzzed through the ranks of the crowd, as the massed goblins debated the extraordinary events occurring in their midst. Bledderag was tempted to argue the point further. He knew that he had been tricked, but if he refused to fight the man, the hated enemy of his people, what would his supporters think?

The goblin prince stared imploringly at Mummichog but the old goblin could not help him; the law was the law and there was no escaping it. The duel must stand.

Bledderag turned once more to face his smug sister and the venom in his eyes promised death and destruction.

"Very well, your majesty!" he spat. "I'll fight your champion; and after his blood has been splattered across the floor of this cavern, yours will swiftly join it!"

"So be it, brother," Okra grinned. "Let battle commence."

Suddenly a bright fanfare of dragonrider trumpets drew the attention of all towards a far entrance. Framed in the torchlit doorway, awaiting a passage through the goblin hordes to form for her, was the Ice Witch.

As she strode into the parting mob, her lieutenants a few paces behind, she was revealed in a breathtaking black robe that hugged her finely carved figure in exquisite pleats and curves. Her fine, aristocratic face was framed in an elegant headress, that dripped at her forehead with delicate silver detail; but the most outstanding feature of her robe, was a luxuriant arrangement of ravens feathers, falling in irridescent layers along the whole length of her figure. The fabulous plumage shimmering in radiant violets and mauves as she moved through the corridor of torchlight. Tuatara was stunning to behold; even her most livid enemies would have claimed it; and as she walked, a long black cane with a silver dragon's head top swung imperiously in her hand. To say that she put the flamboyant Okra in the shade, would have been a gross understatement; the Ice Witch was mesmeric, and she rose like a goddess before the royal goblins at the throne, and they all bowed, as if they were nothing, before her.

"Let's get on with it!" Tuatara ordered, casting only a cursory glance at Thrace. She knew all about Okra's champion and his history, from her goblin spies, but decided that a more detailed examination of the tall gladiator and his potential as yet another important prisoner to present before her master, would have to come later. Gremba was drawing nearer by the minute, and the Ice Witch wanted this little dispute settled once and for all before the northern warlord arrived with his mighty army.

Mummichog tried to voice a protest to Tuatara about the uncertain legal implications of such an unorthodox duel but the Ice Witch cut him short.

"I said, let's get on with it!" she curtly repeated.

Despite being graciously offered the skull throne itself to sit on, Tuatara preferred to be seated on one of the high-backed wooden chairs from her apartments. Okra occupied the throne, much to Bledderag's protestations and the two combatants took their places in a semi-circular arena formed by a curved wall of goblin guards (each bearing a large shield to protect them from stray blows) and the edge of the throne dais.

Tuatara was given the honour of starting the combat, and with a loud rap of her black cane, that echoed ominously through the pillared vaults of the great chamber, the gladiator and the goblin prince took their guard and began to circle slowly.

Bledderag was only two thirds the height of Thrace, but very fast on his feet. The gladiator parried six or seven vicious blows from the goblin before finding the opportunity to execute one good thrust of his own.

The twin battle axes weaved and rotated before Thrace's eyes, their silver points catching the torchlight and tracing almost hypnotic patterns in the air above Bledderag's spiked head. The Gladiator also discovered that the goblin prince was not averse to using his claws and teeth as extra weapons, if the chance arose.

A series of cheers and groans, gasps and roars, lifted from the surrounding mob as Bledderag seemed to gain the upper hand and then swiftly lose it. Tiny rivulets of blood glistened from a pattern of scratch wounds and shallow bites on the gladiator's chest and back, but Thrace stood as solid as a mountain, taking everything that Bledderag had to give and remaining tall and unmoved.

The interested parties watching from the stone platform, followed the progress of the two warriors with avid attention, flinching with every blow, as if they too could feel the force behind them, ducking and weaving on their seats in sympathy with their champions. The eyes of Okra and Mummichog were wide with tension and burning with colour, each grimacing with phantom pain as the two assailants repeatedly clashed together, weapons and bodies entwined.

Bledderag's deadly maces whistled about the gladiator's ears and thundered in a double strike against his shield. Thrace thought he saw an opportunity and launched a swift, crashing blow at the goblin prince's head. Bledderag was ready for it and caught the falling blade with crossed battle clubs, only inches from his face, the force of the blow buckling the goblin's knees beneath him and sending him rolling on to his back, sparks flying from his iron studs as they struck the rock of the cavern floor. The gladiator immediately rushed into a succession of furious strikes at the cowering Bledderag, his gleaming sword raining several bone-jarring hits, not all of them successfully blocked by the goblin's clubs.

Thrace was about to show no mercy to Bledderag; and if the goblin prince did not have the skill to fight his way back on to his feet, the gladiator would simply kill him where he lay.

It soon became clear to all of Bledderag's supporters, that their champion was in grave peril. The large human was toying with him, allowing Bledderag to score a few points, like a dog letting a flea draw a little blood before finally scratching him out and crushing him.

Thrace did not hate Bledderag anymore than any of the other mountain warriors he had slain, since he had been captured from an ambushed patrol and placed in the servitude of the goblin princess. Okra had secretly tested him on many renowned fighters, all of which he had swiftly vanquished, having been trained in the elite gladiator schools of Fforl. In his homeland the gladiator was a hero, a leader of men, respected and adored by his people as a soldier of valour and honour. Now, he had been degraded, stripped of all dignity, and despatching his adversaries was his only means of revenge, for the humiliation of being a goblin's slave.

Somehow, Bledderag sprang free of the relentless assault, leaping out of Thrace's reach. The goblin roared a lungful of well chosen abuse at the gladiator, and then flew at Okra, who was leaning forward attentively in the skull throne. The princess screamed in horror as her brother approached, battle clubs swinging wildy before him. Okra just managed to dive forward from the throne prostrating herself on the platform as Bledderag swiped viciously at her head. The heavy mace tugged out a few strands of Okra's hair as it just missed her forehead and crashed into the back of the throne, obliterating the top four skulls in a sickening splintering blow. Then Bledderag was gone, ploughing through the crowd at the rear of the stone dais and disappearing through one of the large open doorways, that led to the Cave of Spears. Thrace, the gladiator was hot on his heels, not about to let his latest quarry slip from his grasp.

The man caught up with the goblin on a high precipice, overlooking a deep gorge lined with long, sharp stalagmites. Bledderag had been forced to take this lofty route to freedom, as the bridge which normally led across the gorge to the outside of the mountain had been purposely lifted by Okra's camp to prevent any such escape; either by the goblin prince himself or those that had foolishly chosen to ally themselves with him.

A large chunk of Thrace's wooden shield was ripped out as Bledderag suddenly turned and launched an explosive attack with one of his spiked weapons. The goblin's other mace wheeled towards the gladiator's head but was met by the hard edge of Thrace's broadsword. A furious struggle now ensued as the opposing weapons locked together, and the two assailants threw all their weight and brute force against each other, their tussle bringing them perilously close to the edge of the sheer cliff.

Thrace stepped back clumsily on to a loose rock, and with the strenuous heaving of the goblin prince against him, overbalanced and fell across the lip of the gorge. In an instant, Bledderag was upon him, both knees dug hard into his bunched biceps, effectively pinning him to the ground and immobilising his arms. A triumphant grin returned with some surprise to the goblin's sweat-glazed face (the prospect of victory was something he had quite abandoned) as the shaft of one of his battle clubs was rammed hard into the gladiator's throat.

A great cheer reverberated through the honeycombed cave from the crowds of goblins that had followed the progress of the fight from the throne chamber. Even those individuals that did not support or sympathise with Bledderag, allowed their innate hatred of mankind to make them wish for the goblin prince's victory, and the gladiator's death. It was a matter of mountain pride.

Okra and Mummichog had also followed through to the cave and now stood at the head of the mob chanting for Bledderag's victory, the colour rapidly draining from the princess's face.

Bledderag raised his backside to exert even more pressure on Thrace's windpipe, the gladiator's face already a violent purple. Suddenly, as if this was what the gladiator had been waiting for, he brought his knee smartly up, whacking the goblin's buttocks with such force that Bledderag hurtled forwards and back flipped over the edge.

A huge gasp was sucked in by the crowd and the whole mob rushed forwards to peer into the depths, to see what had become of their prince.

Bledderag was dangling from Thrace's gripped hand, the only substantial thing that the goblin had been able to grasp before flipping over. Now the gladiator held Bledderag's life in his palm, the goblin prince swinging helplessly over a bed of glistening rock spears.

Okra screamed at Thrace to drop her brother and condemn him to the cruel stalagmites. Mummichog pleaded for leniency and renewed dialogue leading to possible reconciliation.

The gladiator stared down at the wimpering goblin hanging from his grip, and from somewhere in the deep recesses of his weary mind, he remembered how honour above all was the mark of a true champion, and that if he simply let go of Bledderag's hand, it could never be counted as a true victory. Thrace would still kill the goblin prince but he would make sure that Bledderag died a warrior's death, with his weapons in his hands, even though the gladiator was certain that the goblin would never consider making such a gesture to him.

With the hysterical objections of his mistress ringing in his ears, Thrace hauled Bledderag up from the gorge and set him once again on firm ground. The goblin was drunk with fear, tottering on weak, disobedient legs. Finally he managed to collect himself and reached slowly for his maces, one lying near to his feet, the other at the edge of the cliff. As Bledderag gingerly bent down to pick it up, his head still a little fuzzy from his stomach churning experience, a flash of gold sang through the air, smashing fully into the goblin prince's face flinging him clean over the edge of the precipice into the jagged grin of the gorge.

Luckily for Bledderag, the blow knocked him unconscious, thus saving him from the pain of being impaled on a rapier-like stalagmite, when his falling body finally reached the bottom of the deadly chasm.

A terrible cacophony of raucous voices clamoured in outrage as Okra, breathing heavily from the exertion, stood over the spot where her brother had been struck, the solid gold mace of her father, still gripped tightly in her two hands. A look of exhausted relief and satisfaction flooding into her face. It was all over. The unforeseen return of her brother had been survived and now her plans could continue unhindered as before. She was Queen; rightful and undisputed.

"Congratulations!" Tuatara sneered when Okra eventually returned to the throne platform. "Now you have what you wanted; the throne of your father. I hope it makes you happy, for as long as it lasts. I expect Gremba to arrive from the north with his army at any moment. If you are wise, you will order your people to lay down their weapons and surrender themselves to his mercy. Without a king to lead them, they could never hope to defeat the northern goblins.

It's almost a pity you did not present your father's club to Bledderag and throw yourself over the edge. Hellbender was the longest ever ruler of the Dark Mountains; you shall go down in history as the shortest!"

The goblin queen lay back in the skull throne just as her father had done so many times, and even Hellbender's infuriating broad grin crept across Okra's lips.

"I have no intention of ordering my people to lay down their weapons." she calmly stated. "I do not fear the Lord Gremba. Let him come, I say."

A loud goblin voice sounded in a far off corridor and a host of other voices cried out in alarm at his news. The massed ranks of bemused goblins milling about in aimless groups seemed on the brink of total panic.

Tuatara leaned triumphantly towards Okra;

"He has come!" she said.

The Ice Witch searched the goblin queen's face for signs of fear or disquiet, but Okra's eyes only stared away into the far shadows, a distant, dreamy look inhabiting their gaze, as if rediscovering some long remembered ecstasy. The strangest, almost soppy, smile accompanying her memories.

"Your majesty," Tuatara called to her. "The enemy is hammering at the gate. This is no time for day-dreaming; you must act! Now!"

Okra snapped to attention and turned sharply to the nervously loitering Mummichog;

"You, old crone," she commanded. "As your last official duty before your execution, go and tell my guards to fling wide the North Gates; and bid your new king to enter inside."

A wave of astonishment rose from the crowd; but the look of surprise on their faces was easily outmatched by the wide-eyed expression haunting the face of the Ice

A large chunk of Thrace's wooden shield was ripped out by Bledderag.

Witch.

"New king?" Tuatara gasped. "But how?"

Okra licked her lips with huge self satisfaction.

"My father sent me to Gremba like a common baggage, to be offered as his wife." she began. "I thought we would hate each other. We found just the opposite. During those unforgettable months, Gremba and I planned all of this together, and then just before I left, we secretly married."

"Married!" Tuatara exclaimed.

"Only when I was Queen could we finally be together," Okra continued. "Bledderag rising from the grave was an eventuality I had not accounted for; he might have spoiled everything. If not for Thrace; my beautiful champion."

"You were lucky to have him," The Ice Witch told her.

"Not luck, my Lady. Design." Okra replied.

"What will become of him now?" Tuatara asked. "I can imagine only too well, what fate lies in store for Mummichog, although I would remind you that he is a goblin of vast experience."

"He cannot be trusted!" The she-goblin snapped. "His loyalties lie in the past. Gremba and I must look to the future! As for the gladiator...!"

"He shall come with me." Tuatara stated.

"Yes," Okra agreed. "I have seen the way you look at him. I give him to you!"

Tuatara eyes almost burst with rage at the sheer impertinence that the young goblin queen was displaying. Her newly discovered power seemed to have intoxicated her, and Okra was in grave danger of saying something that she might not live to regret.

"You may return to the Lord of Ice," Okra continued in much the same tone. "And tell him that I: Okra, Queen of the Dark Mountains, have succeeded where my father could only fail. By taking Gremba as my husband I have united all the tribes of the mountains; north and south! And together as one people we shall march forth and smite the enemies of our great lord. Long live the Lord of Winter! Long live the Land of White!"

At last the confused mass of goblins had a cry they could cheer for; the old era was passed, long live Okra and Gremba, long live the Mountains of Menace. The roaring mob surged towards Okra like a giant flock of lost sheep to a seductive shepherdess; they were hers, heart and soul, and she held them all in the sweaty palm of her hand.

"Let us show our new king a real goblin welcome!" Okra roared.

A tuneless orchestra of horns and drums was hastily gathered together, and a strident marching song was enthusiasticly thrashed out by the players, to accompany Gremba's victorious but peaceful entry into the city.

The intimidating skull throne was removed on Okra's orders, and heaved into the deep gorge where Bledderag had perished; the gruesome chair smashed into a thousand pieces of splintered bone, scattering over the spiny bed of the chasm in an exploding white cloud.

In its place, Okra had two new thrones installed, that she had secretly commissioned from sympathetic goblin carpenters, during the last few weeks of her father's reign, bearing the skull motif, the traditional insignia of the Dark Mountains, and a design of ice crystals: the mark of Vrorst.

Tuatara was pleased to see such a public show of loyalty to the Lord of Ice, but not wholly surprised. Okra was wiley enough to realise that without the protection of the Ice Sorcerer, her reign with Gremba would be constantly under threat from the powerful Eastern Alliance to the south. Whilst Vrorst continued to devastate the five kingdoms with a relentless barrage of snow and ice, the goblins were free to terrorise the other noble occupants of the nearby mountains and valleys as they pleased, and, of course, send vast armies south to join forces with the massed legions of the Lord of Ice as well.

The tortured melody that blared through the jagged curve of the cavern, rose to a frenzy as the Lord of the North reached the main doors. A caterwauling choir of screeching goblins erupted into song to greet his approach to the twin thrones. Okra rose reverently as the lone figure neared the stone platform, and descended the few steps to wait for him.

Gremba cast a menacing shadow on the ground. Resplendent in heavy, spiked battle armour, his glaring orange eyes stared out from beneath an elaborate helm, an embossed frontlet of black iron rising to a riot of long hair plumes, the prized scalps of his victims. The face of the wolvine, a huge, evil beast corrupted to serve Vrorst, from the already fearsome mountain wolf, appeared as an insignia on various components of Gremba's armour, and on the shields and breastplates of his northern warriors. Indeed, Gremba and his minions were so feared by the surrounding inhabitants of the northern mountains, that they had been named the Wolves of the North.

Okra presented Gremba with a duplicate gold mace and then hand in hand they ascended the stone dais and took their places on the high thrones.

Tuatara found it hard not to laugh at the spectacle of two ugly, green-skinned creatures, whose smiles bristled with fangs, gazing lovingly into each other's eyes, Gremba's iron spiked gauntlet still clasped gently about Okra's gold-ringed hand.

The idea that these two, hideous individuals could actually feel love for one another, seemed entirely alien to the goblin character. However Tuatara had to concede that there was definitely some sort of bond between them. Okra had shared her throne, when she could have kept it for herself. Gremba could have marched on the city and taken Hellbender's crown by force and had Bledderag and his sister put to the sword. Instead, they were husband and wife, joint sovereigns, and seemingly happy to be so.

As the Ice Witch's party took their leave of the Dark Mountains and rose into the updraughts that would carry them to the Throne Citadel, Tuatara had to smile to herself as she recalled the sharp glint of self satisfaction burning in Okra's eyes, as the combined masses of the goblin tribes, prostrated themselves before her and Gremba, and swore eternal loyalty. Then she had grinned broadly at the Ice Witch, and asked;

"Was I a good girl, my Lady?"

The King of the World

The majestic Throne Citadel, former power anvil of the Wizards of Light had been imprisoned in a fortress of ice. Immense cloud-spearing columns had erupted from the base of the frozen lake, in a glistening explosion of glacial water. The four seasonal bridges had been made permanently impassable by thrusting white spears, that cleaved or ruptured the ancient wooden structures. New platforms had been sculpted across the angular planes of ice rising from the crystal lake, connecting the snowbound belt of lakeside trees with the new entrances of the frozen palace.

The clustered towers that were part of the old building, had been stabbed or encased by shining white turrets, only a handful of the original spires poking free of the gleaming serrated ramparts; the high crystal chamber itself being one of the few.

Daggers of ice burst out periodically from the smooth, sloping walls, to form new dragonports, replacing those lost by the enveloping glaciers. Clouds of swift snowhawks launched into the sharp air, from openings at the base of the platforms, and wheeled about the climbing points of the sparkling palace in screeching flocks. Their pristine-white wings catching the light as they spiralled and soared, making the air above the frozen citadel glitter against the dull frown of the sullen sky beyond.

The main thoroughfare into Vrorst's city had been carved from huge frozen blocks, grown over the ruin of the old Winter bridge. Its wide snowswept roadway was overlooked by an avenue of immense, geometric crystals, jostling for space as they leaned across to one another, creating breathtaking, pointed archways along the whole length of the great road.

The main entrance to the palace was an archway snarling with icicles; those descending from the corners of its mouth had joined with the floor to form rippled, glassy pillars. Similar rapier-like growths abounded inside, lining the walls and ceilings of every corridor and chamber with a forest of crystal teeth; some hanging from the centre of spiny caverns as spectacular glistening chandeliers.

Jonquil might have expected the courtyards and passages of the Ice Lord's fortress to have teemed with busy occupants, much like the Wizards' palace on the Island, but he discovered that it was not so. No one stirred. The glassy halls were empty of guards, attendants, lesser wizards and witches. No creature of any kind could be seen, and the only sound to inhabit the vast structure, was the low rumble of an icy wind coursing unchallenged through an unseen network of empty rooms and corridors. Although, the banf had the distinct impression that for an enemy to assume that the palace was unguarded would be a mistake. As he and the other prisoners were led past fragmented walls of ice, they could feel scores of unfriendly eyes peering through at them unseen from the other side, watching their every move.

The palace of the Ice Sorcerer had an ethereal grace flowing within its columns, which rose into a majestic, natural architecture the beauty of which caused a gasp of steamy breath to exude from the lips of the beholder. But it was also an entirely dreadful place, cold and stark, devoid of hope or kindness. The breathtaking formations of ice crystals that bloomed in profusion at every available space were filled with a shimmering inner glow, but to Jonquil and the other prisoners, the pristine vaults of the palace cast a shadow of blackness over the hearts of those that entered there; a greedy darkness that sought to steal the true light from their souls. Tuatara carried the same hungry glow in her sapphire eyes, and like the magnificent city in which they now stood, her beauty was at once exquisite and terrible.

In the very heart of the palace, if so menacing a place could possibly posses such a thing, there existed a vast chamber, whose walls rose into a towering steeple, and were constructed from perfect angular plates of ice, placed one against another in a giant, irregular mosaic. An army of tall crystals grew from the top of the walls and converged into a spire of prisms, shattering the light from outside into a mesmeric kaleidoscope of rainbow colours and throwing it down to the glassy floor as a dazzling rosette.

Bathing in the full glory of the glittering projection was a crystalline throne, rising from a stepped platform as a great fan of blue ice spears, each spreading column seizing the light from above and splitting it yet further into gleaming shards that stabbed into the very core of the glacial seat.

The prisoners were separated and Jonquil alone was taken into the high vaulted chamber containing the ice throne. Tuatara positioned the banf at the foot of the stepped platform and then moved away from him. There was a soft swishing sound and a gentle rush of frosty air. When Jonquil could resist the urge to look around him no longer, he discovered that he was alone; the Ice Witch had seemingly walked through the wall.

Jonquil crept over to the large panels of ice, whose surfaces were so smooth, they reflected like mirrors. It was the first time since leaving the Forgotten Island that the banf had looked upon his own image. His clothes were tattered and dishevelled, his hair sprang out in wild tufts and his face seemed drawn and pale. It was not a kind picture, and as he began to walk around the perimeter of the chamber, Jonquil found that each sheet of ice gave a different reflection. In some he looked shorter, his slender face squashed into an ugly sneer, others made him look fat, or old, or tall and supercilious; but none of the mirrors were willing to portray him in a generous light. All of the reflections however different were in some way offensive.

The banf decided to move away from the walls, after walking only a short distance, afraid of what he might see in the rest of the plates. There was a morbid enchantment in the ice mirrors and Jonquil did not want to be dismayed by it.

The banf returned to his spot under the gaze of the shimmering light and awaited his fate. Another brief whisper accompanied by a frosty draught caught his attention and Jonquil was just about to turn to see if anyone had entered the chamber, when the light pouring in from above suddenly failed, as if a monstrous storm cloud had drifted over the high roof of the tower, plunging the whole chamber into darkness.

The vague outline of the throne formation could just about be distinguished from the black void, but any figures that might have secretly entered through the walls were lost to the banf's eyes.

The air in the chamber seemed to drop abruptly, not with an icy breeze but with an overall chill. Jonquil could feel battalions of goose pimples rising in waves across his skin.

A pale light began to glow in the core of the ice throne, steadily growing in thin blue lines that bled into the darkness like a bright geometric flower blooming in a black cave. The shining columns grew so intense that a wash of blue spread across the floor until Jonquil's face was stained with the soft illumination.

Then a white star caught his eye. It sparkled on the surface of a large crystal orb that was cradled in the end of one of the throne's arms. Its surface burned with a white halo and streaks of light drifted into the dark from its centre, in slow, spearing arcs. The banf was certain that the orb had not been there before, he could not possibly have overlooked so striking an object when he first entered the chamber.

As hastily as it had arrived, the dark shadow passed over, and the former brightness was once again restored to the hall of mirrors, the internal glow of the ice throne being immediately killed by the return of the refracted daylight.

As Jonquil stood there, still staring at the glittering globe, he sensed that he was no longer alone, that a great presence was nearby, looming behind him. Out of the corner of his eye, the banf thought he could see a tall dark shadow at his shoulder. He was afraid to turn around, fearful of what his eyes might see.

Eventually, after the presence showed no signs of moving, Jonquil tentatively turned his head to look at the dark figure.

The first thing that the banf's eyes fell upon was a large black gemstone, surrounded by a frame of silver filigree, suspended on one of two sweeping chains that contained smaller, different coloured jewels. The black stone seemed almost to pulsate with a cold, menacing power that both repelled and attracted the banf all at once. The chain lay across the chest of a black robe, that dropped full length to the toes of two silver tassled boots; the tongue of a broad white belt fell with it, embossed at its end with more silver and gems.

The chains hung from wide shoulders swathed in luxurious widths of the finest fur that formed the borders of a long purple coat, crafted with the most grandiose folds and gatherings at the shoulders and arms. A stiff, white collar lined with the tiniest silver studsrose extravagantly at the neck of the robe, framing a stern, bearded face, set with the coldest, bluest eyes, that outshone any of the fabulous jewels that adorned the kingly robes. Above two thick, arched eyebrows, there rose a tall, white crown; adorned with silver and gems, culminating in a pastel blue wizard's peak.

With his heart pounding in his ears and a whirlpool raging in his stomach, Jonquil could only stand and stare, frozen with fear, into the face of Vrorst: the Ice Sorcerer himself.

The Ice Lord slowly turned away from the banf and climbed the steps leading to his throne, his fingers brushed lightly over the skin of the fire orb as he seated himself, his touch causing a storm of blue lightning to flicker inside the globe. His deep, calculating gaze returned to Jonquil.

Vrorst had a strong, regal face, that demanded respect. He was lined but unlike his brother wizards did not resemble an old man. Rather, the Ice Lord looked like a king in his prime, vibrant and charismatic, superior and all powerful.

The Lord of Winter was indeed an imposing figure, as he leant back against the magnificent spread of his glacial throne, his hands resting on fingertips at the ends of the long, crystal arms. He exuded an aura of cool malevolence that flowed from his being like a freezing sea. There was no mercy in those narrowed, steely eyes, and under their burning stare, Jonquil felt as though every fibre of his being had been stripped and laid bare, for the Ice Lord's scrutiny. No corner of his soul left unviolated; every thought made naked.

Vrorst's eyebrows knitted into a frown as he stared down at Jonquil.

"And what is this wingless wonder?" the Ice Lord spoke forth.

The Ice Sorcerer's words were deep toned and forceful, and the fragmented walls that surrounded his throne seemed to tremble at his voice.

"I do not know, Lord" another voice answered.

Jonquil turned to see Tuatara standing a little distance away from him. She had once more noiselessly passed through the walls, to wait in attendance on her lord. Her eyes, fixed avidly on the sorcerer, were enlarged into dreamy pools of wonder and adoration.

"What are you?" Vrorst asked of Jonquil.

The banf's throat was so dry that he was sure his voice had gone forever, and his tongue felt as if it had been welded to the roof of his mouth. Eventually, with the terrible glare of the Ice Lord's eyes upon him; Jonquil managed to force out a reply.

"A banf!" he croaked.

"Do you have a name?"

"I am Jonquil."

The Ice Sorcerer exchanged a long contemplative look with the Queen of Witches, and then turned his full attention to the orb. The heart of the crystal globe immediately responded by igniting into a ball of radiant blue fire, and secreted a glaze of swirling stars, that chased and span each other in a glittering rash over its surface.

Vrorst slowly raised his nearest hand towards the shining sphere, his fingers spreading into a wide span. The cloud of busy stars hovering about the orb became so attracted to his palm, that they drew away from its glassy skin and gathered together in a tumbling, sparkling mass. The Ice Lord lifted his other hand towards Jonquil, his index finger pointing menacingly at the banf. Suddenly a tremendous bolt of energy burst from the crystal orb and leapt into Vrorst's hand. A dazzling, star-spangled aura burned about the Ice Sorcerer, as his whole being was set alight by the power from the orb surging through his body. Two, white flames sparkled in his metallic eyes, and then a streak of blue lightning exploded with a deafening crackle from the end of Vrorst's finger, striking the helpless banf squarely in the chest.

Jonquil felt as though his heart had been impaled on a rapier of ice, a terrible stab of pain crumpling his limbs. Every vein in his body screamed in protest as the power of the orb forced its way through him. Freezing fingers slipped inside his head and began to probe interrogatively at his brain.

The commanding voice of the Winter Wizard wrenched his attention back towards the throne.

"You are now a possession of the Orb of Winter," he spoke. "It has dominion over your mind. You have no choice but to speak the truth."

Vrorst then proceeded to demand a great many answers on a wide range of subjects, including the banf's home, his people, and why he was without wings. Like the Wizards of Light, the Ice Sorcerer had been ignorant of the existance of the banfs, and seemed to know even less than the others about the inhabitants of the Great Forest, as a whole. Also like his former brothers, he did become slightly more intrigued when Jonquil spoke of the White Ring. Vrorst somehow recognised that the grand circle of mushrooms surrounding the small kingdom, had a greater significance than a simple wall of defence.

However, the secrets the Ice Lord wanted to know the most, and in the greatest possible detail, was precisely what Jonquil's involvement with the Three Wizards amounted to. The banf found that his replies to the Ice Sorcerer flowed from his mouth quite independently of his will. If the answers to Vrorst's questions existed in Jonquil's mind, then the Wizard needed only to ask and all would be freely revealed.

In a short space of time, Vrorst learned all that had befallen the banf since he and Rattajack had ventured forth from the Banf Kingdom on that distant morning, to start the last of the year's expeditions, an adventure that had not ended yet.

The Ice Lord heard about the battle on the ice, the kingdom beneath the sea, the journey on the black galleon, the long, happy days spent in the comfort of the Forgotten Island, the high council in the Tower of the Stars, the flight on Charlock to Enchantica, and the eventual capture by Tuatara.

Vrorst sat unmoved throughout the whole catalogue of information supplied by the banf. He simply stared stoically at Jonquil, his eyes fixed in an attitude of cool appraisal. The Ice Lord received every item of news without emotion, that is, save two: the discovery of the third haven and the Wizards' spy!

Although he was careful not to show it to the banf, Vrorst was greatly alarmed to learn that the missing spring of Old Magic had finally been unearthed, especially as it was situated so close to home. Mezereon had not yet succeeded in breeding a warrior that could withstand the force of the ancient power, but Vrorst knew that given time, his dark sorcerer would prevail, and produce an army that could assail the borders of the Wells of Hope, destroy the inhabitants and their supplies of Old Magic forever.

The only fear of the Ice Sorcerer was that the Wizards of Light would find their way to the third haven, and establish a new sanctuary, before Mezereon could provide him with his superbreed. Vrorst's spies had assured him that as yet, the Wizards had made no move to depart from the safety of the Island, although there had been a few suspicious banks of thick fog drifting across the ocean. Vakari, the Ice Lord's chief gatherer of information, was satisfied that the Lords of Light were still in residence, as he had heard eye-witness accounts from high flying dragon patrols that there was still an abundant show of life on the sun-drenched stretch of land.

When the Ice Sorcerer had embarked on his next line of questioning, he had not for an instant seriously expected Jonquil to be able to give him a satisfactory answer. Vrorst was intrigued to know how it was that the Wizards of Light were able to second guess almost every major troop movement, or military manoeuvre, that his forces made throughout Enchantica. The Wizards knew about surprise sorties Vrorst had planned with his generals and warned their supporters to withdraw from key rebel camps just in time. The Wizards also knew all about his vision for the future; Vrorst's plans to transform all three of the secret kingdoms in to vast, flourishing gardens, to feed his subjects. Could it be simply coincidence? Vrorst thought not. Then his worst fears were confirmed by the captive voice of the banf.

The Ice Sorcerer's eyes visibly widened when Jonquil automatically spilled out exactly what Orolan had told him about the spy in the Winter camp.

"An eye at my shoulder!" Vrorst exclaimed. "What does this mean? Who is this viper in my midst? Is it one of my henchmen? One of my captains? Speak!"

Tuatara stirred a little uneasily at Jonquil's side.

"I do not know," Jonquil flatly replied.

"Is it some low attendant? Some lesser wizard or witch?" The Ice Sorcerer continued, his calm voice beginning to lose its trained control.

"I do not know," the banf coolly repeated.

"You lie!" the Wizard roared, showers of stars spitting from the crystal globe in angry volleys.

"He cannot, Lord," Tuatara interjected. "He is in the power of the orb!"

Vrorst threw the Ice Witch a look that would have crushed a lesser being, and even she had to fight the desire to retreat in fear, but she held her position and returned her lord's stare with an open face. At last, he relented a little and threw the power of his gaze back at Jonquil.

"Perhaps all one is required to do is ask the right questions," Vrorst thoughtfully considered. "The information may be concealed, somewhere in the depths of his mind; I shall think further on it. Take him away."

Tuatara dutifully obeyed, and led Jonquil out of the mirrored chamber to a dark hall, the entrance to which was watched by a black-cloaked gaoler. The dark figure took possession of the banf and urged him inside. Occupying the long hall was a succession of pyramidal igloos, each faced with a thick slab of clear ice. Charlock and Thrace were already incarcerated in two of the ice cells, Jonquil was roughly deposited inside a third. The transparent door, which was raised by the means of two runners holding it in place either side, slammed down hard in his face. Jonquil's gaoler leaving him without food or water, and to the banf's dismay, any means of communicating with his fellow prisoners.

After witnessing Jonquil's safe confinement from the doorway of the hall, the Ice Witch turned and made her way back the court of the Ice Sorcerer.

On her return, Tuatara discovered that Vrorst was not alone in his throne room; he was conferring in muted tones with a small figure clad in a black child's dress; that was holding something that it clearly considered precious.

As the Ice Witch approached, Vrorst's eyes raised towards her and then he leant forward and spoke something softly to the small figure. The innocent face of a young girl, her fresh features framed with shiny lengths of jet black hair, turned and smiled at Tuatara.

"Ah! Queen of Witches, most loyal of all my captains," the Ice Lord greeted her. " Approach! Allow me to congratulate you on your good work in the Mountains of Menace."

"Thankyou, Lord," the Ice Witch replied. "Although I must confess, the true credit for the unification of the tribes belongs to Okra. She outmanoeuvred everyone, including myself. She is a truly surprising and resourceful individual. I think she will make a strong queen."

"As modest as ever," Vrorst smiled. "The ambitious young she-goblin commits two acts of regicide to make herself queen. Ha! What an auspicious start to her reign; I like her already."

Tuatara smiled politely and found herself a little embarrassed at the constant stare of the child, whose large blue eyes were fixed unwaveringly to her own and were wide with wonder. The Ice Sorcerer seemed to sense her unease and placed a large hand gently on the girl's tiny shoulder.

"I must introduce you, Tuatara, to a very special person," Vrorst began. "This is Hexerne; an orphan child, I have placed under my protection."

The young girl, who could not have been older than eleven or twelve years of age, took a graceful skip forwards and executed a perfect, well rehearsed curtsy, the hem of her dress clasped daintily in the tips of her forefingers and thumbs. It was a delighful display, and one that was rewarded with an uncharacteristicly generous smile of appreciation from the Ice Lord.

Tuatara smiled also, but her expression considerably shallower than that of her lord's. The child was adorably precocious but the Ice Witch did not enjoy watching the beautiful girl stealing Vrorst's attention and his affection, that truly belonged to Tuatara. After a short while, Tuatara longed for the Ice Lord to send Hexerne away, so that the two of them could be alone, to discuss that which had played on the Ice Witch's mind ever since she had left for the Dark Mountains all those days ago; their future together.

However, the Winter Wizard seemed far from bored with his juvenile companion and took great delight in her games and conversation; indeed, at one point, it was Tuatara herself who was in danger of being ignored, not the child. The Ice Witch consoled herself with the promise that when Vrorst finally got around to making her his queen, she would see to it personally that this nauseating little brat was sent far away as soon as possible.

Eventually, Vrorst broke himself away from Hexerne and turned to the Ice Witch, Tuatara thought that at last her time had come.

"You flatter yourself as a bit of a sorceress, don't you, Tuatara?" he asked her. Before the Ice Witch had chance to reply, Vrorst turned back to the child.

"Come Hexerne," he commanded. "Show the Queen of Witches what you have got in your hand."

The young girl, at first a little shyly, slowly revealed the object that she held so closely to her heart. It was a miniature crystal orb, small enough to be concealed by the clasped palms of the child.

"Every sorcerer must have an orb, is that not so, Tuatara?" the Ice Lord laughed.

The Ice Witch just smiled patiently.

"Show her what I taught you, Hexerne. Go on!" Vrorst urged. "The child has a remarkable capacity for learning, Tuatara. I have never seen anything like it. I showed her the basics of a complicated experiment, and in less than an hour, she had mastered it. Give your demonstration, my little sorceress!"

Hexerne giggled with embarrassment but then, steadily gaining in confidence, strode boldly up to the Ice Witch and held the orb up to Tuatara's face, a rash of giggles shaking the young girl's arm.

The Ice Witch was not pleased at being used as a guinea pig, but this little performance seemed to please her lord so she decided to humour the child, and at least pretend to enjoy the experience. Tuatara stared blankly at Vrorst and shrugged her shoulders in mock bafflement;

"What am I required to do? Swallow it?" she jested.

Hexerne burst into peals of laughter;

"No!" she cried. "You have already done it!"

The young girl danced around on the throne platform, her eyes shining with mischief, her petite body shaking with excitement. Suddenly, she threw the small orb high into the air above the throne and let it clatter noisily down the carved steps on to the main floor of the chamber, where it rolled in a wide circle and finally came to rest. A white light flickered inside the crystal ball as a familiar voice echoed loudly around the ice walls;

"What am I required to do? " Tuatara's voice rang out. "Swallow it?"

Hexerne ran over to the Ice Sorcerer and grasped his hand, squealing with delight as she did so. Vrorst chuckled proudly and rubbed his knuckles affectionately across her cheek, a warm expression invading his freezing eyes. An expression that Tuatara had never even seen before, let alone experience at first hand.

"Do you see how clever she is?" Vrorst spoke to the Ice Witch, his eyes not lifting from the child's face.

Tuatara was too furious to speak. She had never grown to hate any individual as fast as she did the little Hexerne. The Ice Witch looked upon the beautiful young girl, with long black hair, who probably looked exactly as Tuatara did when she was that age, as an enemy, a rival, an obstruction that would have to be removed if she was to fulfil her destiny.

"She has the face of a princess. No! A queen!" the Ice Lord continued. "This child has many years ahead of her before she reaches maturity; and in that time I shall fill her young mind with such knowledge! She will grow mightier by the year; until the day when......"

Vrorst snatched a sly look at the Ice Witch. Tuatara's thoughts could be read from her face, as if they had been scribed there in ink. Her eyes were wide with horror.

"Naddyrazz!" the Ice Sorcerer shouted.

A moment later, an old woman swathed in a thick cloak and cowl appeared from the rear of the Ice throne, to where she had clearly effaced herself after accompanying Hexerne into Vrorst's presence. She was the young girl's guardian and constant companion.

You are now a possession of the Orb of Winter!

"Escort the Lady Hexerne back to her apartments," the Wizard instructed, and then addressed a few further comments to the child as she left with the old woman. "Continue your studies, young lady. You have done well but there is so much for you to learn. Be industrious! Let not a moment slip by without profit."

Vrorst's eyes keenly followed the small figure until she disappeared with the old woman, through an opening made by a swivelling mirror of ice in the chamber wall, and then returned with their usual coldness to the Ice Witch.

"I do not seek approval," he said slowly and not without a hint of malice. "Therefore be warned not to state an opinion."

Tuatara fought hard to constrain herself;

"I have no opinion!" she offered her lie.

"That is well," Vrorst accepted.

The Ice Witch tried to ease the difficult atmosphere that had arisen between herself and her lord, by deciding to show an interest in Vrorst's latest protege, despite the painful lump that had developed in her throat. After all, Tuatara was big enough to be charitable to the poor orphan; the Ice Witch had been in the child's position herself once, if a little older. Vrorst had taken her under his wing and bestowed upon her great wisdom and power, and made Tuatara everything that she now was: his, body and soul.

"Where is she from?" The Ice Witch asked.

Vrorst's eyes softened a little and he leant back against the tall Ice columns, into a more reflective attitude. As he spoke, his fingers played along the cool arms of the throne.

"She is the daughter of a low sorcerer and a noble woman," he began. "Her parents died during one of Mezereon's ....experiments? Mercifully she remembers nothing of her ordeal, and seems quite happy and content here, as you will have noticed. I gave her the name of Hexerne; it means 'little sorceress'. I also gave her that small orb you saw; one of Mezereon's lieutenants confiscated it from a goblin raiding party. The stars alone know where they stole it from! It already contained a good deal of power when it was found, far too dangerous a toy for greenskins to be allowed to play with. I can only imagine it once belonged to a Fforlian conjuror, or some other fool meddling in elements beyond his control.

The little trick with your voice, she perfected that all by herself. Unfortunately she sometimes gets her recordings a little mixed up, either that or the orb is fussy about what sounds it captures, but her development is outstanding.

Hexerne has a fine, retentive brain that is able to surmount any obstacle that I throw in its path, and because her mother was noble, the child's mind is entirely pure and unstained; a blank slate upon which I shall write great things!"

"And when she comes of age.....?" Tuatara ventured to inquire.

The Ice Sorcerer looked long and hard into the Ice Witch's eyes, probing for an ounce of weakness that he might exploit, to score yet another victory over Tuatara's pride, but the Queen of Witches was solid, she refused to break.

"When she comes of age, my most loyal and trusted captain," the Wizard toyed.

"I shall make her my queen! And together we shall rule over this world for eternity."

No emotion was betrayed in the Ice Lord's face as he delivered this crushing blow to his henchwoman. He spoke slowly and deliberately, almost as if the content of his words was of little or no consequence. Tuatara inwardly flinched at every word, as though she had been repeatedly stabbed in the heart with a stiletto. The Ice Witch had in part, expected this news, after witnessing Vrorst's hurtful fawning over the child; but the pain of actually hearing the killing words fall from her master's lips was still unbearable.

Tuatara just managed to swallow and keep herself from fainting; that was one humiliation the Lord of Ice was not going to win from her.

"By the time the child comes of age," Vrorst continued. "She will have amassed such a wealth of knowledge and experience that she will be the mightiest of all sorceresses. A worthy consort to the Lord of Winter, wouldn't you say? When I take a female for my queen, she must be my equal......not my servant!"

Vrorst continued remorselessly;

"But let us talk of you," he cheerfully spoke forth. "Before you left for the Dark Mountains, I promised to make you a queen. Never let it be said that the Lord of Winter does not keep his word. I shall make you Queen of the Eastern Realms; and to show my gratitude for your sterling work with the goblins and all your other not insubstantial triumphs, I shall build you a magnificent frozen palace on the Giant Lake, where you shall rule in my name."

The Ice Sorcerer smiled triumphantly.

"Does that please you?" he taunted.

"My Lord is too generous," Tuatara whispered.

"Nonsense." Vrorst playfully denied.

The Winter Wizard watched with interest the maelstrom of emotions whirling inside the Ice Witch, but he resolved that he had taken her lesson in humility as far as it was prudent to go, on this occasion. Vrorst had been only too aware of Tuatara's soaring ambitions, and hoped that making an example of her in this way would deter any of his other high captains from expecting an easy route to his throne. He had never at any time intended to take Tuatara as his wife, even though letting her make wild assumptions in that direction had given him an added lever on her loyalty.

The Ice Witch respectfully asked for leave to withdraw from the Ice Sorcerer's presence; it was granted. Not until Tuatara was a good distance away from the open entrance to the throne room and out of earshot of the great Wizard, did she allow the waves of grief to rise from within, and her head to fall despairingly into her hands.

A small voice distracted the Ice Witch from her pain, and her shaking body froze in mid-anguish, Tuatara's eyes furious at her discovery.

A child's face peered from around the far side of a wide ice pillar, an uncertain smile stretched across her staring features. Hexerne cautiously edged into view and timidly approached the stiffening Ice Witch.

Tuatara's eyes blazed with hostility. The cause of her agonising dejection was standing right in front of her, tantalisingly within reach of her clenching hands. A quick wrenching of that pretty little throat that Vrorst had generously adorned with an exquisite choker of snowstars, and revenge would be hers; but no, that would be too easy.

"Tuatara," the sickly sweet orphan squeaked. "Why don't you like me?"

The Ice Witch could scarcely believe her ears.

"All of the others like me," Hexerne continued, with a nauseating false coyness. "Mezereon likes me."

"Does he indeed?" Tuatara sighed.

"Yes, he does," the child reaffirmed. "I could learn so much from you, if you would only teach me. The more I learn, the more it pleases the Ice Lord; and we both like to please Him, don't we? I promise I shall not forget your kindness, Tuatara. When I become your queen!"

The Ice Witch could scarcely contain her fury, and she had to dig her nails hard into her palms to prevent sparks of blue fire leaping from her fingertips.

"If you want me to like you, dear little Hexerne," Tuatara hissed at the child. "There is one small thing you must do."

"Anything!" Hexerne cried. "If only we could be friends!"

Tuatara bent low to speak privately in the young girl's ear and with the softest voice she could muster, under the circumstances, gave her conditions to the child.

"You must take yourself down to the palace kitchens," she began. "And instruct the chief cook to cut you up into small, succulent pieces and bake you in a pie! I think I would like you that way the best!"

The Ice Witch gave Hexerne a long devouring look before sweeping past her, to continue her progress to her quarters, the young girl's screams of outrage ringing loudly in her ears. A different Hexerne from the timid little thing that had crept from behind the column a few moments before shrieked a lungful of threats and abuse after Tuatara as she hastened away.

"You beast!" she roared. "You are horrible, Tuatara! Horrible! The Lord of Ice shall know of this; see if he doesn't! My orb will have captured everything; it will tell him everything that you have said and he will punish you, Tuatara! He will punish you!"

After Hexerne's hysterical rantings had faded far behind her, Tuatara paused for a moment and thought ironically to herself;

"Punish me! Impossible, Hexerne; I am dead already!"

On turning the last corner before the entrance to her apartments, Tuatara almost ran headlong into the loitering figure of Mezereon.

The High Gaoler of Dragonskeep, was dressed in a long, voluminous black robe, adorned with embroidered symbols and hieroglyphics, that proclaimed in purple, the dark sorcerer's alleged magnificence, and a close-fitting black skull cap, decorated with gold, a brave and rare commodity amongst the high servants of the Ice Sorcerer, who was known to frown upon the precious metal, favourite of the Wizards of Light.

Mezereon's features bore a somewhat ratty resemblence to those of the Lord of Winter. He too had a well attended, pointed beard and long curling eyebrows but lacked the charisma and majesty of his master's face. Mezereon gave the Ice Witch a knowing smile. He clearly knew of her audience with Vrorst and was almost certainly not waiting to offer words of condolence. Tuatara suddenly felt very tired and very much in need of solitude and peace; she decided to waste no time with Mezereon.

"What do *you* want?" she growled.

"Come, come!" Mezereon laughed. "That is no way to greet an old friend."

"You and I may have been many things, Mezereon," Tuatara sighed wearily. "But we have never been friends!"

The Sorcerer leered at her, and there was a familiar lascivious glint in his eyes; the Ice Witch groaned inwardly as she knew what was about to follow.

"Then perhaps we ought to be friends," he said seductively. "Perhaps....more?"

Tuatara rebuffed him with a snapping reply.

"I think not!"

She was just about to stride past the dark sorcerer when a firm hand clamped on to her arm.

"But just think of it," Mezereon persisted. "If you and I were to...join forces! What an invincible combination we should make. We might even decide to challenge for the Ice Throne itself! I don't want that snivelling little brat to share in the fruits of our labours, anymore than you do!"

A desperate laugh erupted from Tuatara's throat and she fell back against a thick ice pillar as if no longer able to support her own weight. The Ice Witch recalled Hexerne claiming that Mezereon liked her, and the lying schemer had undoubtedly told the child that he did. Tuatara's eyes shone with loathing for Mezereon and a mocking smile played wearily on her lips.

"You have finally taken leave of your puny senses!" she sneered. "To even go before Him with such thoughts inhabiting your mind is insanity itself. An invincible combination? Ha!...."

Tuatara paused for more derisive laughter;

"We wouldn't live long enough to climb one step together!"

Mezereon's lips curled into a mocking sneer and his face sharpened to commit injury.

"Perhaps one day, I will prove you wrong, Queen of *only* Witches!"

The Ice Witch visibly winced at this vitriolic reminder of her recent humiliation, but she refused to reward the sorcerer's emotional molestations with what he would claim to be a typically female breakdown. She had just strength enough to save herself from that, and strike a parting blow at her insipid protagonist before withdrawing to the sanctuary of her rooms.

"Dream on, Mezereon!" Tuatara hissed. "Only in your fantasies will you ever become King of the World!"

With the rush of an icy draught, the Ice Witch was gone; and a somewhat crestfallen high gaoler tramped sulkily away to his own imminent audience with the Ice Lord.

Several days passed by in the palace of the Ice Sorcerer, with Jonquil and the others still residing in their frozen cells, at the great Wizard's pleasure. The banf had been dragged before the Ice Lord on numerous occasions, and at all hours, to answer further questions, under the menacing influence of the mighty Orb of Winter.

Vrorst had turned his wrath on almost every servant, in an effort to uncover the Three Wizards' spy; no one escaped suspicion. Each of the Ice Lord's captains had been charged with purging the ranks of their own followers to flush out any traitors. Every inch of the frozen city was scoured in an attempt to find evidence of treachery, the whole citadel practically turned on its head to unearth this viper.

Finally, the Ice Sorcerer ordered that all searches were to cease. A high council was to be held in the Crystal Chamber, attended by all Vrorst's captains; the quest for the Three Wizards spy was at an end.

Vrorst sat at the head of a star shaped table, the pattern of a snowflake embossed in its surface. Mezereon, Vakari, Wargren and Hexerne were amongst those that sat in attendance around the points of the table. Installed in the very centre of the star, held by an ornate cradle of jewelled silver was the imposing form of the Wizard's Fire Orb. Each of the seated figures within the high chamber could not help but stare into its ominous depths and be reminded of the importance of speaking only the truth. The Orb of Winter had a fearsome skill in seeking out and dealing with liars.

The vast crystal windows cast an irridescent brightness over the scene; the jewels and precious adornments of the collected high beings, glinting in a responding chorus of brilliant stars.

"Let us begin," commanded Vrorst.

Mezereon begged leave to speak;

"But where is the Queen of Witches, Lord?" he asked. "Should she not be present?"

"She is indisposed," said the Ice Lord dismissively. "Tuatara is still 'overwrought' from the ordeal of her long journey to the Dark Mountains. We will conduct this council without her. Now, to the business of our spy. I now know that..."

But Vrorst was stopped mid-speech by the sudden entrance of a tall, elegant figure dressed in long flowing robes of white silk, her hair, for once, allowed to fall freely about her shoulders, like cascades of black satin. A simple circlet of silver gracing her pale forehead, was all the decoration she wore on her marble skin. She had discarded all the heavy jewelry and extravagance associated with a queen.

Tuatara rose from the spiral staircase that climbed into the peak of the lofty tower; and floated into the light, her diaphonous robes shimmering with the radiant debris of shattered rainbows. The Ice Witch appeared as a spectacular vision, breathtaking to behold, and all seated around the table of council, including the Ice Lord himself, were stunned into silence as she approached them. Tuatara stood before Vrorst as he had never seen her before. She no longer resembled a queen of witches, she looked like a fair princess; flawless and aloof. Vrorst found the transformation more than a little unsettling, but eventually regained sufficient composure to greet his henchwoman.

"Tuatara!" he said. "You have come."

"Forgive my tardiness, Lord," the Ice Witch said, demurely. "I am here to take my place in your company."

An uncertain smile drifted briefly across the Ice Lord's features and he motioned to an empty place at the star table;

"Be seated then," he told her.

Vrorst ordered Jonquil to be brought before the council. The wearisome banf was rudely bustled up the stone stairs and made to stand on a short stool, positioned directly opposite from the Ice Lord; the Orb of Winter glimmering menacingly between them.

A ring of hostile faces scowled at Jonquil as he swayed with fatigue on the stool top. The frequency of the banf's exhausting interrogations by Vrorst, over the past few days and nights, had dramatically increased as a note of desperation had crept into the Ice Lord's efforts to identify his enemy within.

The searching eyes of the Ice Sorcerer reached across the spread of the table and demanded Jonquil's utmost attention. Familiar words floated through the icy air towards him, and the banf exchanged them for his own same answer.

"Who is the eye at my shoulder?" demanded Vrorst.

"I do not know," sighed Jonquil.

The face of the Ice Sorcerer was frozen in a thunderous expression for several moments and then, almost imperceptibly his stare sank into the depths of the crystal globe, where strange blue fires began to kindle. A low growl suddenly rumbled in Vrorst's throat, building to an awesome roar, and then his lips shaped his raging voice into a string of bellowing words.

"Eye of Winter!" he screamed. "Show me the face of the traitor!"

Plumes of violet cloud billowed up from the base of the orb until its whole surface was filled with the colour. Then gradually it cleared until all that could be seen was the infinite reflections of its own image, gradually reducing to nothing.

A murmur of confused voices broke out amongst the circle of seated figures. The Fire Orb had failed to reveal the spy, what could this mean?

Suddenly Vrorst exploded with harsh laughter, the faces of his captains now thrown even deeper into confusion. The Ice Lord's fist crashed down on the table to silence the mutterings.

"You see, the thing that puzzled me the most," he confided with those before him. "Was why, just as now, the Orb of Winter would not show me the face of our spy. Was the traitor shielded by a cloak of sorcery? Did he have some charm or disguise to confuse the great crystal? Had the Three Wizards devised some powerful protection to keep safe his identity?

I knew that the spy could not be one of you. As willing instruments of my power, you all have much more to lose by helping our enemies, than you could ever hope to gain. So the question remains; who is the spy? How could they steal away our secrets, and yet still remain invisible?"

Vrorst looked into a line of blank faces, no one daring to offer a solution. The Ice Lord continued.

"Is it not true, that the greatest of enemies are created by the most suspicious of minds?" he asked. "I think the Wizards of Light believe so. That is why they sent this creature to dupe me."

"But Lord, the banf-thing was captured....by Tuatara!" argued Wargren.

"He was sent!" Vrorst roared. "As surely as if they had delivered him here in person! I have to confess I am possessed by a grudging admiration for such uncharacteristic deviousness by their lordships. This truly was a masterstroke of confusion!

They filled this creature's mind with a subtle blend of truth and lies; enough secrets to make me believe. And yet, tell him nothing of any real consequence."

"But Lord," whined Mezereon. "I do not understand...."

"Ever since this miserable wretch was brought before me," Vrorst ignored him. "I have been trying to direct this war with one eye constantly looking over my shoulder. I have been chasing my tail like a dog trying to count his fleas! But the fleas keep jumping; so he counts them more than once, and ends up believing that he is twice as lousy as he really is! Spies! I have seen them everywhere! I even began to mistrust my own shadow. And what has been achieved by this grand confusion? Were the Wizards of Light merely having sport with me, through the revelations of this banf-creature? I think not. For what they have achieved is success in distracting me from that which, during these vital past few days, should have been the focus of my fullest attention. Themselves!

Whilst I have been occupied with trying to extract imaginary daggers from my back, the Wizards of Light have made their move, and slipped through my net; they are here in Enchantica! I know it!"

A great uproar of excited voices filled the air of the crystal chamber. Cries of disbelief were mingled with curses and loud recriminations against various members of the council, each captain desperate to deflect any blame from their corner, on to someone elses.

"Silence!" demanded Vrorst. "We have all been played for fools; none greater than myself! I freely admit it! The reason why the Orb of Winter could put no face to our traitor, is because none exists; save in our own imaginations! There is no spy! No eye at my shoulder! If he was real the Orb would show him to us."

"Then how can you explain the leakage of secret information, Lord?" asked Vakari.

"I cannot!" Vrorst answered. "But I will say this; let the Wizards of Light learn of our intentions; let them know of our strengths, our weaknesses! For if they believe that the acquisition of such knowledge will gain them any victories in this war, then they are the greatest fools of all! Vakari, your spies must seek out the kingdom of the banfs; the third haven. That is the destination of the Wizards of Light. If they are already there, we shall lay siege to them; if not, we shall ambush and destroy them!"

A volley of cheers resounded from the council, each captain growling his approval, and with one movement the figures surrounding the star table rose to their feet and praised the Lord of Winter. All except one, that is; the Ice Witch remained seated, and simply stared quietly at Vrorst, an inner smile sparkling in her eyes.

Vrorst allowed a shallow frown to darken his face, as his own gaze met hers. Perhaps Tuatara had changed more than her appearance? The Ice Lord was uncertain about the new glow that emanated from the highest of his servants. She was possessed of a new calm, that was for Vrorst, slightly disturbing, but at the same time strangely intriguing.

The Ice Lord's fascination was interrupted by an insistent tugging of his sleeve. He looked down into the bright blue eyes of Hexerne, demanding instant attention.

"Can I have him?" bleated the child.

"Who?" Vrorst asked of her.

"The banf-thing!" the young girl replied. "Mezereon has shown me some of his experiments. I want to try them out on a live specimen. Can I have him...... please?"

Jonquil suddenly awoke from his half slumber on the stool, on hearing the nature of the little girl's request. He was not sure what being a live specimen for experiments might entail for him, but he imagined that it would not be good. Not after the tales the Three Wizards had told him about Mezereon's unnatural creations.

Tuatara was about to object but Vakari beat her to it.

"But Lord," he interrupted. "Will I not need the banf to guide me to his homeland?"

"He would be of no use to you," the Ice Lord told him. "He could not find his own way there if he were free."

Jonquil took great exception to this foul slur on his navigational skills, but after pondering the accusation for a few seconds, realised that it was probably true. He had never wandered as far away from home as this in all his lifetime; and the Green Sky forest was incredibly big, his flight on Arangast had shown him that. The Ice Sorcerer was right, the banf kingdom was as lost to Jonquil, as it was to the Wizards of Light and the enemy. This new realisation did little to raise his already flagging spirit.

"There is something about this creature that I do not like," continued Vrorst. "And I fear that alive he will prove more useful to our enemies, than he ever will to us. He is not to leave this palace alive!"

Jonquil almost fell off the stool.

"Yes, Hexerne, you may have him." Vrorst agreed. "Do with him what you will, only make sure that he is dead at the end of it."

"I will!" the young child cried. "Can I have the gladiator aswell?"

Tuatara rose sharply from her chair, her composure slightly damaged.

"He has got a lovely big body," Hexerne grinned. "I could turn him into a great ogre!"

The Ice Witch could keep silent no longer.

"My Lord," she began. "Is it wise to allow the Lady Hexerne to mutilate these prisoners, when they may still contain information that could be of use to us?"

Vrorst slowly arose from his high seat and walked over to where Jonquil was still perched precariously on the stool. The Ice Lord gave the banf one long, last appraisal and then shook his head.

"Any knowledge he possesses is merely second hand deception," Vrorst concluded. "Placed there by the Wizards to confound me. I will not listen to it."

Tuatara attempted to voice another objection, but the Ice Lord silenced her with the swift raising of his hand.

"And the only information I need concerning the gladiator's home kingdom of

Fforl, is that it is currently buried beneath a mountain of snow and ice; and will remain that way until the inhabitants of that stubborn domain, lay down their arms, along with their neighbours, and recognise me as their liege lord! So you see, Tuatara, neither captive has any real use, other than providing our little protégé here with a valuable source of education. Does that answer your argument?"

Tuatara prudently abandoned her objections, after quickly recognising the look of unwavering resolve in her master's face and bowed her head in a show of acceptance. This apparently satisfied the Ice Sorcerer and he swept majestically from the high chamber, the excited Hexerne at his side, his captains following closely in their wake, in a jossling subservient crowd.

Tuatara descended from the Crystal Chamber in her own time, no longer gripped by the urge to trot dutifully at the Ice Lord's heels. She decided to pay a visit to Thrace, the gladiator, before he and Jonquil were transferred to Hexerne's study; a loathsome room situated at the top of one of the old original towers, and filled with a gruesome collection of torture instruments. No doubt one of the experiments the child was going to perform with Mezereon was a study in pain, and how best to inflict it.

The Ice Witch had developed a curious fascination for the strong Fforlian. Although he was only a man, and as such far beneath a high being like herself, a part of her felt a twinge of regret at the thought of his fine stature being slowly stretched and torn apart on Hexerne's machines of agony, or corrupted into some monstrous, twisted abhorrence by Mezereon's evil potions.

Tuatara supposed that Thrace might be considered handsome in his own world and by his own females. His face was certainly quite pleasing to the eye, strong bones, a square jaw, soulful dark eyes, and a thick mane of long blonde hair. The gladiator also had a profound gaze that seemed intensely sad and hopeless, as if he had long resolved himself to never again expect pleasure or peace to enter his life. His sorrow somehow reached out to a place within her, to intrude upon the cold sanctity of her dark spirit, a touch that Tuatara found increasingly difficult to ignore, and not entirely unwelcome.

As she wound her way through a honeycomb of connected passageways to arrive at the frozen cells, gliding noislessly through the empty corridors of ice. Tuatara, for a reason that was completely unknown to her, began to smile.

An Unlikely Friend

Jonquil had tried everything to be free of his manacles. He had twisted and wriggled, pulled and wrestled but still the rusty bracelets of iron held him fast. The banf had moistened his wrists by spitting on them and then squirmed like a hooked maggot to try and ease his bony hands through the squeaking hoops, but they would not release him. After a frenzied bout of struggling, the banf flopped back against the damp wall, panting breathlessly, his reddened face glistening with sweat, shiny wounds at his wrists testifying to the furiousness of his efforts to escape.

When he glanced over to the shackled form of the gladiator, Jonquil was disturbed to find that Thrace was making no attempt to test the strength of his chains. He simply hung from his arms, limp and forlorn, indifferent to the fervent exertions of his smaller cellmate. Seemingly resigned to whatever fate lay in store for him, uninterested in evasive measures, perhaps even contently anticipating the final release from the misery of his life.

The only movement that Jonquil managed to inspire from the man, was a slow lifting of his head and a long, pitiful gaze from the gladiator's melancholic eyes, after the banf had launched a barrage of abuse - most of which, Jonquil, was quite ashamed for later - chastising him for submitting to the enemy and giving them an easy victory. Thrace gave no answer to the banf, to explain his apathetic capitulation, he simply returned his eyes to the rush strewn floor beneath him and waited.

The round, stone built, room against whose wall they had been securely attached, was lit by a handful of torches, the light from which was reflected in an ensemble of strangely shaped flasks and bottles, carefully arranged on a series of worktops and shelves. Some of these scientific vessels contained boldly coloured liquids or powders, a few of which glowed quite brightly in the semi-darkness. Others imprisoned dark shapes that jumped against slippery sides or scuttled endlessly around the edges of glass bottoms. From the conical rafters that rose away into thick shadow, a host of wicker cages hung down like giant fruit. The rope suspended baskets were continually on the move, unseen creatures flapping leathery wings or shrieking to one another as they bounced off the walls inside. Whenever the cages inevitably clashed together, tiny clawed hands would reach out through the woven bars to scrap fiercely with their neighbours, an explosion of shrill screams and raking claws accompanying the fracas. Jonquil was afraid to imagine what nature of aggressive, little, hybridised demons they were, whose cages swung so ominously above their heads.

The floor of the room was filled with a great many large machines and equipment the purpose of which was not clear, although the inclusion of various arrangements of straps, spikes and blades, suggested that these were not devices of idle pleasure.

Hexerne, the Ice Lord's protégé - and for as long as he remained in the Throne

Citadel, Mezereon's pupil - had personally supervised the shackling of her two prisoners. The banf and the gladiator were very precious to the child, her very first live specimens. She wanted to be absolutely certain that they were strongly secured and not able to escape. Hexerne had made the gaoler and his men test the chains several times before she was satisfied, and after doing as they were bid, over and over again, eventually retired to their beds grumbling irritably under their breath.

The child would have started work on her experiments there and then if she had been allowed, such was her excitement, but Mezereon persuaded her that great sorceresses need lots of sleep, if they are to become all powerful, so better to leave her sorcery until the morning. And more to the point, the High Gaoler of Dragonskeep had a flagon of the finest elfen wine, taken from the cellars of some ransacked woodland palace, waiting for him in his quarters, and if it was a choice between coaching a nauseating brat in the fine arts of torture or slowly sipping a goblet of the most excellent beverage with his feet up in front of a glowing crystal orb; there was no contest.

Consequently the prisoners had been granted a brief reprieve until sunrise, the thick, heavy door to the room having been locked and bolted, Hexerne insisting on guarding all the keys herself.

Jonquil decided to give his sore wrists one more coating of spit and try to twist them through the tight bands before finally admitting defeat and cease his struggles, to prepare himself for the horrors that would follow the dawn. As he urged and cajoled his left hand to scrunch up even smaller and ease out of the biting iron, his face fixed in a grimace of pain, two things happened: the fluttering torches suddenly died and out of the corner of his eye, the banf saw something small, with a long thin tail, scuttle quickly across the barred imprint of moonlight cast on to the floor from a solitary window. Jonquil stopped and tried to locate the swift creature, in the now complete darkness, he did not relish the thought of a hungry rat gnawing at his ankles, whilst his hands were useless to him. The small animal was nowhere to be seen. The banf tried to listen for it with his sensitive ears, rustling over the dried rushes towards him, but there was no sound either. It could not have simply disappeared!

Suddenly, there was another movement. The creature had made itself invisible on one of the dark bars of the moonlit silhouette and now it had trotted into the one of the broad white bands and stood quite still, regarding the banf keenly with tiny, gleaming eyes.

It was a lizard, and at first Jonquil presumed it was an escapee from one of the live collections on the shelves, searching for the quickest route to freedom. The banf was just about to wish the small reptile good fortune, when it reared up on to its hind legs and slowly began to grow before his eyes, casting its own enlarging shadow in the moonlight.

Despite packing his pupil off to bed, Mezereon never made it back to his apartments to sample his rare liquor, his return journey was interrupted by a messenger from Vrorst, summoning the dark sorcerer yet again into his master's presence. The Lord of Ice wanted a progress report on what new biological creations had emerged from Mezereon's dreaded laboratories in the dark dungeons of Dragonskeep. With a few well muffled curses uttered to himself, the dark sorcerer turned from his path and wearily followed Vrorst's messenger through the dark halls leading to the throne room.

On his arrival, Mezereon found the ice chamber to be deep in shadow, but seated upon the great throne, which shone with a spectacular blue radiance, emanating from its core, was the fearsome silhouette of the Lord of Ice, his features softly picked out by the glowing Fire Orb, at his right hand.

"Ah, Mezereon!" cried Vrorst. "You have come!" he said, as if the dark sorcerer had had any other choice.

"You must tell me," the Ice Lord continued. "How fares the dwarf dungeons of Dragonskeep? And the fantastic creatures they contain?"

Mezereon had already given the Ice Sorcerer a brief résumé of his work in the deep laboratories but had declined to quote precise details until the final results of his latest endeavours had been brought to him by fast dragonsteed from the north. The dark sorcerer having to leave the conclusions of his many experiments to his assistants after being summoned to leave for the Throne Citadel in such haste. Vrorst had received word that the awaited messenger had duly arrived, earlier in the evening and now demanded a full report.

The first subject that the Ice Lord was impatient for news on was the Sentinel of the Mines. Even though the entrances to the tunnels which led to the veins of the Three Wizards' power crystals had long been sealed, Vrorst had commissioned a guardian from Mezereon, a terrible beast that would lie amongst the rubble of the collapsed caves, to ensure that no one would ever dare try to enter the mines again.

The dark sorcerer was delighted to be able to tell his master that the long awaited beast was born, and with the aid of concentrated sorcery would grow to full maturity in only a few weeks. It was a dragon of colossal stature, larger and more powerful than any of the four Guardians of the Vessels, and better yet, had hatched from its massive egg with no less than seven heads. The beast was named Massazauga, which in the old tongue of the Wizards meant, many headed terror, and from all accounts was growing into the fiercest, most deadly creature Mezereon's servants had ever seen, and that was high praise indeed.

The Ice Lord wanted to know what steps his high gaoler had taken to remove the pockets of resistance from the deep caves and tunnels of the Marble Fortress, a thin scattering of dwarfs who had refused to surrender to Mezereon's forces and had sought refuge in the endless maze of tunnels that burrowed far into the ancient mountains. The rebel dwarfs had been impossible to remove by conventional means. The small armies of goblins - the only creatures at Mezereon's disposal suited to such dark and inhospitable terrain - had been gradually slaughtered by the roaming bands of dwarfs, who were perfectly adapted to their subterranean existance and knew every twist and turn of the honeycombed depths like the wrinkles in their faces. Not surprisingly after a time, the goblins refused to venture into the tunnels to seek out the dwarfs, which meant certain death.

So Mezereon had decided that where brute force failed, sorcery would have to succeed, and told Vrorst of a breed of swift moving serpents he had perfected, who had been raised solely on a diet of dwarf flesh, and were able to slither through the smallest openings in search of their prey. The serpents hunted by scent and so would not be affected by the dark, and were built for speed and stamina, and a relentless love of the kill. These murderous creations were due to be released into the potholes of the mountains very shortly, and would, Mezereon predicted, locate and destroy the dwarf resistance within a matter of days.

The dark sorcerer also spoke of many other horrific beasts that he had created for Vrorst's new empire, including, giant sharks that could outswim the mer-folk, terrorise them in the open water and even attack their undersea cities. Eggs had already been hatched and a few fingers lost.

Huge lizards called Gracklins, that stalked the earth on two, long, taloned legs, rows of dagger-like teeth arming their powerful jaws, had been developed. Ideal for use against forest dwelling enemies, such as the enchanted folk or the banfs, where winged dragons would be made redundant by the closely growing trees.

Vrorst gave a wry smile when Mezereon told him he had created a race of even faster snowdragons, if such a beast was possible, that flew like the north wind, called snow-darts. The best of these had already been presented to Wargren, captain of Vrorst's dragonriders, to create a new, élite flight. The crowning glory of these white blurs was called Snowthorn, a dragon of supreme poise and elegance, the fastest creature alive.

Mezereon was truly obsessed with making yet further refinements to his already perfect flying machine. The humiliating defeat of his white flocks at the Battle of the Bay of Voices had urged him beyond reason to redesign their fighting power, and now he was confident that if the same battle was to be fought tomorrow, the outcome would be very different.

Vrorst was impressed by the work of the Grand Corruptor, and greeted the descriptions of all of the fearsome creatures with an excited glint in his eyes. But his expression fell into dismay when Mezereon admitted that he had still not been able to produce the Ice Lord's most desired servants of all: his superbreed of warriors; even though he was getting closer.

"Go back to your cauldrons and your test-tubes!" commanded Vrorst. "And do not come before me again until you have an army of my new soldiers with you. I cannot claim total victory over the Wizards as long as there is one place in this world, where I cannot reach them! The Wells of Hope!"

And so, Mezereon was dismissed angrily from the presence of the Ice Sorcerer, and sent back to his quarters to pack his things. He would be leaving the citadel that same evening; no time to take even a moments rest or the smallest sip of elven wine. By the time his dragon flight was prepared, the dark sorcerer was not in the happiest frame of mind, and his servants returning to Dragonskeep with him, pitied the first prisoners to be pulled from the dungeons to be Mezereon's next batch of victims, for his rage would be their agony, and the dark Sorcerer's rage knew no mercy.

Jonquil could hardly believe his eyes, as he stood against the wall of the tower room, witnessing the fantastic transformation taking place in the small patch of moonlight before him.

The lizard had grown tall indeed, and its back legs had become long and straight; its forelegs, pale skinned arms, that rose into small, delicate shoulders; its scaled flanks had been sucked in to form curved hips and a thin waist. The long, weaving tail shrank away like a fleeing snake, disappearing into the body. The reptile's head was the last to change, its pointed face crumpling into the finely carved features of a beautiful woman; flanges of skin draped along the lizard's neck grew into a thick mane of silky hair, darker than the night, falling behind her naked body, in shimmering waves.

A gulp of disbelief rumbled in the banf's ears, and if his hands had been free, he would have used them to rub his eyes, to make sure that he was not dreaming. The strong beams of moonlight caused her milky skin to glow with an hypnotic luminescence as she stood against the blackness of the room. She remained as still as a statue; like a goddess, carved from the purest marble, perfect and serene.

Jonquil knew this had to be a dream, or an apparition, or some evil trickery of the Ice Lord sent to harass them in their last hours. After a long, intense silence, the vision spoke, her voice faint but familiar. The woman stared out of the window, her face bathed in the full rays of silver light, and as the words flowed from her snowy lips her eyes never strayed from the broad smile of the moon.

"I have tried to serve you," the pale figure sighed. "With my whole body I was devoted to the glory of your name."

Jonquil did not even begin to understand the meaning behind the woman's words, but soon realised that her lamentations were not directed at him but elsewhere. The figure continued;

"I would have laid down my life for you a thousand times over. Robbed, killed, betrayed; all these things I have done for your profit; and never once questioned your most extravagant desires. And now I am discarded, redundant, excluded; no longer at your side, or welcome in your confidence. Mistrusted, accused, rejected; this is my reward. This is my future!

You have denied me the means to serve any other destiny. All that I am, you have made me. What is there for me now?"

At last, the sad face turned from the moon and gazed emptily at Jonquil, two shiny tracks falling from her glistening eyes. The banf could feel only pity for the broken woman standing before him, and wonder at the cause of the grief and misery, of which she was so deeply stricken, his own state of misfortune, for the moment, quite forgotten.

"I cannot remember the name of whom I was before," she said. "He named me Tuatara. In the old tongue it means 'lizard'. Well, Lord of Winter, King of the World, beware! This lizard is about to change her skin!"

The Ice Witch then gave Jonquil another of those deep analytical stares that he had almost come to expect from the higher beings of the outside world. He had never been the focus of so much attention in all his life. The banf wished he knew just what it was about himself that was so astounding. He was just an ordinary banf, nothing

This Lizard is about to change her skin.

more! Tuatara obviously saw differently;

"You are a change-bringer, Jonquil," she began. "Wherever you go, the past is overturned and new fortunes are made. There is a power within you that brings all this about. That may be the reason why Vrorst fears your freedom. Perhaps all of your kind are catalysts for disruption; I do not know. You are the only banf the higher world has ever encountered.

Be that as it may, I shall not let you die in this barbaric place; not at the hands of that little butcher! You must take flight upon the wind of fortune; as must we all."

The Ice Witch glanced once more at the moon;

"A lizard you made me, and as a lizard I come to betray you!" She cried.

With that Tuatara turned away from the window and disappeared into the darkness. Jonquil strained his eyes and ears to try and locate the Ice Witch within the room but it was useless, she was cloaked in thick shadows and as silent as the grave. The banf turned to Thrace, to view his reaction to the incredible visitation they had just received. To his dismay, Jonquil discovered that the gladiator had slept throughout the whole episode, and that the banf alone had been a witness to the naked metamorphosis of Tuatara. When he turned back to the moonlit scene and saw no trace of the Ice Witch or the lizard she had once been, Jonquil had to question whether the fantastic happening had really taken place or had it been an astonishingly real trick of his overwrought mind. Perhaps Thrace really did have the best idea, forget life and just sleep!

Suddenly, there was a blinding flash and a crashing roar as timber and stone were wrenched asunder. Silhouetted in the white explosion was the naked profile of a tall woman, arms outstretched, commanding the wall to burst, her long hair flowing out behind her with the force of the blast. The broad beams of moonlight streaming in through the barred window, became thick with clouds of dust and debris that rolled over the prisoners like a choking blanket.

The demonic ménagerie hanging from the rafters exploded into a cacophony of alarmed screams as their baskets buffeted wildly in the backdraught, each creature angrily lashing out at its neighbour, as they swung into reach, as if blaming each other for the disturbance.

When the air finally cleared, Jonquil and the now - not surprisingly - wide awake, gladiator could just about distinguish a gaping hole in the round wall of the tower, from the rest of the general darkness. The banf even thought he could see one or two stars set in a deep violet sky beyond.

The sound of large flapping wings approached the opening, and then it seemed as if a tall, winged shape blocked out most of the night sky as it alighted on to the jagged bricks of the ruptured wall. The wide, leathery membranes folded away and the creature ventured inside. The banf could hear the heavy snorting of the dragon echoing in the darkness.

"Jonquil!" the voice of the Ice Witch cried, "Come, you must hurry, the noise will have been heard!"

The banf was just about to shout back to Tuatara that he was shackled to the wall, and consequently unable to go anywhere, when his arms suddenly fell limply to his sides, the iron rings broken. He carefully made his way over to Thrace and found that the gladiator was also free, together Jonquil and the man guided each other towards the hole, where the banf was overjoyed to discover that the dragon they had heard was none other than Charlock, his faithful friend and carrier. As he stepped gingerly over the rubble, Jonquil could feel a new weight around his waist, and hear a strange jingling sound about him, like thin chains. When the banf reached down to investigate, the mystery was solved. By some miracle, Jonquil was wearing a flying harness, that had definitely not been there a few moments before; but knowing there was no time now for idle curiosity, he did not stop to question, but scrambled over to Charlock to prepare to flee.

To the banf's further wonderment, his groping fingers revealed that the carrier-dragon was fully harnessed and provisioned in readiness for a long flight. There was certainly no way that Charlock could have equipped himself with such vital accessories, whilst languishing in the dank, dungeons below the ice, which passed for stables for the captive carrier-dragons. No doubt Tuatara's enchanted hand was at work here, and Jonquil would have loved to have asked her why she was doing all of this to help them, but the need for great haste denied him.

Jonquil finally managed to buckle himself on to Charlock's harness securely after a degree of blind fumbling and then turned to try and thank the Ice Witch.

"You must hurry!" a disembodied voice hissed from the blackness. "Or the snowhawks will catch you!"

"But what about Thrace?" Jonquil asked.

"Do not worry for him," the voice assured. "I will see to it that he is safe. Now go!"

A scaled hand slapped hard on Charlock's rear and the dragon leapt into the frosty air, weaved precariously through the towers of ice, and swept away from the clustered crown of the Ice Sorcerer, following the winds northward over the mountains.

Once Jonquil and Charlock were a reasonably safe distance from the palace, they dared to put down amongst the snow and ice for a short time to try and regain their bearings.

The banf was all in favour of turning westward to try and find his homeland before the Wizards arrived there and found his people unprepared. He also had to warn King Merlion of Vrorst's army that was setting forth to lay siege to the Banf Kingdom. Charlock however strongly disagreed.

"We must not go that way," the carrier began. "They will expect it, and there is no way that I can outfly the Ice Lord's snowhawks. They will easily recapture us. No! I believe our safest route lies to the north. To Dragongorge, my homeland. The enemy will never expect us to fly that way, and with an extra ounce of good fortune we may just make it. In any case, I know the way to my homeland, you do not know the way to yours. We might waste valuable time searching for it and get caught before we find it.

Let me take you to my brethren, Jonquil, and from there we will decide a way to get you home. What do you say....?"

Jonquil was stunned, he stared at Charlock with eyes like saucers, when he finally could speak, his voice emerged as an astonished squeak.

"Y'Y'You c'can talk!" he stammered. "You can talk!"

"Well of course," Charlock casually replied.

"B'But why have you never spoken before?" the banf asked.

"I was warned by the Lord Orolan," the dragon told him. "That it would be safer for you, should we get caught, if you believed that I was just an ordinary carrier-dragon. So I was instructed only to speak should it be absolutely necessary, such as now."

Jonquil smiled and patted Charlock warmly on his neck;

"Well, I am very glad that you did," he said. "Because you are right, my friend. We cannot go westwards. After our escape has been discovered the skies in that direction will be thick with snowdragons. I was speaking without thinking. As much as I long to see my homeland again, I concede that the best route must take us to yours. Let us away!"

Charlock spread his wings and lifted them both into the night, with a clear sky the stars were easy to read and the carrier soon plotted a straight course to the foothills of the Marble Fortress and Dragongorge: the canyon of the dragons.

Vrorst greeted the news of the escape with a great deal more calm than his young protégé, who became instantly hysterical when she was told that Jonquil was gone, the gladiator was gone, the carrier-dragon was gone and Tuatara was gone also. Although privately the higher offices of the Throne Citadel proliferated with rumours of betrayal and treason, much to the bewilderment of his other captains, Vrorst refused to make a public condemnation of the Ice Witch, or openly accuse her of the crime.

Of course he knew that she was responsible, and in his own time he would punish her; but for the time being he was willing to let her go, let her keep her small victory.

The Ice Lord had to admit to himself that he was unable to fathom out quite how the Ice Witch had executed so perfect a rescue. The hole in the wall and the release of the carrier-dragon explained the banf's departure from the tower. But what of Tuatara and the gladiator? How had they escaped? The guards who had rushed to investigate the explosion had found the heavy, iron door to the high room still locked. The carrier would have been unable to bear more than one small person such as the banf to freedom, so how had the other two escaped the locked room? The only other possibility was that they had climbed down the outside of the tower; but then that was nonsense, for the gladiator would simply have frozen to death.

The only other information that the guards had felt a need to report, was that a few of the live specimens must have been released from their bottles by the force of the blast. Because, as soon as the door was opened, two lizards darted out of the room, moving far too fast to be caught, raced down the descending steps and disappeared into the darkness of the spiral staircase. The guards were not sure if the specimens were important or not!

"Lizards?" Vrorst mused to himself. "Little tuataras. I wonder!" Then he smiled broadly and laughed with renewed admiration.

Tuatara had freed the prisoners as an act of vengeance, to repay Vrorst for daring to reject her. He admired her courage, if not her good sense. The Ice Lord would allow her to flee to her secret castle, somewhere in the foothills of the North

Mountains, to ponder over her folly in crossing the King of the World. He was confident that in a short while Tuatara would return to him, stricken with remorse and wise with the knowledge, that the only life that could provide her with the power and influence she craved, was the one that Vrorst offered her; without him she was nothing.

The Ice Lord would wait for the Ice Witch to prostrate herself before him and beg for mercy, and then he would have her even deeper within his power, and her loyalty would be doubly his.

Vrorst would soon recapture the banf-creature and restore him to the inconsolable Hexerne to experiment on. Only this time he would have to be permanently incapacitated to ensure there was no repeat of his rescue, perhaps the removal of some vital limbs? As to the gladiator, Tuatara could keep him as a toy, if it pleased her; he was no great loss to the dissecting table. There would be plenty more where he came from, to give to the eager child, once the gates of the Eastern Realms were thrown open in surrender.

Just as Charlock and Jonquil had predicted, Vrorst ordered Wargren to send forth his fastest dragonsteeds to search the western airspace between the Citadel and the great forest, confident that the relatively slow-flying carrier-dragon would be easily overtaken by Wargren's new, even swifter snowdarts. Indeed, such was the Ice Lord's confidence, that he did not even hurry to give out the order, and with his foolish delay gave Charlock and the banf valuable time to make good their escape to the north.

The hunters and the prey were locked in a deadly race, but thanks to the Ice Sorcerer's arrogance, in opposite directions!

Alone in the Green Sky

A trail of four-toed footprints followed the weary figure, as he battled alone through the banks of deep snow clinging to the bases of the thick trunks. Mercifully, the snow had not been dumped heavily over the whole of the forest floor. Directed by the harsh, freezing winds, it had mostly drifted into huge waves and mounds, that although occasionally presented great walls of frost hardened snow to negotiate, also afforded long trenches and smooth plateaus to walk upon. As long as the lonely traveller could keep to these natural trails, his progress was not too difficult.

The terragon was relying on his strong instinct to guide him to his destination, not being at all familiar with the part of the forest in which he now found himself. Only time would tell if his feelings were taking him along the right path.

After being so cruelly wrenched from his friends by the terrifying storm, Rattajack had ridden inside the ferocious wind tunnel for many long hours, his feeble wings not strong enough to challenge the urgent forces that carried him. The maelstrom had originally been surging eastwards, when it swallowed the three travellers, but shortly after Rattajack was sucked from Charlock's back and the carrier and Jonquil spat out into oblivion, the windstorm had changed its mind and doubled back to roar into the west. When Rattajack finally succeeded in slipping from its grip and dived for freedom, he found himself coming to rest at the very eaves of the Green Sky forest. The windstorm had in fact saved the terragon many gruelling days, traversing the treacherous snow desert that now covered what used to be the rich, verdant plains of the Southerns.

Rattajack had spent the night curled up inside a gnarled cage of roots that enveloped the feet of an ageing green oak. The tree provided friendly shelter for the exhausted terragon as it stood sentinel on the forest border, tough and stubborn, defying the biting gales of Winter to do their worst. Green oaks above all other trees exuded an atmosphere of ancient strength and goodness, and this dependable old character was no exception; like a warty old grandfather, it welcomed Rattajack into its protection. A hidden cache of dry leaves beneath the snow-laden net of roots provided a cosy bed for tired limbs, an unexpected treat, and within moments of nestling down and closing his large, fearful eyes, Rattajack had been consumed by a deep, dreamless slumber.

When he awoke at daybreak, the first thought to leap into the terragon's conscious mind was of Jonquil. He had an overwhelming fear that the banf was in danger and that he and Charlock were powerless to avoid it. Rattajack squirmed with frustration, his place was with Jonquil, the banf should not have to face such terror alone. But the terragon could only sigh and face the realisation that fate had decreed they should not be together, and the only thing that Rattajack could do now to help his beloved companion was return to the banf kingdom with all haste and somehow tell the great Wizards of Jonquil's plight.

As Rattajack journeyed deeper into the forest, he found that ahead of him the trees grew much closer together, the gaps between some of the trunks being barely wide enough to pass through. One consolation, however was that the quantity of snow lying on the ground was considerably lighter, and in a few places none existant, the original leaf-lined forest floor clearly visible.

After a while, even the leafy ground disappeared, a mess of interweaving roots enveloping it, wrestling with their neighbours to gain access to the soil, forming an entangled platform between the fibrous trunks. Some of the twisted growths were slimy with moss and made walking treacherous, more than once causing Rattajack's feet to slip from beneath him and his hands to fly out to a nearby branch to save himself.

The air was getting noticeably warmer, even humid, and the snow seemed to have taken great exception to this part of the forest and shunned it completely. Patches of mist drifted lazily about the dripping trunks, like earthbound clouds imprisoned beneath a network of branches spreading overhead like a giant cage. Beards of feathery moss hung down from the crooked stems in long tresses, brushing against Rattajack's sensitive ears at unexpected moments, making him start nervously and cringe at every touch. The further the terragon ventured into the forest before him, the uneasier he became; his eyes could see nothing to be afraid of, but his senses screamed danger.

The banks of floating mist began to join forces until Rattajack was enveloped in a milky haze, the trees fading to pale memories more than a few strides away from him. Strange hoots and shrieks sounded intermittently in the far distance, either side of him, calls and cries that no bird, the terragon knew of, could ever make. The noises seemed to be messages, questions and answers in some secret code flying to and fro over his head; but what did the sounds mean, and who was making them? Meanwhile the mist grew up and became a fog, thick and inpenetrable, and Rattajack's careful stepping was suddenly a blind stumbling, his hands thrown forward in an effort to feel his way around the approaching buttresses.

Then abruptly, the terragon ran out of trees and all that lay before him was a featureless wall of white. Rattajack paused for a few moments to consider his choices. The overwhelming sense of peril that had gripped him earlier was stronger than ever and seemed to be emanating from the path ahead. Similarly his navigational senses suggested that the route to the banf kingdom also ran through the blank void that faced him, and that to retrace his steps and attempt to skirt around the menacing fog would add considerable time and effort to his already mammoth journey. Rattajack resigned himself to procede and hoped that for once his fears would be unfounded.

He had edged forward only a short distance from the last trunk when his toes met with a firm obstruction. Thinking little of it, the terragon carefully stepped over the object he just presumed to be a rock or a hummock and continued forward. Much to his dismay, Rattajack found a great many more obstacles to negotiate, some of which lay across his path like a tangle of fallen branches. Soft plumes at the ends of hard stems brushed against Rattajack's skin, as he eased his way across the white void, the terragon assuming they were merely the seed heads of common cotton grass, that always flourished on open ground; and paid them little heed.

Suddenly his long toes snagged on a large, unyielding mass that like all of the other hindrances had a cold, smooth surface. The terragon was just about to step over as before, when something made him stoop to investigate.The terragon had to squat with his nose almost touching the object in question before the thickly veiled air would allow him to recognise its form. When his squinting eyes slowly reached a decision on the nature of the obstacle they were staring at and Rattajack realised what it was, he drew back in alarm. He had just stubbed his toes on a section of goblin armour, and from the solid feel of it, lying heavy on the ground, it was not empty.

Hesitantly creeping forward, Rattajack followed the profile of a dark shoulder plate as it rounded towards a pale leaf shaped object, that turned out to be an ear. It protruded from the side of a curved helm, armed with a bed of sharpened spikes, and framed within it was the dew-spottled face of a goblin warrior, its eyes screwed up tightly, its fang-filled mouth bared in a grimace of pain. Rattajack scanned his eyes over the rest of the creature's body and discovered both its clawed hands clasped across a seeping wound below its breastplate, thin wisps of steam still rising from its dark blood.

The terragon stared for a long time into the goblin's tortured face, it had clearly met with a most violent death, and despite the creature being a soldier of Vrorst, Rattajack could not help feeling a twinge of pity for it. However, with a shriek of horror, the terragon's pity turned to abject terror when the goblin's eyes suddenly opened. Rattajack scrambled backwards in blind panic and in doing so lost his footing again and came crashing down against a large, metallic mound. As he picked himself up from the wet ground the terragon's eyes met with the lifeless yellow gaze of another slumped body, and a second yelp of alarm escaped his trembling form. Suddenly a new chorus of 'amimal' calls echoed through the fog around him, this time sounding much closer.

Accompanying the unnerving noises were pale sheets of colour that occasionally flashed from somewhere out in the milky sea, like the distorted afterglow of burning flares or forked lightning, and at one point the terragon's keen sense of hearing thought it could hear the faintest traces of.....music? It might just have been a forest breeze weaving through the matted branches, its hollow moan curved and sculptured by the writhing boughs; but Rattajack was sure that he could hear the gentle undulations of woodland flutes, playing only half-heard melodies in some far off glade.

The newly opened eyes of the first goblin, were now vacant and empty but the terragon began to feel the attention of other stares from beyond the battlefield. Eyes hidden by the wall of mist that could somehow see through it and keenly observe his every move. Eyes that knew the power of sorcery and enchantment, for Rattajack had decided that the blinding veil that obscured the world about him, had not been formed by natural means but by devious manufacture. As if to confirm his suspicions the smothering fog abruptly departed.

An energetic breeze whipped up from nowhere and wafted boldly across Rattajack's face, the sea of white that coccooned him immediately yielded to the surprise intrusion and began to disperse with an unnatural haste. A wall of trees faded in and out of view as great plumes of fog raced past, the last remnants of the pale cloak taking only moments to be disrobed from the forest, and then all was astonishingly clear.

The wall of trees continued into a wide circular clearing, the approximate centre of which the terragon had now reached. Rattajack's startled senses could hardly believe the monstrous spectacle which surrounded him. He was standing in the middle of a grisly battlefield, which was covered in a carpet of slain goblins.

A whole company of Winter servants had been cut down within the confines of the clearing, their strewn bodies bristling with white flighted arrows. There was no cotton grass. It had been the soft touch of trimmed feathers slotted into the ends of the long wooden shafts rising from the bodies of the dead that had brushed Rattajack's skin, as he had innocently trampled over the sprawled bodies of the slain. Their was no sign at all of the goblins' foes, no opposing soldiers lay amongst their enemies on the blood stained ground. It must have been a mighty army indeed, Rattajack decided, that could massacre so many green-skinned invaders and not lose a single warrior in the process.

Suddenly the faint snap of a twig was heard by his large ears and Rattajack stared into the line of trees to try and locate the source of the noise. It was then that the terragon discovered that it was he himself who was being watched by a great many half concealed figures, whose mottled green garments made them blend almost perfectly with their arboreal environment.

They looked at first glance at little like banfs, and for one ecstatic moment Rattajack thought he had been found by his people, but then he noticed the longbows slung over their shoulders and the half filled quivers of white feathered arrows and quickly realised that they were not his mushroom dwelling friends. The faces of the green-clad figures were not dark or evil like the servants of Winter; but they were not entirely kind or welcoming either. As one or two of the watchers moved into the open, large crystal-like wings trapped fragments of daylight and scattered them within delicately lined segments as they played against the steady breeze. The eyes of the winged people were cold and suspicious and some of them slipped the bows off their shoulders as they began to cross the wide circle of ground towards the terragon.

Rattajack decided that he did not like this strange race of beings, even if they were forest dwellers like himself, and urgently searched about him for a gap to escape. He thought he had found one and smartly galloped towards it, the closing ring of archers making no attempt to stop him. The terragon managed to hop over the procession of twisted bodies without stumbling once and leapt with the briefest burst from his wings into the thick cover of the first few trees. Rattajack could see nothing but open forest ahead of him. The green warriors had foolishly left this route through the trees unguarded. The terragon was just about to congratulate himself on the spryness of his escape, when without warning a glistening, web-like net suddenly filled his vision; Rattajack unavoidably charging headlong into it.

As the silver threads drew tight about his thrashing body, the terragon suddenly began to feel very drowsy, as if the fine trap was laced with a strong enchantment. Rattajack battled valiantly to lift his sagging eyelids and keep himself awake, but it was hopeless, he was steadily being drawn into an irresistible sleep and before the first of the forest archers arrived to claim him, the terragon was deeply unconscious.

Eyes in the Dark

Where the great 'Green Sky' Forest was fractured by the foothills of the Marble Fortress, a long meandering chasm of immeasurable depths cleaved the first soaring peaks asunder. It was Dragongorge, the birthplace of all true dragons.

The almost vertical walls of the vast canyon were lined with a thin scattering of small, intensely resilient, evergreen trees, that despite their arduous life, clinging to the bare rock and at the mercy of the cruellest elements, flourished in triumphant, sporadic communities along the mean ledges.

Before the voice of Winter had commanded all the rivers to cease, majestic waterfalls had plummeted from the high mountain valleys, to thunder into oblivion amongst the jagged occupants of the canyon's belly; a rising haze of white spray drifting across the dark cliffs like a flightless cloud.

Tall sceptres of wind-blown rock rose dramatically from the deep floor of the weaving chasm, their heads and shoulders sprouting with a green cladding of high-borne trees. They stood like slim giants, straining on tip-toe to peer over the lips of the trench, as if trying to catch a glimpse of what life might be like on the slopes of the world above. The formal ridges of the striated columns had been dusted with a light covering of snow, as had the clefts and ledges of the weather-hewn cliffs. However, the Lord of Winter had spared the great gorge from the worst of his season, to allow his dragon-slavers easy access to the caves of the free winged beasts; condemning yet more wild carrier-dragons to a life of miserable servitude and bondage.

Charlock had borne Jonquil over an endless succession of snow-capped peaks that formed the spine of mountains fencing off the Great Forest from the northern plains. When, after three days journeying, they had arrived at the wall of daggers which guarded the southernmost lip of the giant canyon, they found that Dragongorge had disappeared. A sea of morning mist had blanketed the divide, erasing all beneath it. Only the highest points on the other side reached through the pale blue veil to greet the climbing sun; the lonely mountain ramparts transformed into islands of shining rock suspended in the milky air.

The carrier-dragon did not hesitate. He plunged determinedly into the white void that concealed the deep canyon, falling in a steep dive into its fathomless depths. Confident familiarity allowed Charlock to weave skilfully between the long fingers of rock pointing upwards from the floor of the abyss, which suddenly appeared out of the mist before them and then swept past, almost within touching distance, to disappear again behind them. Each and every rising formation was permanently engraved in the dragon's memory, and he banked to the right or left with perfect accuracy to negotiate the potential hazards as he approached them; even though in the thick haze he was blind to them all. Jonquil could only marvel at Charlock's superior knowledge and bow once more in praise of the wonderful supersenses that dragons of all kinds seemed to possess, his beloved Rattajack included. Truly they were the most precious of creatures.

Eventually the carrier flew them out of the mist, the rising cloud already beginning to disperse as the sun made the new day a little warmer. As Charlock and Jonquil emerged from the lifting veil, the banf gazed on in wonder at the vast expanse of Dragongorge that now opened up before him.

The sun played along the fragmented faces of the mountainous cliffs, revealing places where dramatic rockfalls had occurred. The awesome power of the ice, which had seeped into thin cracks and flaws as harmless water, had ultimately ripped great slabs of stone away from the sheer walls and shattered them into a thousand tumbling pieces, to add to the mounds of debris already littering the floor of the chasm. Turgid rivers that had once hurled themselves from the high precipices, now hung from the frost-glazed rocks in dripping clusters of white needles, their points glistening with wriggling drops of awakened water, adding still further to the frozen beards of the silent cascades.

A towering chimney of rock, its rugged profile fringed with a shaggy halo of evergreens, loomed proudly in their path. Charlock dipped slightly to glide across the surging updraughts and pass close by to the giant's craggy skin. Its surface was a riot of ragged vertical columns, splintered by horizontal flaws and seams, that in places had caused the body of the crumbling spire to fall away and reveal deep scars or caves. As Charlock wheeled about the great needle, Jonquil suddenly realised that there were figures perched on the narrow platforms and ledges. Some of them casually testing their long wings on the surging draughts that hugged the towering rock, others letting themselves fall into the strong winds and swooping away from their companions, only to return a few moments later in graceful effortless arcs.

Although the assembled creatures were all carrier-dragons, no two of them were the same. Dragons of bright yellow were perched alongside fellows of fiery orange or red; silvers, blues and greys flew with mauves and russets. Jonquil saw one individual that was the colour of the Green Sky's canopy and another that was as purple as the stone which sparkled in the forehead of the Ice Lord. The wild carriers shared Charlock's delicate, refined bearing, long, dished faces with high, intelligent brows, that arched above large sensitive eyes. Charlock drew attention to himself with a loud, piercing cry, that echoed on through the canyon for miles, and his people all lifted into the air to greet him. In a short while the air was filled with a cloud of excited dragons, each one shrieking with joy at the return of their prince. Charlock returned their enthusiastic salutations and dipped away from the tall column to fly to the myriad caves, which were the homes of his people, a multicoloured stream of spiralling carriers following in his wake.

The caves of the dragons were situated in a part of the chasm where the walls fell from the surface in immense vertical planes, and had once been reflected in a majestic sheet of water that filled a shallow basin lying at their distant feet. The shimmering lake was now a whitened lid of ice and the gentle rivers that served it, just frozen memories.

Charlock and Jonquil were given a rapturous welcome by the population of the caves. The former had many old acquaintances to renew and was eager to hear news of the gorge and what was happening with the dwarfs and Dragonskeep. Unfortunately, as Charlock was the only carrier who could speak in the tongue of the Wizards, Jonquil was unable to follow the intense discussions between the prince and his people, which to the banf's unaccustomed ears sounded like indistinguishable exchanges of rapid, chattering noises.

Charlock's consultations lasted for most of the day, and involved him making a few reconnoitring flights with small groups of his fellows, to see for himself the extent of the Ice Lord's influence over his homeland. Jonquil therefore was unavoidably left to his own devices, not that he minded a great deal. It was nice, he decided, to have his feet once more on firm ground and was quite happy to leave the rediscovery of the chasm to Charlock. Jonquil was much more interested in exploring the long, winding tunnels which led from the bowels of the deep caves, and when the prince of carrier-dragons finally met up with the banf, early that same evening, Jonquil asked him where the dark passages led to.

Over a simple but surprisingly sustaining meal of cone nuts, gathered by the carriers from the fruits of the evergreens, Charlock answered all of Jonquil's questions and also informed the banf of the grave tidings that the carrier had gathered during the day.

Charlock had discovered that many of the friends he had known before leaving Dragongorge to serve the Wizard of Summer, were now either dead or enslaved. Mezereon was capturing more and more free carriers to use for his evil purposes in the dungeons of Dragonskeep, none of whom ever returned to the cliffs of their homes. The dreaded dragon-slavers on their evil snowdragon mounts, patrolled the depths of the canyon with increasing frequency. Indiscriminately ensnaring any luckless individuals that should fly across their path. At first it was solely the young female carriers that were taken, for breeding stock; but now, any dragon that could fly, young, old, male or female was considered worthy quarry. The time was nigh, Charlock concluded, for the inhabitants of the caves to resist the creeping darkness of Mezereon and his Ice Master, whilst there was still enough of them left to make a fight of it.

Jonquil nodded his head sadly. He could imagine a similar decision being made within the boundaries of the White Ring before very long. The banf only prayed that he would be present to attend that council when the time came.

Charlock then spoke of the dwarfs, the vast majority of whom had been captured and enslaved within the huge vaults of Dragonskeep; only a small number managing to retain their freedom to form a resistance. The huge castle that had once been a place of noble toil and industry, was now a massive gaol, overseen by Vrorst's dark corruptor, Mezereon. Prisoners gathered from all over Enchantica were housed there, many of them never to see the light of day again, or if they should, not in the same form in which they last viewed it. Indeed it was said that the cavernous cellars of Dragonskeep crawled with the twisted, deformed shapes of creatures that could only be described as Mezereon's mistakes. Why these tortured beings were left alive to continue their suffering was unknown, unless the dark sorcerer derived some sort of depraved enjoyment from their agony. Perhaps he kept them as a living reminder of what can result from costly lapses of concentration, to spur him on to create the perfect beast, the ultimate in biological invention. The carriers could not be certain, but there were strong rumours that the dark sorcerer had spawned a new demon to pursue the fugitives dwelling within the secret recesses of the mines. If this was true, the remaining dwarflords surely had but a few days left to live, for Mezereon's creatures were accomplishing their objectives against the noble races with increasingly devastating effect.

Finally the carrier prince told Jonquil about the tunnels. As far as he knew, the whole range of mountains that made up the Marble Fortress were honeycombed with millions of interconnecting holes and caverns, riddled throughout their very fibre like giant sponges. Therefore, it had to be said that the tunnels found at the rear of the dragons' caves, could lead anywhere. Possibly up to the surface, or down into the very bowels of the world. However, the oldest of the dragons living in the great chasm told tales of the ancient tunnels being a secret path to the mines of the Wizards, and that perhaps the only safe way to find the surviving dwarfs, now that flying in the air beyond the gorge was too dangerous, was to venture in to the dark passages and walk beneath the mountains.

Jonquil did not relish the thought of 'walking beneath the mountain' and getting hopelessly lost within the world's largest labyrinth. But at the same time, he was no use to anyone hiding in the dragons' caves, not even the dragons. So what other choice did he have? Charlock was not about to carry him down to the banf kingdom after flying all this way, and finding his people in such need. Therefore if the banf's long path home, had to start at the mouth of the first tunnel leading into oblivion, so be it!

Charlock was sorry for bringing Jonquil so very far from home and apologised for condemning the banf to such a lonely fate.

"If only I had been able to fly faster," he said. "We might have lost that snowdragon patrol over the Great Forest and avoided capture by Tuatara."

"And if that had happened," Jonquil consoled him. "You would not have arrived here just in time to save your people from disaster. You must forget your misgivings about me and lead your people to victory!

Do not worry," Jonquil continued bravely. "I'm not that easy to get rid of!"

The banf wished he felt as heroic as he sounded but at least Charlock seemed to be a little more at ease.

"Of course by remaining with my people," the dragon told him. "I am breaking my vow to the Lord Orolan. I promised him that I would be your constant guide and companion."

Jonquil gave the carrier a warm smile.

"I am sure that he would understand," he said.

"If you wished it, my friend," Charlock ventured. "I would still come with you and share your darkness."

Jonquil thanked the dragon for his generous offer but would not hear of it, Charlock's place was with his people and this was where their journeys had to part. The banf was resolved to venture on alone.

After a good night's rest and another wholesome meal of cone nuts, accompanied by a bowl of the most delicious spring water, that the dragons had somehow managed to acquire from some secret source hidden within the rolling clefts of the low foothills, Jonquil was ready to begin his subterranean adventure.

Charlock gave him a fond farewell and then together they cried;

"Till we meet again in victory!"

The banf gathered together the few stores and provisions that were left over from their long journey from the Throne Citadel, filled the now empty waterskins with fresh icy liquid, lit the first of the small collection of torches that he had made and marched purposefully into the gloom.

The torches cast a weak, insignificant light and lasted only a ridiculously short time. Before the banf had travelled very far along the damp progress of the tunnel, he was groping his way in complete darkness, wishing with all his heart that the comforting presence of his favourite terragon was padding along beside him.

Jonquil never knew that the dark could be so dark. His eyes were filled with a blackness so fierce that not even his imagination could lighten his surroundings. The greedy, black void stole everything, his hopes, his memories, even the mental pictures he tried to paint of the stone walls that coccooned him. Every thought that tried in vain to boost his morale was sucked away leaving a cold vacuum of despair.

The tunnel continued unchanged for a great distance, and as far as the banf could tell he had not missed any secondary channels leading off from the one he was carefully following. There had been no abrupt draughts or change in temperature as one might expect with passing a wide opening. The main passage had started to rise shortly after Jonquil had commenced, almost imperceptibly at first, but then gently increasing until it simulated the climbing of a low hill. By the time Jonquil took the first of his many rests, he was puffing like an old banf. He assumed that like hope, the air was fairly thin beneath the mountains.

Abruptly, the floor of the tunnel levelled on to a broad plateau; the panting banf slumped in relief against the right hand wall and sat a while to catch his breath. It was then that he felt a cold whisper across the tip of his right ear, and on reaching along the wall with his hand discovered the jagged mouth of another passage. Further investigations of his immediate surroundings revealed that the banf was actually standing at a rough crossroads of tunnels. The route that he was travelling on had been invaded by a second channel, suddenly offering an alternative path to his original steep climb.

Jonquil stood for a few contemplative moments. Should he take this new tunnel? And if so, in which direction? Left or right? The banf seemed to remember Charlock mentioning that the entrances to the dwarf mines lay directly above Dragonskeep, and when the carrier-prince had flown from the cave to spy on the great castle, he had planed to the right, travelling further on down the chasm. That meant, from where Jonquil was now standing , Dragonskeep would lie to his left. Therefore he resolved to take the left passage and quickly bustled himself inside before doubt made him change his mind.

The new tunnel was a little smaller than the first and twisted and meandered a great deal more. Various enticing openings beckoned him from both sides, but the banf ignored them, determined to stay faithful to his present course.

After a good many hours struggling over fallen boulders, squeezing through tight obstructions and doggedly following the winding progress of the narrow passage for a good many difficult miles it seemed, Jonquil arrived at a place where the tunnel became an opening to a cavernous void.

Somewhere within the unseen vault, an underground stream was chuckling, the welcome noise reverberrating along walls that seemed to house only a modest chamber. It sounded as though the stream gurgled into a small pool, and then escaped as itself again, on the other side, to chatter on to another part of the buried world. Jonquil decided the safest way to procede was on his hands and knees, feeling his way around the base of the walls, lest the darkness should conceal deep pits or shafts in the floor of the cavern. The banf discovered a number of interesting openings as he crept around the edge but dismissed them all until he found one of reasonable width, that he judged to be as near as possible, continuing in the same direction that he had journeyed in for so long. After carefully crawling to the icy pool, taking a few startling sips and replenishing his almost empty waterskin, Jonquil made to continue on his way through the entrance of the new tunnel.

Suddenly he heard a faint rustle on the far side of the cavern followed by a few distinct clicking sounds. The banf's body froze in its prone position and he prayed that he had imagined the noises. Jonquil listened intensely for the next few terrible moments, and was just about to console himself that the sounds he had heard must simply have been distorted echoes of his own movements, when a volley of similar noises erupted from all over the surrounding chamber.

Tiny claws scratched against stone as small bodies leaped and bounced off the walls and floor, whistling through the air in front of Jonquil, some of them chilling his face with their draught. Each frenzied manoeuvre punctuated with a series of loud staccato clicks.

The first thought to grip Jonquil's mind was that these swift moving creatures must be the infamous demons manufactured by Mezereon to conquer the rebel dwarfs. In his blindness the banf imagined them to be hideous gargoyles, peering at him with hungry, sneering eyes, springing around the chamber from pillar to rock on long scaly legs, their sharp clicks emitted from snarling jaws, armed with needle-like fangs.

In a furious bout of stumbling, Jonquil seized his waterskin and tried desperately to relocate the entrance to the tunnel, ramming himself hard against the cold wall more than once in his efforts. A whine of panic mixed with frustration emerged from his lips, as the banf's hands groped franticly for the opening. The instant he found it, all movement inside the chamber abruptly ceased and a soft, almost musical voice rang out in gentle echoes.

"It doesn't want to go that way, Sollo-Sollo. No indeed!" The voice cried.

A chorus of rhythmic clicks resounded in agreement.

"Bad tunnel, Sollo-Sollo. Danger! Danger!" the voice continued.

Suddenly one of the mysterious creatures leapt from its perch and landed with a splash in some part of the central pool. It fired a stream of searching clicks in the banf's direction and Jonquil had the distinct feeling that he was being measured and probed by the piercing sounds; his dimensions, both internally and externally, being noted and generally observed.

"It is lost, Sollo-Sollo," the voice said at last. "We will help!"

Then the figure launched itself from the water, bounced off the wall closest to the now seated Jonquil, so close in fact, that a few droplets of water moistened the banf's cheek, and then landed with the barest sound right next to him.

"Do not be afraid, Sollo-Sollo," said the voice. Jonquil was startled to hear the creature so close to him, he felt as though he could reach out and touch it.

"Who are you?" the banf nervously asked, almost certain that the strange tribe of beings gathered before him were not Mezereon's demons, but not sure if he was wise to trust them.

To the banf's utter amazement, a pair of luminous orbs slowly appeared by his outstretched feet, occasionally flashing on and off, as if blinking. The orbs tilted up and down and from side to side, a thin pool of grainy light running over every corner of Jonquil's face and body, the glowing eyes studying him with great interest. The banf stared into the blackness before him and was astonished to see at least a dozen sets of twin lights shining back at him.

Although not completely sure if he should, Jonquil told the small creatures what he was doing in the deep labyrinth of underground passages, and where he was bound for, and despite his initial reservations, allowed the small beings to persuade the banf to follow them along a different route than the one he had intended to take. For some reason Jonquil found the glowing eyes, which shone so brightly in the wall of darkness, quite irresistable.

They went before him along a comfortably sized tunnel, and in the pale light from their collected eyes, the banf could just make out the rugged face of the curved walls that enclosed him. Jonquil delighted in the acrobatic progress of his hyperactive guides. They seemed to live by the doctrine that one should never step in a straight line, when a score of frantic hops and bounces every which way but forward will do. Their eyes, which for the most part seemed to stare back along the tunnel at the banf as they moved, drew oscillating lines of light across the darkness, creating the most hypnotic patterns. The dancing beams plotted every leap of the energetic creatures as they bounded to and fro inside the wide passage, never once colliding with their companions during their frenzied gymnastics.

Eventually they came to a point where Jonquil began to make out a different light, softly illuminating the jagged contours of the tunnel. As the banf and the creatures rounded a gentle bend the source of the unknown glow revealed itself. It was an elegant cluster of luminous toadstools, growing like a natural candelabra out of a small notch in the wall. The thin, shaggy-capped fungi shone with a delicate purple hue, and Jonquil's face blossomed into a beaming smile as it was bathed in the wash of soft light.

"Witches' Lanterns!" the banf gasped.

A series of curious clicks sounded inquisitively nearby and suddenly a great many flickering pairs of lights gathered closely around Jonquil staring at the glowing fungi.

Jonquil assumed the creatures were waiting for further comment.

"My people use these in the winter," he explained. "To light the root caves, during the long nights. We call them Witches' Lanterns. This is the first time I have ever seen them growing outside the White Ring. They are really quite rare."

Jonquil turned to stare into two gleaming orbs only inches from his face, which turned to look at him at the same time. The eyes blinked and a voice said;

"Lots of them here! Sollo-Sollo!"

Another voice from the opposite wall of the tunnel cried,

"Come! Burra-Burra! We will show!"

The tightly packed group of creatures gathered about Jonquil, suddenly exploded into a storm of frantic activity. The general direction of the jumping figures leading on into the tunnel. As the weaving lights of the creatures eyes painted yet more mesmeric pictures before him, the banf came across further crops of luminous fungi nestling amongst various holes and crevices in the walls. To Jonquil's surprise not all were Witches' Lanterns. There were numerous species growing out of the damp rock that were quite unknown to him, uniquely shaped toadstools that glowed with a variety of bewitching colours.

The bizarre procession had travelled between the fungi studded walls for some time, when far ahead of him, Jonquil was able to see the tunnel veer sharply to the right, the reflection of an intense glow, much greater than the singular clumps of fungi, reaching boldly around the corner. The jumping creatures bounded on ahead, a chorus of excited clicks reverberrating in their wake. They disappeared from sight in a riot of dark blurs, briefly silhouetted against the backdrop of illuminated rock, before entering the bright light. Jonquil was left to turn the mysterious corner alone.

The stunning scene which greeted the banf as he tentatively rounded the corner, made his light-starved eyes almost burst with wonder. Arrayed before Jonquil, in a splendid pillared cavern, that opened into a series of arched cloisters, was a breathtaking garden of incandescent blooms. Fabulous sloping carpets of red, green and purple capped toadstools burned with determined splendour, each delicate spire seemingly trying to outshine its huddling neighbours. Angelic clusters of white parasols rose from the luxuriant spread beneath them with a ghostly, pristine beauty, bestowing a pale, ethereal luminance on the rock faces around them. The rough walls of the partitioned chamber were stained in a patchwork of shimmering colours, thrown up by the brilliant banks of exultant fungi beneath. The dripping ceiling was adorned with a luxurious downpour of shiny rock formations, tiny pearls of water hanging at their points. Each crystal tear imprisoned a minute inverted replica of the fabulous garden below in sparkling detail, causing the high shadows of the cavern to glitter with stars of reflected radiance.

Jonquil stood and marvelled before rising infernos of flame coloured cones that towered above him like dazzling mountains of fire. It was from these magnificent beacons that the strongest light shone forth, filling the cavern with a burning intensity.

The network of tunnels and passageways that led away from the exquisite vaults were also illuminated by pockets of bright fungi sprouting from convenient recesses in their walls. They appeared to Jonquil to resemble the gaily lit halls and corridors of some magnificently opulent subterranean mansion, the doors to which the owners had left foolishly ajar.

On exploring his cave of treasures further, the banf disovered a modest pool, disturbed by a lazy, rock-laden waterfall. The bubbling waters fractured the surrounding landscape of light into a rippling mosaic of multicoloured sparks, that radiated from the frothy water to visit every corner of the dark pond. Small colonies of toadstools even grew behind the stream of falling water, set like brilliant jewels amongst the damp rocks, their enchanted light briefly borrowed by every bubble or droplet inhabiting the crystal liquid that chuckled before them.

Movement from above attracted Jonquil's attention and he turned to stare into the clusters of wrinkled points suspended from the ceiling of the cavern. A pair of huge, round eyes, as black as the blackest cave, twinkled back at him. The eyes were set in a small face with neat, rounded features. Two enormous ears fanned out either side, dwarfing its head, straining in tandem with its twitching nose to drink in every detail of Jonquil's being. Then it was gone, leaping from one stalactite to another, its long bushy tail sailing through the air behind it.

The banf found many other pairs of dark eyes observing him as he took a closer interest in the roof of the chamber. The remarkable creatures seemed able to cling to the smooth surface of the dripping rock with the aid of suckers on the ends of each digit of their hands and feet. Long back legs were permanently tucked in to their bodies, ready to spring away in any direction. The long bushy tails, not only mid-air rudders, were also used as extra limbs to coil around the long columns of rock or whichever perch they found themselves attached to, enabling the versatile little creatures to secure themselves to practically anywhere.

Another peculiar little quirk that Jonquil noticed about the creatures, was that whenever they spoke, they always included strange words, the meaning of which was lost to the banf. He could only guess that the words were a means of identification, a vocal signature, a name. After listening to the same leading individuals for some time, he became familiar with a few of the jumping creatures: SolloSollo, BurraBurra, ManuManu and RioRio. Everything about these delightfully eccentric beings seemed to posses a certain rhythm, their chattering sonar clicks, their rapid movements, their manner of speech and even the words they affixed to themselves that Jonquil chose to call names. Indeed the more the banf thought about it, the more it made perfect sense. How else would the creatures know which of them was speaking, when they were exploring deep in the darkest caves, unless they identified themselves in their speech?

Jonquil sat down by the glassy pool and took a few blissful sips of chilled mountain water, then he suddenly became aware of a fast moving object zig-zagging off various rocks about him with incredible agility and coming to rest with the lightest touch close to one of his feet.

A silver-grey furred body crouching behind two huge, staring eyes, its banded tail curled neatly about its feet, peered inquisitively at him

"You like the agamid, SolloSollo?" the creature asked.

For a moment Jonquil was a little confused and then he remembered that agamid was the Wizards' name for mushrooms.

"Oh yes!" replied the banf. "Very much. I have never seen anything like this before. It's magical!"

"Yes, indeed, SolloSollo!" agreed the creature. "There is much enchantment bleeding from these rocks."

SolloSollo dragged a pointed finger along the ground and then rubbed it against his other bulbous digits as if to suggest that the enchantment was so great, it could be felt in the very dust of the cavern.

Suddenly a loud burst of clicks erupted alarmingly from the other creatures around the chamber and with a weaving dark blur, SolloSollo was gone from the banf's side and reappeared peeping nervously from behind a stout stalactite, in the direction of one of the softly lit exits.

Jonquil was unable to see the mouth of the tunnel which all of the alarmed creatures were staring at, because of a series of awkwardly 'grown' rock pillars, effectively blocking his view. Only when the banf cautiously rose to his feet and crept out into open space did he discover the cause of the excitement.

Standing upon the threshold of the fabulous cavern, their heavily bearded faces boldly illuminated in the accumulated glare, iron lanterns in one hand, long spears in the other, were three, stocky dwarf warriors.

Their stern faces were fixed in quizzical expressions, as if they had been disturbed by a mysterious sound and had come to the illuminated chamber to investigate. The three short figures scoured the walls and ceiling with their sharp eyes, searching for the cause of their concern. Jonquil suddenly felt a little exposed, crouching out in the open, and slowly began to edge backwards into the shadows. It was then that he felt the kiss of cold steel across the nape of his neck, and the menacing hiss of a grim voice.

"One false move, my long eared friend," it snarled. "And I will stick you like a pig!"

The owner of the harsh voice slowly wheeled around the banf, firmly brandishing the spear, until he was standing in front of him. Jonquil gazed up into a weary, battle-worn face, red rimmed eyes glaring from beneath an arched, frown-scarred brow. The sad dwarf's beard, which in former days would have been impeccably groomed and well kept, hung in dirty, bedraggled tails. His armour was rust stained and neglected, his clothes torn and unkempt. A helmet, battered almost out of shape sat awkwardly on his head. His whole appearance was more like that of a desperate fugitive than a proud miner.

The point of the spear shook with the trembling of the dwarf's hands, as he held it fiercely against Jonquil's throat. The banf could plainly see that the tough little character before him, who seemed slightly younger than the others although it was difficult to tell in his toil-worn condition, was not quivering with fear, but with exhaustion. The dwarf's cheeks were deathly pale and the deep circles beneath his eyes suggested that the extent of his deprivation included sleep as well as food. Despite the inherent disquiet at being held at spear point by a desperate, hostile character, Jonquil could not help but feel an ocean of pity welling up within his soul for the poor wretch that threatened him.

The dwarf called to his fellows and soon four pairs of unfriendly eyes stared suspiciously at Jonquil. They wanted to know every thing about him; who he was, where he came from and more importantly what he was doing in the tunnels.

Unfortunately, as the banf feared, the dwarfs had never heard of the banf kingdom or its inhabitants, and listened to his fantastic tale of adventures since leaving the company of the Wizards, with a growing air of scepticism. Despite Jonquil trying his very best to convince the four short warriors that he was a friend not an enemy, the general consensus of opinion amongst three of the dwarfs - the fourth, who looked somewhat older and less impulsive, mysteriously remaining silent - was that the banf was a spy, probably created by Mezereon himself to resemble a harmless windsprite, and sent into the deep recesses of the mountain roots to seek out the dwarfs' hiding places.

The fact that Jonquil had started his journey from the caves of Dragongorge made his position even worse, for the three dwarfs were convinced that the carrier-dragons had sided with the Dark Sorcerer and were allowing their caves to be used by the goblins to launch raids into the tunnels. The banf's ardent protestations to the contrary seemed to hold little water with his captors, and his story of Charlock, prince of the dragons, returning to unite the free carriers against the enemy, was dismissed as pure invention.

Jonquil could see that many months of hiding in the dark caverns beneath the mountains, fighting for their survival against impossible odds, had made the dwarf miners reasonless and bitter. In a world of blackness where it was virtually impossible to choose between friend or foe, the dwarfs had decided it was much safer to trust no one but themselves.

"What shall we do with him then?" the gruff voice of a dwarf called Gart asked.

"Let's execute him here and have done with it," Brak, the younger dwarf who had discovered Jonquil, answered him. "It's too dangerous to take him back to the hide-out, there may be others lurking in the tunnels."

A third dwarf, Orsa, was undecided.

"He may possess some useful information," he said. " Think how helpful it would be to us, if we knew just how extensive Mezereon's knowledge of the mines really is."

Jonquil burst into their discussion;

"But I am not from Mezereon!" he cried.

"Silence!" snarled Brak, prodding the banf's throat again with point of his spear.

"No I will not be silent!" Jonquil roared, pushing the head of Brak's spear aside and climbing to his feet. "You have to listen to me. Your lives and those of your people may depend on it."

The fierce younger dwarf brandished the spear with renewed menace and growled malevolently at the banf through clenched teeth.

"Your life is forfeit! You may depend on that!" The dwarf thrust murderously with his spear at Jonquil's stomach but the banf quickly side-stepped the rushing point and with a movement too fast for the dulled reflexes of the tired dwarf, snatched the spear clean from his hands. The other three tensed themselves but made no move. Brak responded by pulling an iron headed hammer from his belt and waved it furiously at Jonquil. Suddenly the fourth dwarf, who had remained silent thus far, made his voice boom through the chamber.

"No!" he bellowed. "Let there be no killing!" It was Tarbet, the only member of the original circle of senior dwarfs, who had sat within the secret chamber of the mines and listened to Tuatara's lies, who still remained at liberty. Hest, Blick, Hepna and all of the others had either been taken or killed by Mezereon's hordes. Tarbet was the only one of the twelve left to lead the remnants of his people in their struggle for life.

"But he is an enemy!" Brak cried. "He must die!"

Tarbet slowly pulled the tightly gripped hammer out of Brak's fist and pushed it back into its home in the younger dwarf's belt. Then he spoke softly to him, his words heavy with a wearisome sigh.

"Have you forgotten all of your wordly knowledge, young Brak," he began. "The servants of the enemy cannot bear to be close to agamid. Look around you, are we not surrounded by the fruit of the magic fire?"

The younger dwarf was not convinced.

"Y'Yes b'but he might still be a spy, Tarbet. Acting under the influence of the Dark Sorcerer!"

Tarbet's eyes lifted to the glistening ceiling and he called into the stalactites.

"SolloSollo!" he cried. "BurraBurra! PiaPia! Please, show yourselves, we will not harm you."

The dark recesses above resounded with the rattling of uncertain clicks, and then after a short while a flurry of swift shadows weaved their way into the clusters of hanging rock closest to the banf and the dwarfs. Before Jonquil knew it SolloSollo was perched on the skin of a thin pillar right at his shoulder, so close to the banf that the strands of fur fringing the creature's ear, brushed teasingly against his own. The rest of the large eared creatures, peered down at the group from behind the lowest of the dripping points, forming a crescent of attentive, starry eyed faces.

Tarbet continued his discussion with Brak.

"No one gets past the peepers unless they are filled with good intentions," he said. "They will not suffer any evil creatures to walk freely within their tunnels."

Gart interrupted.

"Indeed not," he began. "I have been saved many times from marauding goblins by these wonderful beings. With the hypnotic lights from their eyes, they can either guide unsuspecting explorers to safety, or to their deaths."

"Their deaths?" Jonquil gasped, casting an uneasy glance at his closely perched friend; SolloSollo returning his look with one of almost childlike innocence.

"Indeed yes!" Gart answered him. "Some of these twisting, black tunnels are riddled with pits and potholes, bottomless most of them. If the peepers had led you down one of those, we would not be standing here having this discussion."

Jonquil gulped in astonishment.

"If only there were more of these wonderful creatures inhabiting the roots of the southern mountains," mused Tarbet. "Our fight against the enemy would be a much easier one. But unfortunately these caverns lie at the very edge of their range, the greatest populations of peepers are concentrated much further to the north. However, that is not important now. You said you had some vital news for us. Will you tell us, now that we know you as a friend and not an enemy?"

The banf said he would, and proceeded to repeat to the dwarfs exactly what

Charlock had told him about the terrible creatures Mezereon was planning to unleash on the rebel miners. The four dwarfs stood and listened with grave faces, the news that Jonquil brought to them was like another hammer blow to their already flagging spirits. When the banf had finished the dwarfs heads were bowed with the weight of dread and despair.

"I know you came here with thoughts of aiding us, my friend," Tarbet sighed. "But I wish that you had not come. You have cast an even greater darkness over our hearts, and yet, in the end your black tidings will prove to be of little consequence. We are starving. All the supplies we gathered up when the enemy entered the mines have been exhausted. What little food we have now, we have stolen from the goblin raiders, and what vile sustenance it is; but soon that also will fail. It is almost certain that our people will die from famine before Mezereon's devils can reach us. We are without hope."

Jonquil felt miserable for bringing yet more shadows of doom to darken the lives of the already persecuted dwarfs but then brightened when a wonderful idea came into his head.

"There is always hope!" he cried. "Why do you not bring your people here, to this place of good enchantment. Surely, the mushrooms..I mean.. the agamid will protect you from Mezereon's evil servants. Not even his new demons would dare to enter here!"

The banf was dismayed to see that his idea was met with little or no reaction from the dwarfs. At last, Tarbet answered him.

"This thought is not new to us," he began. "We have considered these caves of light as a place of refuge before. But even if we did as you suggest and gathered together the residue of our people and brought them here, how would it help us? We would still be without food."

"Without food!" Jonquil exclaimed. "But these caves and tunnels are full of food, it is all around you!"

The four dwarfs were suddenly swept by a wave of incredulity and surprise.

"What manner of madness is this?" Orsa cried. "Where is this hidden cache of food?"

"It is not hidden," Jonquil replied. "It is here!"

The banf swept his arm through the air as if to encompass the whole garden of fungi with his gesture. The dwarfs were quite bemused.

"Are you mad?" the impetuous Brak demanded of the banf. "Every creature knows that agamid are poisonous!"

"Only some of them," Jonquil told him. "Most of them are quite edible, and a few quite delicious, when prepared properly of course. I should know, where I come from we eat little else."

The four dwarfs were truly amazed at this new revelation and suddenly seemed much happier to be in the banf's company. They begged Jonquil to show them which of the fungi they could eat and which they should avoid. Using the skills which he had learned and developed over a lifetime of residing within the mushroom filled boundaries of the banf kingdom, Jonquil guided the dwarfs around the glowing caverns, introducing them to the wide varieties of enchanted species in which they might soon be placing the lives and fortunes of their people. Even the peepers seemed impressed and followed the five figures throughout the caves in an erratic lunging cloud. Finally Tarbet turned to the other three and clasped them warmly on their shoulders.

"Brothers!" he boomed "I believe I can see the light of hope beginning to burn in our darkness."

Jonquil felt a wave of joy wash over him as he watched the dwarfs embrace one another, long neglected smiles breaking across their bearded faces.

"Bring your people here this very hour," the banf urged. "And then, once you are renewed and made strong again, let the peepers guide you to the caves of Dragongorge, and join with the carriers in their fight against the hordes of Mezereon!"

SolloSollo leapt into the centre of the circle of figures and fervently clicked his approval.

"Good counsel! Good counsel! SolloSollo!" he then announced.

Tarbet rushed forwards and firmly gripped Jonquil by the wrist.

"It is good counsel," he said."And we will do as you say. Ah, brothers! I long to face Mezereon's devils on open ground and let them feel the true mettle of our father's seed. Too long have our people languished in the bowels of the earth, let us lead them into the sun. We shall build forges here and craft great battle axes and swords like our ancestors wielded. However, we must be careful to respect this enchanted place, not to spoil or stain it with our industry, and leave it as we discovered it, a flourishing haven of goodness."

And so the four dwarfs who had entered the caves of light with hearts soaked in dread, now made ready to leave it with buoyant spirits and new hope. Naturally, they asked Jonquil to accompany them, a request he was happy to accede to but to the astonishment of the banf and the dwarfs, SolloSollo would have none of it.

The peeper and his fellows were quite insistent that Jonquil should go with them, although they refused to give any clear indication why. The banf was not sure what to do, he had no desire to offend either party, but to his surprise the dwarfs did not contest the wishes of their small friends and advised Jonquil to follow the peepers. Tarbet informing him that the wise creatures would not voice such an urgent request without a very good reason for doing so. The banf obediently accepted the old dwarf's counsel and said farewell to the four warriors, vowing to pray for their good fortune.

After a brief rest and sumptuous meal, Jonquil placed himself in the small hands of the peepers and allowed them to lead him from the precious caverns.

Banfs with Wings

SolloSollo, BurraBurra and the others guided Jonquil into a new realm of darkness, far from the comforting light of the shining garden. Whenever the banf asked any of the peepers where they were taking him, the only answer they would give was, "Up, up, up!" However, the confusing thing for Jonquil was that since they had departed from the illuminated caverns they had not climbed anywhere; their journey had progressed in a distinctly horizontal direction.

Finally, the bright lights of SolloSollo's eyes weaved back down the tunnel and landed before the banf. Jonquil stopped, not knowing quite what to expect. For a few seconds the peeper said nothing but just gazed and clicked softly at him, then suddenly the peeper's eyes flickered towards the ceiling of the tunnel and he cried,

"Up, up, up!"

Jonquil followed the glowing stare of his small friend and gradually, as the rest of the peepers gathered around the banf, lending the light from their eyes also, the softly lit rock above revealed a black hole.

A sharp draught issued from the mouth of the shaft, wafting tantalisingly across Jonquil's upturned face. It felt cool and fresh as if the air had not had to travel all that far from the surface to reach him, suddenly he longed to be free of the dark caves and walk in the daylight again.

"Up, up, up! SolloSollo!" the peeper insisted, and with a deep breath Jonquil prepared to negotiate the steep wall of the tunnel. A few of the peepers leaped inside the hole and peered downwards, to light the banf's entry into the shaft. The rest of the creatures positioned themselves as best they could, either side of him on the wall, to guide his hands and feet with their eyes, to the safest footholds.

Jonquil's ascent inside the narrow chimney was slow and difficult, and for the best part of an hour he struggled upwards, not daring to stop and rest, constantly cheered on by the small crowd that accompanied him. The banf liked to think that he was a strong climber, having many times scaled the wide, craggy trunks of vast Green Oak's to sit for a while in the cradle of their lofty branches. However, the walls of the shaft were not so generous and in places had been worn smooth and treacherous by the ancient trickle of seeping water.

After a long, exhausting climb the peepers guided Jonquil to a place where one side of the narrow walls abruptly shrank away to form a deep ledge. Rising at the base of the short platform was a tall, narrow rupture. Jonquil allowed himself enough time to catch his breath and drink a little mountain water before squeezing through the gap, at the behest of the peepers, to complete the final part of his journey.

The slim passage wriggled its way through the fibre of the mountain for some distance, occasionally opening out into cleft hollows and domed caves, or narrowing into meagre cracks that even the lean, sinewy Jonquil had some difficulty in scraping through. The steady stream of fresh air, that had flowed over the banf ever since he had climbed up into the vertical shaft, was much stronger now, and seemed to grow even more prolific with every corner he turned. Jonquil could sense that he was frustratingly close to the outside and expected every twist of the jagged tunnel to be the one that would lead him to the light of the world; but to the banf's continuing dismay the walls of rock ahead of him remained in darkness.

The peepers kept assuring Jonquil that his journey was nearing its end but the banf was losing heart. Once more he was beginning to fall prey to the oppressive darkness of the tunnels, which despite the shining eyes of his companions, seemed to heap exhaustion upon his shoulders in unbearably, heavy loads, only the smell of the cool breeze keeping him scrambling forward.

Jonquil fought his way around a particularly intrusive buttress of rock and then by the light of the peeper's eyes, saw the walls of the passage disappear into a rough arch of black.

When the banf staggered through the opening, he found himself emerging on to the edge of a high cliff, which looked out upon the wide expanse of a vast pit. Boisterous updraughts surged over the lip of rock pushing playfully at his shoulders, his hair tossed this way and that in the turbulent air. At first glance, Jonquil assumed the great void before him to be yet another giant cave imprisoned within the belly of the mountains. But after SolloSollo had urged him to look, "up, up, up!" the banf discovered that the ceiling of the 'chamber' was twinkling in clustered formations. He was staring at the open sky.

In the wash of pale starlight, Jonquil could see that the floor of the pit was buried beneath great heaps of ancient rubble, as if, at one time, this had been a complete cavern with a thin roof of rock, its ceiling no doubt adorned with copious collections of hanging points. Thousands of years ago, a monstrous earthquake must have shaken the mountains, and smashed the vulnerable lid, sending it crashing down below, transforming a capacious chamber into a deep crater.

The peepers told the banf that the ledge upon which he stood, wound around the steep walls like a giant spiral stairway, and that with patience and a good stride, it would eventually bring him to the very lip of the crater. Then in a riot of leaps and bounds his briefly met friends were gone, disappearing back inside the dark opening, to continue their endless vigil of the black caverns beneath the mountains. Not even giving Jonquil the chance to thank them for bringing him to this high place, or more importantly asking them why they had done so.

The most unpleasant feeling suddenly swept over the banf as he slowly trudged along the blustery ledge, heading for the surface. For the first time in his entire life, he was alone. Truly alone that is, not languishing by himself in a cell as someone's captive, but out in the wide world, free and his own master, without any company. Jonquil sighed heavily; it was a miserable feeling, and for the next hour as he followed the dark trail of the rising ledge, not knowing where he was or where he was going, he thought only of Rattajack.

A high pitched squeal wrenched Jonquil from his slumber. He had only intended to sit and rest for a few moments, curled up against the wind inside a little nook at the base of the cliff ledge, but long ignored weariness had crept up on the banf and coaxed him to sleep.

Now he was awake, Jonquil wondered if he had dreamt the noise. The great well of darkness before him held no clues, the only sound to fill his ears was the constant whine of the wind that swirled within it. Jonquil rose stiffly to his feet and walked to the edge of the cliff to embrace the chilling draughts. The banf threw out his arms in a deep yawn and filled his lungs with the sharp air. Suddenly a black shadow riding swiftly on the draughts swept up before his eyes, the wind roaring beneath its wings. The bird-like silhouette was darker than the night and rushed at the unsuspecting banf so closely that Jonquil was thrown on to his back with surprise.

The figure continued on the breeze until it merged again with the darkness, seemingly unaware of the banf's presence. Another squeal echoed around the crater; it was a young girl's cry of joy, the deeper voice of a boy followed it in merry, excited tones. The shouts grew louder, as the two figures slowly circled on the wind and then the two of them rose in glorious unison before Jonquil, whoops of exhilaration bursting from their soaring bodies.

Jonquil was dumbfounded. The young couple's voices were the voices of banfs. The musical ring of their laughter, the soft clarity of their happy calls, they were unmistakable; but no banfs that Jonquil had ever known could fly like an eagle! He decided it was about time the two fliers became aware that they were not alone in the crater, and with a loud, clear voice he called into the dark void.

The young couple were alarmed at first, when they heard Jonquil's cry, but then after a brief mid-air conference and with true banf-like curiosity the boy and the girl swooped over to the high ledge to investigate.

They landed on the ledge a safe distance away from where they had heard the banf's cryand cautiously crept their way closer. Luckily Jonquil had the presence of mind to keep talking to them. Firstly, so that they would not feel threatened by not knowing exactly where he was in the thick gloom, and secondly, so that they would hear the similarity between his voice and their own, which hopefully would make up for the fact that they could not see his features.

Jonquil told the young pair anything and everything that might convince them that he was a friend, and as far as the banf could tell, they were listening sympathetically to his words.

Eventually the banf dared to ask a few questions of his own, such as what what manner of beings were the young couple - that sounded like banfs but flew like birds.

"Oh, falcons of course!" the boy proudly answered. "What else could we be?"

"What else indeed?" Jonquil thought to himself.

"Are you otherwise known as windsprites?" the banf inquired.

"There are some that call us that," the boy replied with a slight tone of distaste. "But we prefer falcons!"

The boy went on to explain why he and his younger sister had come to the crater. Hillstar, the young girl, had just come of age and had been eager to try out her new wings on the strong updraughts and so she and Fleet, her brother, had slipped away from the falcon settlement, that nestled amongst the higher peaks, to fly in the starlight. Jonquil had the distinct feeling that the young couple's parents would not have approved of their offspring's midnight excursion into the foothills, alone and unprotected in such dangerous times. The boy more or less confirmed as much by announcing to the banf that he and his sister had best start their journey back before they were caught out by the light of dawn. Jonquil smiled to himself as he wondered which it was the young fliers feared the most, discovery by a flight of snowdragons, or the wrath of their parents at finding two empty beds in the morning. The young couple that sat with him in the darkness sounded and behaved so much like banfs it hurt, and Jonquil fondly recalled the nightmares he had given his own family in his adolescence, by sneaking off with Rattajack to explore the dense bowers of the Green Sky Forest, beyond the protection of the White Ring.

A streak of light attracted the banf's eyes upwards to the mouth of the crater. He first thought it to be a shooting star but then gasped as he watched the tiny spark fall in a slow arc against the dark mass of the far walls. Another burning light followed it inside the vast opening, and another and another. Until soon a whole stream of glistening stars flowed in ordered procession around the deep well of the crater. Anxious voices called out in the darkness, and as the crescent of lights drew nearer, Jonquil could hear the names of the two youngsters perched near to him reverberrating about the craggy cliffs.

Obediently the two young windsprites made themselves known to the search party, in rather sheepish voices, but were saved from too grave a reprimand by the excitement caused by the discovery of Jonquil along with them. At least a dozen fliers stood around the banf, each one bearing a globular lantern, and stared intensely at the face and form of the stranger in their midst.

For some time the windsprites spoke only amongst themselves, discussing the remarkable similarities between Jonquil's features and their own, and wildly speculating on the origin of this wingless duplicate. The boy flier muttered privately to a tall, hooded individual, who listened intently as the adolescent spoke of his meeting with the banf. Then the figure, who seemed to hold some position of authority amongst the gathering, stepped forward to address Jonquil directly.

"I give you greeting, stranger," he began. "I am Judruff, King of the Falcons, that some name windsprites. My young friend here informs me that you call yourself a banf. Is this true?"

"Indeed yes!" Jonquil affirmed.

Judruff moved even closer to him and held his lantern so that both of their faces were fully lit. The king windsprite looked deeply into Jonquil's emerald eyes, and for the first time the banf was able himself to see the face of one of the winged people. Apart from the rise of two large folded wings at the king's back, Jonquil might have been beholding someone from his own village, the prominent cheekbones, the upturned nose, the curve of the mouth, he even shared the same eye colour as the banf. Jonquil was speechless, the resemblance was uncanny. The king seemed more than a little stunned himself but finally overcame his surprise sufficiently to voice a few breathless words to Jonquil.

"It has been many long years since I have heard the word banf spoken aloud," he said.

Jonquil was amazed;

"You have heard of us?" he gasped.

"Oh yes," replied Judruff. "We have heard of you. These are indeed grave and mysterious times, and I do not know what strange purpose brings our two long divided races together once more. But if you will come, we will take you back to our settlement and give you rest and shelter, and perhaps talk a little of our two great peoples."

With the possible exception of being magically jaunted back to the banf kingdom, at that moment Jonquil could not think of anything that he would desire more, and promptly told the king so.

Judruff was delighted and told the party of fliers to make ready to return home. A final word of warning was delivered in the strongest terms to the two young flyaways, Fleet and Hillstar, who bowed their heads in woeful repentance and then the king held a brief conference with two of the burliest windsprites that were present. Jonquil felt his stomach churn like a whirlpool when Judruff told him of the method he was intending to employ to air-lift the banf to their settlement.

With one hand firmly gripped under each armpit, the two strong fliers rose from the ledge, Jonquil dangling in terror between them. The banf watched the rubble strewn expanse of the crater floor pass by below his feet, as he was steadily hauled into the sky. An awesome starlit mountainscape opened up before him when he emerged from the mouth of the broken chamber but Jonquil was too busy praying that his two, winged bearers strength did not fail them and lose their grip to truly appreciate it.

By the time the flight of falcons began their descent to the settlement, Jonquil's arms were dead from the pressure of the two fliers grips on his circulation, and once he had been placed back down on firm ground, the banf's first impressions of standing within the windsprite city were marred by a ferocious attack of pins and needles. To add to his misery, Jonquil could not speed up the return of blood to his veins because he had no spare arms to rub them with. Mercifully, his two bearers must have sensed the banf's discomfort and kindly administered a brisk massage upon his prickly limbs and within a short space of time the feeling buzzed back into his lifeless fingers.

As Jonquil later discovered during a long night of tale-swapping with Judruff and his people, the windsprites were originally a tree-dwelling race. Constructing their homes out of the living branches, plaiting them into woven domes that grew in harmony with the tree amongst its thick boughs. Since their exodus to the lofty reaches of the Marble Fortress, however, the fliers had been forced to change their lifestyle somewhat. The windsprite settlement nestled at the base of a high corrie, a wide, snow-laden mountain lake lying at its feet. The circular wall of rock that reared at its back, rose into knife-edged arretes, standing so proud and severe, they threatened to slice great wounds in the clouds.

The windsprite's houses consisted of clusters of curved stone-built chambers, illuminated by circular shuttered windows. The individual rooms themselves were not necessarily perfectly round but they contained no straight lines, the winged people seemed to have a great dislike of regimented geometric shapes, much like the banfs, who carved similar shaped rooms out of the growing house mushrooms.

Rising occasionally out of the huddled buildings were tall towers of wooden scaffolding, wide circular platforms spreading at their tops. These bizarre erections served a dual purpose for the windsprite community. They provided lofty vantage points to watch over the approaches to the settlement, and also made excellent launching pads for uncertain novices, who had just acquired their wings but were too nervous to use them.

When Jonquil followed the king and his entourage into the domed halls, he found the inside of the windsprites homes to be vastly different from their rather dour exteriors. At first sight, it looked as though an inner skin of woven, leafy tree branches had been crafted to cover the plain stone walls, but on closer inspection the banf discovered that the natural screen was infact only an image, a trick of the eye, an astonishingly realistic mural painted upon a rendering of dried mud. The gifted artists had even managed to capture the illusion of sunlight peeping through the fibres of the knitted walls, the cladding of green leaves vibrant as they bathed in the potent gaze of the summer beams. It was an effort to recreate the feeling of the past, to remind future generations of windsprites where their people came from and just exactly what they had lost.

Judruff headed the crowd of falcons as they filed into a wide hall, large piles of pillows stuffed with shale, had been laid in a rough circle about its centre. The king windsprite and his followers casually slumped into the mounds of heaped pillows, reclining on their stomachs, and invited Jonquil to do the same. After they had all settled, a team of attendants emerged from various side entrances and began to serve endless rounds of fruit and flavoured waters. The fruit consisted mainly of berries gathered with extreme caution from the high belts of scrubland that inhabited the low foothills, just inside the snowdragons' range. The fruit flavoured cordials that the windsprites specialised in, Jonquil found to be delicious and quenched a ravenous thirst with a host of cupfuls.

As soon as the last mouthful of food had been swallowed, the flow of attendants recommenced and every trace of the banquet was cleared away. Then three more windsprites entered, one carrying an ornate iron basket, another a sack that seemed to be full of small rocks and the third a lighted torch. With proficiency borne of familiarity, the basket was laid down in the middle of the gathering, filled with the contents of the sack and swiftly set to flame. The banf stared in wonder at the fire basket, each of the rocks it contained now glowed with a different colour of the rainbow, and the tongues of flame that rose from the enchanted coals burned with the same brilliant hue.

Jonquil felt a nudge from Judruff;

"A gift from the Wizards," he smiled. "Everlasting fire rocks, and not their only gift!"

Suspended from the ceiling of the domed chamber was a frame in the shape of a spoked wheel, from which a ring of gilt lantern globes hung down on long chains. After the special fire had been laid in the basket that stood on the floor, the high wheel was slowly rotated and each lamp extinguished. Gradually, the brightness of the round hall was dimmed until the only flame left to illuminate the faces of the reclining figures was the softly flickering glow of the mutlicoloured brazier. Judruff told Jonquil that now the scene was set for a good bout of story telling, and once again Jonquil had to smile at the close comparison with his own people. The banfs liked nothing better than to gather around the dying embers of a log fire, after a good meal, and recant heroic tales until the early hours.

Jonquil had to force himself to stifle an insistent yawn. He did not want to offend his hosts but wondered if he would manage to stay awake long to enough to hear all the old yarns, or even complete the saga of his own adventure. The firm pillows, although they were stuffed with hard flakes of shale, were surprisingly comfortable and slumbersome.

Judruff offered Jonquil a draft of green juice. The cool liquid jarred the banf's throat with its sharpness but after he had politely drained the small cup, he suddenly found himself feeling wide awake and refreshed. The king gave him a wry smile and invited Jonquil to begin the proceedings with his own tale, impatient to hear about the Green Sky Forest and the Wizards, and fearful that the banf might succumb to his fatigue, despite the uplifting cordial, and drift into sleep before he had the chance to tell all.

And so, Jonquil began to speak to the select ensemble of windsprites, more or less giving them his entire life story, which, after countless meetings and captures during his adventure, he had become quite proficient at. The winged audience were enraptured, especially with the banf's description of his homeland and his people's strong association with the mushrooms of the forest. The king and the others frequently interrupted Jonquil at certain places in his story, to ask him to enlarge on details that he had only briefly mentioned, that were of great interest to them. The banf found them to be especially eager to hear news of the Autumn Wizard, the Lord Waxifrade, for whom the fliers seemed to have a particular fondness; the banf was later to find out why.

The saga of Jonquil the banf, and friends, took a good two hours in the telling and by the time he had finished, the weary traveller felt wearier still. However another stiff dose of green cordial from the king sharpened his senses, and after moulding a comfortable impression for himself in the bed of firm cushions beneath him, he settled down to listen to the sad history of the windsprites, as Judruff, their king, retold it.

As Jonquil had already guessed, the ancestral realm of the windsprites was not the higher peaks of the Marble Fortress, where they now dwelled; the mountains were merely a temporary place of refuge. The true home of the falcons was the majestic kingdom of the Fruit Forests of the West, that swept out from the shadows of the Western Mountains.

More than a hundred years ago, Judruff told the banf, the windsprites had lived beneath the generous canopies in peace and prosperity, weaving their homes amongst the thick branches, existing in perfect harmony with their arboreal environment. They were not known as windsprites or falcons then, for back in those blissful days they had no wings, and knew nothing of the gift of flight.

Judruff had to confess that until that night he had not been able to recall the name that, as a child, the ancient ones, who could still remember the early times, had told him was the former name of their people. Now he was sure that the ancient word had been, 'banf'.

Jonquil's mouth fell open in astonishment; no wonder that he had been thought a windsprite throughout his entire journey, they were one and the same people.

"I am convinced that we have common ancestors, my dear Jonquil," Judruff announced. "Hundreds of years ago, the founders of my people must have dwelled within the sanctuary of your hidden kingdom. For what reason I cannot guess, a large community of banfs must have resolved to depart from their brothers and seek out a new land in the north. After a long journey, which took them over the Western Mountains, they must have happened upon the rich vales of the Fruit Forests and there decided to found a new kingdom. Mushroom eaters became fruit lovers and the memories of those that could still recall the great journey became confused with the mists of time, and soon the links between our two proud peoples were lost as the old ones died and their legends ignored. The new banfs were happy, excited by their pristine, untrodden world, they had no need for old stories. They adapted to live in the trees and forgot about their mushroom dwelling brethren.

As you can see from the wall paintings, we have no intention of forgetting the home of our forefathers, and even though we have dwelt here amongst the high peaks for many generations, one day our people shall return to the West, to take back what shall always be ours."

Jonquil was speechless; this whole revelation was too enormous to comprehend. He had always thought his own tribes to be dull and complacent. The knowledge that he was not the first banf to venture far beyond the White Ring and know real adventure, filled him with an exciting but disquieting glow.

"Of course those were kinder days, when the races of Enchantica were young." the king continued. "Before the evil of Winter began to leave its curse on the noble soil. The world has changed forever since then. Such leisurely migrations would be impossible now."

"But what happened to your people?" Jonquil asked. "Why did they leave these wonderful forests? And how did ground loving banfs become sky-soaring windsprites?"

A great sadness darkened Judruff's eyes as he recalled the terrible events that had led to an entire race of people abandoning their homeland and fleeing for their lives. The king's body trembled with loathing as he finally put a name to the powerful creatures who had entered their world and become the evil bane of the windsprites. He called them, the Destroying Angels.

A volley of angry curses resounded from the circle of fliers at the mention of the accursed enemy, coupled with repetitions of the age-old vows to reap vengeance upon the murderous hordes and restore the once bountiful tree realms to their rightful occupiers.

The Destroying Angels were yet another product of the Dark Sorcerer's evil imagination. Mezereon himself, according to the falcon king, was the grand architect of his people's downfall. Working as one of Vrorst's servants in the bowels of his frozen palace in the far north, Mezereon had created a race of monsters so rich in dark powers, that neither he nor his fledgling master could control them. Yet rather than destroy them and save Enchantica from their menace, as would have been a kindness, the sadistic Lord of Ice ordered that the fearsome creatures be freed from their bonds and set loose upon the world, whilst he and Mezereon sat back and laughed at the oceans of death and misery that the evil spawn wrought upon the noble races they infested.

Mezereon's creations may have been as dark and as devastating as any monster ever conceived, under the skin, but to the eyes of the innocent beholder they appeared as pale and beautiful winged maidens and youths. Their fair countenance was the mask that concealed their black malevolence, for they were the corrupted souls of captured fairies who had been transformed by deep sorcery into dreadful, diaphonous visions that sucked the breath of life from all living things and left behind them a black sea of destruction. The foulest of all products to emerge from Mezereon's laboratories lured their victims by casting a web of sweet seduction about their shimmering, veiled forms. Once their prey had gazed into their longing eyes and listened to their haunting songs, they were irresistibly ensnared. One kiss from the monster's lips and they were infected, doomed to perish from this world, as their lifeforce slowly seeped into the soil, and were consumed by darkness.

Judruff told the banf that after escaping the vaults of the frozen palace, the Destroying Angels had drifted across the mountains in search of fresh victims, for only by preying on the living could they be sustained themselves. Eventually they had entered the Fruit Forests and claimed the innocent dwellers of the high canopies as their latest quarry. They surrounded the largest concentration of new banfs in the heartland of the forests and slowly began to tighten the noose.

"The people were simple tree-dwellers!" Judruff exclaimed. "They had no weapons to fight these creatures of dark enchantment. They were powerless. All the banfs could do was sit and wait for the end. They could not flee, they were surrounded by monsters!

Then, the very night before the first trees of the main settlement were to be claimed by the terrible creatures, a spirit arrived at the home of the king. A fairy, clad in robes of red and purple, a real fairy that is, sent by the Lord Waxifrade himself to aid the stricken people of the fruit forests. Too late the Lord of Autumn had received word of the evil disease which had been released from the confines of the ice palace, to save those who had already fallen before the drifting plague, but now he had sent his spirit, Fossfex to save the remainder of the forest dwellers, and by sparing those, in some way make amends.

The Autumn Fairy carried with her a gift for the beleaguered banfs. A spell, an enchantment, that transformed our forefathers from the likes of you, to the likes of us; and so, the banfs became the windsprites. Fossfex had time to give the would be fliers only the barest instruction in the use of their new gift, and with a great fear and trepidation in their hearts, they gathered their courage together and rose from the treetops."

"So that explains why the Wizards had heard of the windsprites but not the banfs!" Jonquil exclaimed.

"Even though the banfs are the older race," Judruff concurred. "Although, it has to be said, if it was not for the need to escape the Destroying Angels, the windsprites might also have remained undiscovered by the world. The flight of our people across the occupied realms of the fruit forests, is a legend within itself. Barely two hundred survived the journey to set down upon the safety of the western foothills. From there they crossed the vast shoulders of the Great Forest and made this high place their journey's end. I have vowed, my friend, that I, Judruff, shall be the last king of the falcons to reign in this desolate place. I made my son, Indri, a promise on the day of his birth, that the throne he accede's to, will be the throne in the ancient realm of the Fruit Forests of the West.

However, before we depart, our people must first settle their score with the Gaoler of Dragonskeep. Mezereon must be made to pay for his gift of death to the world!"

A rousing cheer followed the last of the king's words and all those present, bathed in the flickering glow of the firelight, raised their fists to the air adding their support to the motion. Jonquil was suddenly gripped by a rush of bravado and loudly hammered his fist on the stone floor, almost immediately the cries died down and all eyes in the hall turned towards the banf.

Jonquil took a deep breath and then addressed the king.

"Begging your majesty's pardon," he spoke forth. "That is what you must not do!"

A collective gasp emerged from the circle of fliers but Judruff was unaffected.

"With respect, your majesty, we must go to the Banf Kingdom, that is where the Wizards are. We must seek their counsel and then decide our strategy. You cannot go up against Mezereon alone, his snowdragons would tear you to pieces. Leave the storming of Dragonskeep until Vrorst has called the main forces south, and then join with the carrier-dragons and the free dwarfs to deal with the Gaoler."

Judruff fixed the banf with a long thoughtful gaze and then, to Jonquil's surprise, a wide smile grew across his face. Finally, he spoke to the banf.

"You are as wise my friend, as you are courageous," he said. "To attack Mezereon now would be suicide. We shall go to the Banf Kingdom, moreover, as I think of it, my heart aches to go there. But how is this to be achieved, my friend? I cannot ask my two strong brothers here to carry you all that long way, can I?"

Jonquil smiled weakly, this of course was the fatal flaw in his plan. The windsprites may only have been banfs with wings, but he was definitely a banf without wings. They could fly to the Banf Kingdom, but he could not.

"Jonquil, my friend, it has been a long night, and I crave your forgiveness for keeping you from your well earned rest. Do not concern yourself too deeply about the problems that face us. One way or another, we shall get you home, I promise you!"

After the gathering was dismissed, Jonquil was taken to a room that had been specially prepared for him. It was round, of course, just like all the others he had seen, the walls and ceiling merging into one complete dome, decorated with the same predominant theme of interwoven branches. One arched window, shuttered against the night, fitted neatly into the bowed wall. The windsprites had furnished the small chamber as best as their limited resources would allow. There was a bed, a few coloured flames licking at a small pile of fire rocks inside a modest fireplace, an essential provision with the cold, mountain nights, a wash bucket and a large, elaborately decorated gilt drinking bowl containing a cordial.

Jonquil fell on to the bed and lay staring at the ceiling. Fatigue bore down upon him like a lead weight and his eyelids flickered and sagged. However, despite his exhaustion, sleep was reluctant to take him and his attention was drawn to a shimmering pattern, dancing in a rough circle on the ceiling above him. It looked exactly like green-stained sunlight thrown up on to the trunks of rugged oaks by one of the busy little forest brooks that trickled through his homeland. The banf sat up and tried to locate the source of the strange illusion. To his surprise, it seemed to emanate from the bowl of cordial, kindly provided by his winged hosts for his nighttime refreshment. Jonquil rose from the bed and walked over to the table supporting the bowl. The liquid looked quite still but there did seem to be a faint glow radiating from deep within it. Jonquil did not know if it was just his tired eyes or did the shimmering shapes inside the greenish liquid really look like sunlight attempting to penetrate the thick, green canopy of his beloved forest. Whatever the source or the nature of the strange submerged lights, above his head the glittering mosaic continued.

As Jonquil bent over the bowl peering into its depths, a wonderful smell filled the air. The tangy smell of old wood, softly blended with the heady odours of fresh mushrooms. It was the scent of home and it was irresistible. Jonquil took a long sip from the gilded cup. The cordial was delicious and by some magical coincidence tasted exactly like one of his very favourite drinks, the juice of crushed gemberries. Jonquil suddenly discovered an unknown thirst and he tipped the bowl to his lips once again.

Impossible. The cordial now tasted like a fine brew of spearherb tea, another of his favourite beverages. This was strange indeed. Jonquil drank again and once more the cordial presented a different flavour. He took another drink and another and each time the taste was radically different, each mouthful more exquisite than the last. The more Jonquil consumed, the more he wanted to consume, his thirst was insatiable; the mysterious liquid continuing to reveal yet more varieties, never repeating itself lest the banf should lose interest and leave it unfinished. It was almost as if the cordial wanted to be drunk, right down to the very last drop. Finally, the vessel was drained and Jonquil found himself gazing rather sadly at the bottom of the bowl. Not a trickle was left. He carefully placed the beautiful cup back on to the table and was immediately seized by a huge yawn which forced its way through every fibre in his body. As the giant stretch left his tired limbs, the heavy fatigue rushed back in. He slumped back on to the bed and fell swiftly into a deep sleep.

Then followed a vivid, disturbing dream, so real it could have almost drawn breath.

Jonquil was floating through the air, held aloft by urgent breezes that twisted and turned him like a hapless, autumn leaf. He was enveloped by billowing plumes of mist that drifted about him so thickly they formed an endless sea of white cloud. To his surprise, the banf found that he could actually land on the denser of the fluffy formations and dive and snuggle into them as though they were immense flying pillows. He could even bounce across the void from one cloud to another, tumbling into their soft, voluminous bodies and springing forward on to the next, gliding

Mezereon, the Grand Corrupter.

through the air as light as a feather. Jonquil's only discomfort was a slight pain between the shoulder blades that gave a twinge now and then as he frolicked in the gently yielding texture of the cloud balls.

Suddenly, the clouds beneath him parted and Jonquil could see rolling hills, pockets of dark green woodland and thin, blue rivers painting the land far below. The banf was hanging in the air far above the world, with only the merest breath of wind to play against his outstretched arms and hold him there.

All at once, Jonquil became unsure. The rotating spread of the distant hills and valleys that he was floating so high above, assaulted his confidence, and he was afraid that he might fall. Jonquil suddenly felt as heavy as lead and knew that the spongy clouds would no longer hold him. The familiar pain between his shoulders came back to haunt him, as if to add to his misery. He started to panic and as he did so began to lose his buoyancy. He tried desperately to hold on to the clouds but now they had no substance and slipped invisibly through his fingers. It was no use, Jonquil's own crumbling faith had become an irresistible force dragging him down. He was falling, plummeting towards the ground at heart-bursting speed. The inevitable scream which rose from his belly was snatched away by the roaring wind and his terror-filled eyes could only watch the wide, spinning world rushing up to meet him.

Jonquil's scream travelled back with him to consciousness and his sensitive ears recoiled with the intensity of his own voice echoing around the small room. It was morning. Thin beams of pale sunlight peeped through the gaps in the shutters and cast bright lines upon the painted walls. The terrible dream that had seemed so short and horrific had apparently lasted all through the night, or at least what had been left of it. Jonquil lay motionless, staring into the web of branches, that weaved across the ceiling. A thin glaze of sweat glistened across his forehead, his heart beat its loudest drum inside his ears, and his hands gripped fistfuls of bed-clothes by his sides. Jonquil's whole body was taught with tension and the pain in his back had multiplied tenfold, he felt as though he was lying across two sharp rocks, and no end of shifting himself into different positions would bring relief.

At last Jonquil could stand no more and decided to get out of his uncomfortable bed, but no sooner had he tried to rise to his feet, than a mysterious weight pulling at his back caused him to topple backwards on to the mattress. A single white feather pirouetted downwards before his eyes, finally landing on his chest. Jonquil stared at it in bewilderment. Where had it come from?

After a short spell of pondering the banf concluded that the small plume must have been dislodged from the wings of a previous occupant of the room. The feather had probably been lying on the rim of the lantern wheel hanging from above and was disturbed from its hiding place by the draught of Jonquil's fall. As to his sudden giddiness, perhaps the delicious cordial, so generously provided for him, had contained more potent substances within it than he had first realised and was only now experiencing the side effects. He attempted to rise to his feet again, and this time with a little more care and a steadying hand on the back of a nearby chair, he succeeded in remaining upright. There was still the uncanny feeling of some strange weight behind him trying to pull him back down again but the banf felt he was winning. Very slowly, Jonquil made his way to the only window in the round room and drew back the shutters. A thick beam of bright morning light instantly invaded the small spherical chamber and the banf looked out on the crystal clear panorama of the foothills of the Marble Fortress.

As Jonquil turned away from the fabulous view, his eyes fell upon the image of his own body profile, projected against the opposing wall in silhouette. At first he took no notice of his dark outline, his eyes not yet fully awake, but a sharp double-take quickly confirmed the bizarre image the morning sunshine had revealed to him on first sight. His mouth suddenly became very dry, his eyes exploded into giant saucers of disbelief.

A large curved shadow, rose and fell from his back, creating a most familiar shape. The banf tentatively reached behind him, and his searching fingers brushed against layers of soft feathers. Jonquil almost screamed with shock when the incredible realisation of what had happened to him eventually sank in. During the night, he had grown wings!

What would Meadolarne and Old Yargle say if they could see him now? Jonquil stood in the sunlight and gazed in awe at his new silhouette. A broad grin exploded across his face as he watched the two arched shadows open out either side of him in a breathtaking span. The banf strained to try and glimpse his outstretched wings for himself, and there they were, hanging in the air either side of him, pale and magnificent. Jonquil's fingers trembled as they ran down the quill of a long, white feather, lying flat and firm with its fellows, all of them taught and strong and unbelievably grown from his own body.

Could he still be dreaming? Or was this some cruel joke of the windsprites? Had they stolen into his room whilst he slept soundly and attached false wings to his back? If this was so, the banf could not find where they had hidden the straps. And how was it that Jonquil could feel the wings and move them independently? It had to be real; but how?

Then the banf's eyes fell upon the empty bowl sitting innocently on the table and he remembered the delicious potion. Suddenly it all became clear, Judruff had promised Jonquil that somehow they would discover a way for him to travel with the windsprites to the banf kingdom, and of course the most obvious way was to make the banf one of them. So the cordial was the gift Waxifrade had made to the windsprites to allow them to flee the Fruit Forests of the West. A delicious brew that turned banfs into birds!

Jonquil decided that now he had acquired wings he might aswell learn how to use them. He tried to concentrate on his two extra limbs and see if he could control their movements. It was like having another pair of arms, completely independent of his two originals and twice as long.

At first, every time the banf tried to coordinate a flap, he either wafted his arms up and down instead or fell over. His wings seemed to have a mind of their own. After several dismal failures and a good deal of hot blood and curses, Jonquil roared in frustration, clasping his arms tightly across his chest. As he did so, the energy he created bypassed his crossed arms and surged into his wings. They both beat down hard against the air and his whole body was lifted a short distance off the floor.

Jonquil screamed with delight and wasted no time in trying to repeat his first success. In a short while he could flutter on to the seat of a chair, then the top of a table. Unfortunately the banf was occasionally subject to sudden, involuntary changes of direction, which usually resulted in him hurling himself against the walls or crashing into the furniture. It was not long before the bed was the only item in the room still in one piece.

Not surprisingly the succession of violent sounds that emanated from Jonquil's quarters attracted a good deal of attention. A rather concerned party of night sentries, who had taken alarm at the series of shouts, screams and crashes, had summoned help, and soon the king and his sons had arrived to investigate the disturbance. Judruff did not wait to knock, the chorus of noises that greeted his ears on arriving at Jonquil's door, convinced him that the banf was being attacked by several assailants. The windsprite king seized the door latch and charged into the room, closely followed by his sons and others.

The room was deserted, practically every stick of furniture had been broken. Judruff stood in the middle of the room and surveyed the damage. He could only surmise that Jonquil had been taken by force through the open window, as even the wooden shutters had been demolished. The king was just about to charge out of the room to rally forth a rescue, when a small white feather drifted down from above in a lazy, breeze blown spiral, brushed his cheek and then floated nonchalantly to the floor. Judruff bent down to retrieve the feather, and then held it up to his eyes. As he did so, a broad smile brightened his fearful face and his curious stare lifted towards the ceiling.

The king tried to suppress a laugh but his shoulders began to shake uncontrollably, and those that stood around him in the doorway were also infected, as their eyes fell upon the hilarious sight above them. Jonquil had not been kidnapped by dark forces, of course; he was hanging upside down from the lantern-wheel, his legs threaded precariously through the spokes. He smiled weakly at Judruff and with a rather red, upturned face said,

"Sorry about the mess, your majesty. I seem to be experiencing a few difficulties with my wings."

Judruff and the others exploded into a storm of bellowing laughter, unable to contain themselves a moment longer. Even Jonquil had to see the funny side of his entangled predicament and joined them with a few bursts of inverted chuckles. Judruff's sons had to help Jonquil down from his lofty perch for the king himself was doubled over with laughing, and for a long time after Judruff would suddenly start to giggle, for no apparent reason, when he was reminded of the highly comical look on Jonquil's face as he hung from the ceiling like a giant, ungainly bat.

The next few days in the falcon settlement Jonquil spent in earnest, trying to perfect the flying skills that would have to carry him on the long journey home. In light of the expected increase in snowdragon patrols over the Great Forest, with the coming of the Wizards, Judruff had decided that only a small number of windprites, apart from himself and Jonquil would be making the dangerous trip, a mere handful of fliers being much more difficult to spot. The greater number of his falcons would remain in the mountains with, Indri, the eldest of his two sons, to aid in the uprising against Mezereon whensoever it came. Judruff's youngest son, Comet, was to accompany his father, the banf and four other strong fliers, on their long flight southward.

The high lookout towers had been Jonquil's first challenge on the way to mastering his wings, but had ultimately proved to be the merest of obstacles, after an initial apprehensive peep over the edge and a friendly shove from behind. After a short while, Indri and Comet, who had designated themselves the banf's personal instructors, had Jonquil climbing up to the high platforms and throwing himself with absolute confidence into the air, spiralling his way to the ground in slow, graceful glides.

One amazing thing that had struck the banf after he had made several similar flights, was that he no longer felt the cold. Before he had drunk the magic cordial and grown his wings, the icy mountain gales had knifed through his clothing as if it had a purpose. The winds still gusted with the same venom but now he did not notice them. Even when he was far from the ground, slicing through the sharp air in a speeding dive, the cold made no impression on him; as a windsprite he was simply impervious to the breath of Winter.

The two falcon princes were delighted with the banf's progress. He was quick to learn, courageous and enthusiastic, and in no time at all, was not only gliding down from the high towers but flying up to them from the ground aswell.

Jonquil had once asked Judruff why only the adult windsprites had wings, not the children. The king told the banf that long ago it was decided that the mountains were too dangerous a place for inexperienced youngsters to be given the gift of flight. So only when a young person came of age, was he or she permitted to imbibe of the sacred potion at a solemn ceremony, and be transformed from a falconet into a fully fledged falcon. Judruff apologised for the underhand way in which they had 'changed' Jonquil, but confessed that he and his advisors had been unable to think of a suitable alternative and dared not risk a flat refusal, were they to ask the question. The banf assured the king that he was far from unhappy with his winged condition and even ventured to thank Judruff heartily for giving him the wonderful experience of being able to fly like an eagle.

Flocks of fledgling falcons were escorted daily to the deep crater, where Jonquil had been abandoned by the peepers, to test their young wings on the wild but reliable draughts that permanently circled inside.

Jonquil now realised that SolloSollo and friends had only left the banf alone, in the sure knowledge that it was simply a matter of time before a flight of windsprites visited the crater and found him. Somehow the intuitive peepers had known that the fliers, whom Jonquil resembled so closely, not the dwarfs, would be the people to help him find his way home. Although perhaps even the perceptive cave dwellers would have been surprised to see the method the windsprites had employed.

On the suggestion of his two hard taskmasters, Jonquil joined the regular procession of new falcons, flying to and from the great open cavern, to learn how to ride the urgent draughts. After a few intense sessions, following a stream of fellow novices and then alone with the two princes, soaring and diving, wheeling and hovering, up and about the high cliffs, hour after hour after hour, the newest recruit of them all was declared ready by his teachers. Jonquil had been forced to acquire in only a few brief days, the level of skill his windsprite counterparts would have been allowed weeks to learn; at the end of it all he was thoroughly exhausted.

Finally the sun bled into the dawn of the day they were to leave. Judruff, Comet and the four other falcons bid an emotional farewell to their loved ones and people, and with the wind tugging impatiently at their outstretched wings, turned with Jonquil to face the southward spread of the Green Sky Forest.

In the Shadow of the White Ring

The four ancient Green oaks that rose from the heart of the Banf Kingdom, towered above the rest of the trees with a majestic prowess. Their all encompassing canopies swept out beneath the sky, spreading their wide eaves ever further into the surrounding forest. Such was the great age of the trees, each one known to be more than nine hundred years old, that aerial roots had grown down from the knuckles of the mighty boughs to form strong vertical pillars. These tall, straight supports, which held up and enabled the elderly limbs to sweep out from the now obscurred main trunks, grew down in close profusion, giving the four old men of the forest an almost cathedral-like magnificence. The feet of the descending columns erupted into a riot of twisted roots that wrestled and writhed with their neighbours to gain access to the soil. Nearer to the vast trunks of the Green oaks, where the mess of tangled growth was more prolific, a honeycomb of nooks and caves had been formed, affording excellent accommodation for Wintering banfs. Indeed, cradled amongst the lower branches of one of the oaks, within a bower of matted roots, were the halls of King Merlion and his court. Perfectly sheltered from the ravaging winds of Winter and gently shaded from the ardent attention of the Summer sun.

The gnarled chambers of the banf king had suddenly become the focus of great excitement. News had arrived from the borderlands, near to the boundary line of the White Ring, of a grand procession of fantastic noble beings, marching in glorious ranks along the forest trails leading to the white wall. Merlion, who had been thrown into complete disarray by the confused tidings, hastily gathered together a formidable reception of high banfs and hurried them down the cascade of winding roots that formed a natural stairway to his elevated palace, and along the weaving paths that would take them to the relevant section of the great mushroom wall.

In the meantime, various envoys who preceded the arrival of the Wizards, came before the banf king in his oak dwelling, to announce the coming of their great lords, and to ascertain if Merlion had received knowledge of their plight from another source, namely Jonquil.

The King sat in a throne that had been cleverly crafted from the entwined stems of the far wall of his main chamber. He was a banf of middling years, probably somewhere in age between Jonquil and Old Yargle, with strong, intelligent features and insistent green eyes. Sitting proudly upon his tied back chestnut hair, greying a little at the temples, was a domed wooden crown, carved many centuries before, for an early banf king, from a fallen Green oak bough in a decorative representation of an acorn cup. Merlion's robes, although seemingly very simple in comparison with other monarchs, were cut from the finest cured mushroom leather and woven herb flaxes, gathered in abundance from the plentiful forest realm.

The King, who for a long time could only stare in complete wonder at the brightly coloured fairies and elves, never before having laid eyes on such fair beings, eventually rather shamefully informed them that he was quite ignorant of the dark machinations of the outside world. The Wizards' messengers, who included Piraruchu and Limpkin of the elves, and Pippitril and Vinivet of the fairies, then told the King of the fate of the world, and the danger that now threatened every noble race of Enchantica. The envoys did not mention the Three Havens, or the great role the Kingdom of the Banfs was about to play in the ensuing drama. They decided that such news would be better borne by the Wizards themselves.

Merlion was more than a little bemused. He knew nothing of the terrible tidings the four emissaries had brought to him, and understood them even less. However, the banf king was wise enough to know that if the noble players in this mighty confrontation were seeking refuge within the protective boundaries of his kingdom, the dark side would be sure to follow and bring the ugly shadow of warfare along with them.

After due consideration, the King of the Banfs bade the small band of messengers return to their high lords and bid them enter through the gates of the White Ring and be welcome. The banfs may have been, for such a long time, a secret and separated race, but the time had come to count themselves amongst the children of the world and as such play their part in its rescue.

Rumours of the fabulous host gathering outside the White Ring spread quickly amongst the ever curious banfs, and in a short while large crowds had mustered from the neighbouring villages and beyond to await the arrival of the exotic visitors.

Pippitril, Vinivet and the other envoys hastened back to the approaching caravans of the Wizards to brief them of Merlion's words. The Lords of the Seasons dismounted from their horse drawn vehicles, their handmaidens the high witches at their sides, and began the long procession through the modest gap in the mushroom wall that constituted one of the many gates into the Banf Kingdom beyond.

The narrow path leading to the city of the King was lined with cheering banks of mushroom dwellers, none of whom had the faintest notion of who it was they were welcoming, or why. The richness and the splendour of the Wizards and their supporters as they filed past the wonder-filled eyes of the banfs, caused occasional gasps and astonished sighs to blend with the chorus of vigorous cheers.

Fantazar and his entourage were the first to enter beneath the eaves of the powerful ring and greet the awe-struck faces of the banf people. Bruntian, the High Witch of Spring walked beside him, a fine lady, whose graceful figure flowed in luxuriant emerald robes. These two splendid beings strode out along the frosty trail with almost regal poise, a small army of green-clad attendants following noisily in their wake, singing joyous chants and merry poems to the delight of their enchanted audience.

Orolan and Vijian, High Witch of Summer, came next with their golden retinue; radiant and dazzling in the sudden accompanying sunshine.

Last to emerge from between the pristine columns of the towering white mushrooms, was the Lord Waxifrade and Quillion. The crowds of cheering banfs seemed to sense the special sympathy that the Autumn Wizard and his followers felt for the forests of the world and their inhabitants, and raised their voices even higher as the handsome red and purple procession marched past.

Perslane, Carobus and Hoolock, the three high wizards of the seasons had remained behind on the Forgotten Island with a small residue of the former population. Their task was to keep the small island sanctuary alive and flourishing, a living reminder of the works of the Lords of Light if ought should go amiss with their quest, and also so Vrorst would think that the Three Wizards themselves were still in residence and not suspect their migration across the ocean. It would prove to be a weak deception on closer scrutiny, but might provide sufficient delay in Vrorst's manoeuvres to allow the three Wizards time to prepare.

The large gatherings of excited banfs were in no mood to return to their villages after what they had just witnessed, so they happily joined on the end of the Autumnian train and followed the progress of the Wizards to the palace of the King, eagerly awaiting some explanation for this colourful invasion. After a journey of some several miles from the gates of the White Ring, Fantazar and Bruntian, now riding on white ponies, passed through the first pillars of vertical roots supporting the outer reaches of the giant Green oaks. The grand reception that Merlion had despatched to welcome the Wizards, striding proudly to the fore. The banf king had come to the head of the natural stairway, ready to greet his illustrious guests, but the sight of the great lords and their supporters, extravagant robes and vibrant banners arrayed in a blaze of flamboyant colours before him, suddenly made Merlion feel very small and insignificant. Nevertheless, the King of the Banfs threw back his shoulders, pouted his chest and after the deepest breath of his hitherto uneventful life, prepared to receive the mighty Lords of the Seasons.

King Merlion and the Three Wizards were locked in heavy council for many long hours, only the briefest respites for food and refreshments halting the lengthy consultations. At the end of it, the king emerged tired and drawn, burdened with heavy knowledge and confident that never again would he be able to ease away his life, reclining in the lap of blissful ignorance. However Merlion was not sorry for the coming of the Wizards, even if he was afraid of the consequences. He was grateful for the secrets they had shared with him concerning the Three Wells of Hope, and for his part assured the Wizards that he had always known of the uniqueness of the Banf Kingdom; it was an innate feeling shared by all those that dwelled within the enchanted boundaries of the White Ring.

Merlion was also intrigued to hear about the heroic exploits of a certain hitherto unkown banf named Jonquil, and took more than a little pride in the Wizards' retelling of his brave deeds and adventures. The Three Lords had been deeply distressed, if not wholly surprised, to find their envoy not safely arrived long before them. As they explained to the banf king, mischief and Jonquil seemed to have an irrestible attraction for one another, the young banf seemingly unable to make his journeys have an end. The banf king resolved to have the family and friends of this remarkable individual informed of his vital errand, lest the young wanderer should innocently happen across them first before making himself known to his King.

The Three Wizards agreed that this was wise, then together with Merlion stepped out to face the large numbers of curious banfs converging on the spreading roots of the giant oaks. All of the mushroom dwellers were hungry for knowledge, but none of them prepared for the horror story the Wizards and their king were about to describe. For the first time in living memory, the peace loving banfs were about to become acquainted with the cold dread of warfare.

A few days after the Lords of the Seasons had finally succeeded in explaining why, of all the races in Enchantica, the forces of Winter had chosen the banfs to be the focus of their massed aggression, and had persuaded the shocked mushroom dwellers to join with the Wizards in preparing for the coming of the enemy, just beyond the sight of the newly installed lookouts on the White Ring, a wall of darkness crept through the trees.

The evil shadow drifted over the ground like a black mist, seeping through the tangle of trunks and branches that lay before it, swallowing all in its path. The occupants of the dark cloud stared out with hateful, yellow eyes at the distant gleaming line of white mushrooms.

The Wizards of Light had brought a new warmth and freshness into the Banf Kingdom, with their arrival, the power of their Fire Orbs instantly banishing the white season from their presence. After many dark months of Winter the banfs were filled with a strange joy as the air steadily grew warmer and the frost and snow began to fade and retreat towards the eaves of the White Ring. Virgin blades of grass speared through the hard ground, tight leaf buds relaxed their guards and allowed their green inhabitants to burst forth into the world, in a bold show of confidence in the change of season. For a short time it looked as if the spell of Winter had been truly broken. But it was not to last, and the impatient new foliage was soon to regret its premature emergence.

With only the briefest reign of balmy days having passed in the land of the banfs, the elements of Winter launched a counter attack. The sun, which had only just begun to shine again, with true sincerity, was rudely smothered by a sweeping pall of bruised storm clouds. The inhabitants of the Banf Kingdom were once again thrown into dismay as soft white flakes of snow began to float into their faces, borne aloft on rising winds of icy breath, flowing over the flat tops of the White Ring with a building rage.

Orolan, Fantazar and Waxifrade exchanged grave looks with one another as the returning frozen gales howled their challenge through the cage of root pillars, leading to their shelter within the caves of the Green oaks. The Three Wizards knew they were discovered and that the Lord of Winter had come to take them.

Reclining in the opulent fur-draped seat of his magnificent snow chariot, framed against the jewel-encrusted points of a spectacular ice star, was the quietly appraising figure of Vrorst. His spies, who lived in every shadow of the forest, had finally located the secret kingdom of the banfs and now he had come, with the full might of his armies to smash the white power of the mushroom ring. The Ice Sorcerer's fingers played idly over the skin of the Orb of Winter, mounted at his side, as he slowly calculated his next move. He had been too impatient to wait for Mezereon's race of superbeings, before leading his first assault against the Wizards. Therefore, to compensate, rising from the legions of assembled goblins, hidden from noble eyes within the cloak of gloom, were immense wheeled vehicles, mighty machines of war that may have been crude in appearance but were devastating in operation. Catapaults, giant spear-launchers, battering rams, every device and tool of destruction that could possibly play a part in the crushing and tearing up of the White Ring, had been included in the powerful armoury of the Ice Lord. The black veil, which had been conjured forth from the dark crystal depths of the Orb of Winter and cast over Vrorst's circling armies, was designed not only for concealment, but to act as a screen to allow the dark creatures to drag the great engines of war within range of the mushrooms, without the intense glare of the white wall burning their eyes.

Victory hung so sweetly in the air, Vrorst could almost taste it. The Three Wizards were somewhere behind that vulgar sprouting of Old Magic, perhaps even standing beneath it peering out into the gloomy depths of the trees, searching for a sign of their Winter foe. Vrorst smirked, the poor fools would not have long to wait.

Wargren reported to his waiting lord that the last of their forces were in position. The Kingdom of the Banfs was competely encircled, the Wizards could have no escape. The Ice Sorcerer smiled to himself once more and told the dragonlord to start the attack. As Wargren strode purposefully away, Vrorst's right hand slowly spread over the curve of the Fire Orb at his side and his eyes rose swiftly to the skies.

Without warning or transition the howling gales roared into screaming blizzards so thick with snow that none could bear to face into them. Any banfs that were caught out in the open by the sudden onslaught were blinded by the biting snow cleaving through the frosty boughs in merciless horizontal sheets. If they were not quickly helped to shelter by a comrade they were buried where they fell by the waves of drifting white peaks flowing between the forest of Green oaks in an unstoppable white flood.

Out of the dreadful din of the snow-laden winds an even louder noise rumbled forth. It was thunder and a more deafening, pulsating sound had never assailed the sensitive ears of the cowering mushroom dwellers. Frightened banf children buried their heads in their mothers breasts to try and escape the noise but still the menacing din roared its way through. Then the thunder was no longer thunder, it was drums, drums being pounded maniacally; but not scores of drums or even hundreds, it was thousands, thousands of drums being hammered in every corner of the outlying forest, without rest or mercy.

Old Yargle did his best to comfort Meadolarne and her mother, even though the very ground beneath their feet was shaking with the force of the raging noise. The Old One and his family had been forced to leave their house mushroom, as had all banfs who lived close to the rise of the White Ring, and were now sheltering amongst the caves of the giant Green oaks with their fellow refugees. Old Yargle and Meadolarne had prayed together that Jonquil would return before the enemy appeared, but now it seemed that their prayers had failed for the forces of Winter were upon them and only the enchantment of the White Ring could save them now. Jonquil, if he was out there, Meadolarne thought to herself, would be better off dead than be at the mercy of the Ice Lord's hounds. She wished with all her heart that she could be with him and share his danger, wherever he was.

The circle of darkness began to close on the wall of white mushrooms that forbade entry into the Banf Kingdom beyond. The mighty machines of destruction moved steadily beneath its veiled embrace, heaved forward by sweating teams of grunting trolls. No sooner had the malevolent engines rolled into firing range, than trained packs of eager goblins swarmed over them, working at the straps and pulleys and screaming their commands at more ranks of dimwitted trolls who were loitering aimlessly nearby with huge rock missiles cradled like lethal babies in their arms. Other roughly made contraptions were loaded with immense, sharpened stakes or spears, and once all were armed and ready, the Ice Lord reduced the ferocity of the turmoil from the skies and gave his blessing to fire.

The Wizards of Light were horrified as the huge boulders and spears were flung at the delicate mushrooms, crashing into their fibrous stems and ploughing into their perfect caps, ripping huge segments away with their force. The King and the other banf leaders, who, from a safe distance, were watching the attack with the great lords, assured them that the White Ring was made of sterner stuff than at first it seemed. Indeed, no sooner had they spoken than most of the crumpled stalks and damaged gills sprang back into place, as if some unseen force had suddenly pumped new life into them. Even those pieces of precious flesh that had been torn away and now lay on the ground, still shone with a brilliant light, their enchantment intact. Nevertheless the Three Wizards were deeply disturbed by the damage that the enemy had inflicted on the wall, and hastily drew their banf comrades into a huddled conference to devise some counter measures. The Wizards and the banfs discussed the possibility of allying the power of the Fire Orbs with the enchantment of mushroom spores. The Lords of Light were especially interested in obtaining spores from the White Ring itself.

Vrorst could not have been more delighted with the initial throes of the battle. For once his armies had performed perfectly and the first blood was his. After the fiascoes of the Green oak and the Bay of Voices, the Ice Lord had resolved to direct this final conflict in person, to ensure faithful employment of his commands. The goblins and trolls were now directed to fire at will until a suitably large section of wall had been demolished to allow the mighty gracklins to be herded through to reap murderous devastation on the land of the mushroom dwellers beyond. The huge dragon headed lizards were straining at their heavy chain tethers, their cruelly clawed talons pawing impatiently at the snow. They had been promised a feast of banf blood by their keepers and the fearsome monsters were eager for their meal.

The groan of an awesome machine drew Vrorst's attention to his left, as a nearby catapault launched an immense rock at its white target. The attendant goblins watched spellbound as the colossal boulder roared through the air, falling from a great arc upon the tall fungi. A jubilant cheer rose from the waiting crew as their missile smashed through the thick fence of stalks, decapitating a splendid specimen, sending its magnificent cap rolling dramatically along the ground. Although Vrorst was a little dismayed to notice that the white mushrooms still retained their magic after being broken from the main body, he was not greatly concerned. A liberal dumping of snow from his attending storm clouds, hovering patiently above, would soon dull the shine of the enchanted debris.

The Ice Sorcerer had just congratulated himself on a brilliant start to his campaign and had decided to simply lean back and let his fiercely enthusiastic minions work themselves into a frenzy, destroying the barrier between him and his threefold prey, when a powerful flash of coloured light exploded from the stillness of the Banf Kingdom beyond the white wall..

The intense volume of the drumming that up to now had remained constant and booming suddenly faltered as the bright light bounced off the trunks about the players, a touch of hesitancy creeping into their insane rhythm. The feverish work of the goblin bombardiers abruptly halted and their eyes grew wide and fearful as they waited for the inevitable backlash.

At first it seemed as though none would come, as if the Wizards' bright explosion had failed to develop into the weapons of sorcery that they had intended, but then the faint hum of a rising wind could be heard drifting over the broken line of white mushrooms towards the enemy, in the now complete silence.

Vrorst shifted uneasily in his seat. The power of the three Fire Orbs was at work, he could feel it. But what could the Wizards possibly hope to achieve with instruments only capable of noble, constructive acts? For the moment he would wait and watch.

The mysterious wind gathered momentum and seemed to be filled with the mournful cries of lost souls wailing piteously for the fate of the world, the haunting screams little improving the confidence of the apprehensive warriors. Then a soaring chimney of spiralling draughts lifted from behind the white wall, the weaving tunnel striped with rising bands of luminous colour and studded with glittering flights of spinning stars. Clouds of snow powder were thrown up by the dazzling cyclone, hanging in the charged air like a brightly stained curtain of flickering hues. Eventually, the towering kaleidoscope narrowed into a single, gleaming star, which gradually drew all the climbing colours inside it. The star finally swelled into a giant radiant sphere, that hovered like a visiting sun above the gloom of the forest floor, impatient sparks jumping from its surface.

The moaning winds subsided, dying away to an uneasy stillness, and the few moments of suspenseful silence that followed inspired a restless tension in the surrounding legions. Vrorst was just about to blast the menacing orb out of the air with his own power, when it suddenly exploded of its own accord. Stars in every shade of the spectrum were showered across the wall of firing machines, the ear-splitting sound rattling every branch of the inlying trees, causing an avalanche of snow to descend on to the armies below. When the mists of ice particles finally cleared, the now highly agitated creatures attending the great machines, discovered a glowing crop of stars burning brightly in the snow amongst them. Their captains immediately ordered the dark warriors to snuff the vibrant flares out but the fearful minions were reluctant to go near, the multicoloured stars sparkled with the power of Old Magic and seemed to tremble with an unfulfilled energy. At last Wargren could stand no more of this mindless paranoia and barged a small group of goblins aside to stamp himself on the nearest of the intense flames. The dragonlord had to squint in near blindness to approach the fallen star and with a roar of rage and contempt raised his foot to strike.

Suddenly, the star flared up in Wargren's face, singeing his beard in its fury, and shooting up from the exposed ground where the star had lain, a vigorous rash of tall, white mushrooms sprang forth.

A scream of absolute terror erupted from the ranks of goblins close by and, without a moment's hesitation they abandoned their posts and fled from the mighty engines. Similar growths of blinding fungi burst from the other stars glittering in the snow around the machines and were greeted with equal horror by the gangs of dark creatures they surprised. Wargren screamed in pain and fury as the uncontrollable stampede rushed over him, thunderous packs of trolls, their eyes filled with a terror-struck madness, pounding his trampled body even further into the snow. By the time the last of the magic stars had germinated and borne fruit, the entire wall of artillery had been infested with rampant fungi, and to the eyes of the enemy, the log-lashed structures of the mighty catapaults and spear launchers, were illuminated in a most terrifying and excruciating light: the glare of Old Magic.

Vrorst was incensed, he had lost his instruments of destruction and, although the White Ring was greatly damaged, too much of it remained intact to allow a frontal assault. Vrorst concluded that there was only one option left to him, he must summon forth the full majesty of the Winter tempests, combine all the mightiest blizzards his dark season could muster, and bury the Kingdom of the Banfs, the Old Magic, the Wizards of Light and all. To achieve this titanic feat, however, would require more power than the Fire Orb at his fingertips could bestow. The great Vessel of Winter itself would have to be brought into the forest. Only then could Vrorst raise high his arms and begin to conjure forth the converging storms of catastrophe, and sound the doom knell for the forces of Light.

By the power of the Orb of Winter, Vrorst spoke with Vakari, who had remained behind in the Throne Citadel with a modest retinue to continue the necessary administration and government of the empire in the Ice Lord's absence. Vakari was able to inform his master, with some relief, that Tuatara had finally heeded the call to arms and had garrisoned her great host around the shores of the Crystal Lake, to guard Vrorst's retreat to the ice palace, so she claimed. Although the Ice Witch had not come before Vakari to explain the tardiness of her arrival, she had sent word to Vrorst's captain, saying that she had finally decided where her true loyalties lay and that the Ice Sorcerer may be sure that she would act accordingly.

Perhaps if Vrorst had not been too preoccupied with his lust for blood and victory, he might have felt uneasy at Tuatara's words, but the Ice Lord was too eager to command his archcaptain to send forth Grawlfang and the Winter Vessel, to take notice of the prickles of suspicion rising on his skin.

Vakari had received his command. Tuatara was in place. The tool of mass destruction was on its way and that was all Vrorst was prepared to care about as he stared out at the self regenerating wall of the White Ring. The Lord of Ice would not allow anything to distract him from his single purpose, until those that sheltered within the third Well of Hope were frozen to death beneath a deep tomb of ice.

The break in hostilities, however brief it might prove to be, at least provided the Wizards and the banfs with an opportunity to repair the damage inflicted upon the brave white wall. Despite its injuries, it was still a formidable barrier to be overcome and it seemed to those that dwelled within the Ring that as yet, Vrorst and his minions had not discovered another way to assail it. The Wizards observed with growing unease, however, that if anything Vrorst had increased the strength of his siege around the Banf Kingdom, clearly not ready to admit defeat just yet. The Ice Lord seemed to be waiting for a new opportunity.

A jubilant roar greeted Grawlfang the Terrible as he drew himself out of the dark, jagged mouth of the dragonport and stood proudly upon the high platform. Doubled ranks of palace guards were assembled across the frozen lake below to cheer the great guardian and his precious cargo on their way. The hour of their final victory was at hand and Vakari had thought it only proper that Vrorst's elite warriors should be lined up to witness the beginning of such an historic flight.

Hexerne and Vakari personally tested the security of the special harness that had been rapidly adapted to accommodate the priceless passenger. They were only too aware that it would be their heads on the block, if ought should go amiss with the vital mission. Then the young girl climbed aboard the great dragon herself, her small body clad in thick furs to protect her from the biting aerial gales. Vrorst's protégé had insisted on accompanying the Sacred Vessel on its momentous journey herself, so that she alone would have the honour of personally presenting her master with his instrument of invincible power. Vakari, like all of the other Winter captains, dared not refuse the requests of the precocious child, not whilst she could still command the full attention and favours of the Ice Sorcerer. The henchmen of Vrorst had seen on numerous occasions how Hexerne's poison whispers in the ear of her guardian had spelt ruin and disaster for those who caused her offence.

Once Vakari was satisfied with the strength of the harness he glanced upwards to make sure that Grawlfang's escort was in place. Flocks of wheeling snowhawks shrieked impatiently far above the crown of clustered spires, the swift white dragons just visible against the growing turmoil of the sullen sky. Vakari could only assume that the snowdragons above were of Wargren's flight, as instructed (all other flying activities having been temporarily forbidden) but the circling white beasts were so high above the Citadel, it was impossible to make out their command insignia. The archcaptain was only allowed to ponder these thoughts for the briefest moment, until the shrill voice of Hexerne demanded his attentions return to her. She haughtily announced that she was ready and that he might give the order to depart. At the risk of courting the child's petulant anger, Vakari refused to do so until he had thoroughly inspected, once more, the harnesses that held the chest to the dragon and the child to the chest. He had no intention of incurring the murderous wrath of his master by allowing either passenger to be sucked into oblivion by the buffeting winds.

The touchpaper of the rocket flare was finally lit and after a few tense seconds it screamed into the air to explode into a brilliant fireball, the signal to the snowdragon escort that Grawlfang was about to take wing.

However, the smug smile that Vakari wore, as he visualised the glorious massacre about to be wrought upon the Forces of Light, was changed to a frown of dismay as the first of the descending snowdragons swept past the mouth of the dragonport. Rather than Narian or Brabast, two of Wargren's finest lieutenants, leading the flight, the face that greeted the eyes of Vakari was that of Hawkhood, Tuatara's henchman.

Hexerne had been too busy fussing with her fur wrappings to notice the change in escort and snapped furiously at the transfixed archcaptain, demanding to know the reason for the delay. The child was also too engrossed in herself to notice the wall of archers emerge from the shadows of the Lake Forest, their arrows aimed threateningly at the columns of the Ice Lord's élite guard.

Suddenly a tall female figure stepped out on to the ice platform beside the quaking Vakari, her long black hair falling upon a white robe of silver threaded silk. Tuatara looked even more serene and beautiful than her previous transformation. The last traces of painted colour had been cleaned from her face and now she looked fresh and youthful, even soft blushes glowing in her cheeks. Vakari shrank away in fear at the sight of this vision, he could perceive that Tuatara was finally free of the Ice Sorcerer's influence and that made him afraid. Hexerne did not realise that something was wrong until she finished preening herself and casually scanned her eyes over the distraught form of Vakari. Then she saw the Queen of Witches.

"What are you doing here?" she spat violently at Tuatara. "Why aren't you with your army?"

The Ice Witch smiled confidently at the pouting child and then swung out her hand in a sweeping arc, gesturing towards the lake.

"But I am, my Lady," she sweetly replied.

Hexerne stared down at the frozen bridges and saw that the cream of Vrorst's warriors, who a few moments earlier had stood in a glorious, cheering parade, had been replaced with Tuatara's power. Every bridge and vantage point leading to the citadel that could be seen from the high dragonport, was now lined with heavily armed ranks of her soldiers. Hexerne recoiled in horror, her knuckles clenched white on Grawlfang's reins.

"What is the meaning of this?" she cried. "Do you intend to add grand treachery to your ever growing list of crimes?"

"I do!" Tuatara coolly answered.

Vakari advanced on the Ice Witch, his hand unwisely reaching for the hilt of his scimitar. She turned and held him with her sapphire eyes, his body freezing mid-stride.

"Foolish Vakari," Tuatara warned. "I may no longer hold favour with the Ice Sorcerer, but I am still a witch of some power."

The archcaptain smiled rather sheepishly and then with a scowling glance at Hexerne turned and fled into the main building to gather together his servants and engineer his escape, the fury of the young girl's screamed abuse and condemnation ringing for some time afterwards in his ears. Hexerne then returned her venom to Tuatara.

"One word from me," she began. "And Grawlfang will take to the air. Then with or without an escort I will deliver the Vessel to our Lord and the final victory will be his."

"You will not surrender the Vessel to me?" Tuatara asked of the child.

"Never!" came the hissed reply.

"Then," the Ice Witch sadly announced. "You leave me no choice."

Tuatara took a step closer to Grawlfang and Hexerne tensed at the Ice Witch's approach, her right hand slipping into her pocket and involuntarily clenching the small crystal orb that lay at rest there. Then, suddenly, the Ice Witch threw wide her arms and launched into a wild song of enchantment, its riotous melody vibrant with jarring dischords and ear-piercing notes. She sang with every fibre of her being to agitate and enrage the great dragon, to bore into his mind with her grating phrases and shrill refrains, to coax him to madness. The response of the dragon was immediate, for just as Tuatara had the power to sooth and placate the mighty guardian and bring him to peaceful slumber, she also had the skill to reverse the spell and inspire a blind fury to explode within his powerful body, that was at once devastating and uncontrollable.

A scream of terror burst from Hexerne's lips as Grawlfang threw himself on to his hind legs to claw the air before him, his snarling head rising to release a thunderous roar that shook the walls about them, splintering the very fabric of the ice with its force. The dragon then spun around in savage circles, thrashing the opening of the dragonport with his tail, causing volleys of ice spears to crash around him from above. Grawlfang's wings flailed the weakening ice platform beneath him, raining penetrating blows upon its damaged structure, his powerful jaws gnawed at the edge of the crumbling projection, ripping up vast frozen chunks and hurling them at the lake below.

Tuatara's army wisely broke ranks and dispersed to seek shelter from the raging dragon. Hawkhood swooped daringly at the thin promontary, his dragonsteed's talons closing firmly about the Ice Witch's waist and snatching her to safety. A few moments later the dragonport platform finally shattered beneath the trauma of the Guardian's madness and the great white dragon was jettisoned to the wind. The cowering forces below were forced to throw themselves flat to the ice as Grawlfang screamed across the surface of the lake in a surging white storm, the hysterical, screaming Hexerne still attached to the loosening chest on his back. The tunnels of arched pillars that rose over the bridges were systematically smashed into showers of giant debris that crashed about the ears of Tuatara's warriors, as the mighty dragon vent his anger on the towering ice formations. After launching similar attacks on the high ramparts rising from the Citadel, Grawlfang gradually spiralled upwards into the low ceiling of dark clouds and swept into the western horizon.

As Tuatara watched the Guardian of Winter disappear over the tree line, she could only pray that the Sacred Vessel would never be laid to rest at its master's feet.

Grawlfang continued to wrestle with his inner torment as he sped over the roof of the Green Sky Forest, thrashing and biting at the wind with a boiling frustration; the Vessel and the girl still strapped to his back a growing source of feverish irritation.

Every sound that Hexerne tried to make was stolen away by the violent draughts, the dragon was deaf to her pleading and blind to their quest, he surely meant to destroy them all. As the white dragon dived and looped in his endless rampage, the child could only sit and watch in helpless horror as the body of the silver chest began to ease out of its moorings. The elaborate harness, charged with holding it in place, had tried its best but had never been designed to withstand such an aggressive test, and Hexerne feared that the squealing of the fastenings preceded the snapping capitulation of the sorely stressed metal. The wind gripped the young girl's shoulders as if to say, 'with the next dive you are mine!'

As expected Grawlfang's incensed aerobatic raving finally took his passengers' bonds beyond their limit and with a loud squeal from the ornate buckles and an even louder scream from the terrified Hexerne, the dragon, the chest and the girl parted company in mid air.

The lid of the Sacred Vessel suddenly burst open with the force of the gusts bullying its damaged clasp and the powerful Winter gems it contained spewed out in a priceless black arc, to fall as a glistening shower over the naked canopy of the Great Forest. The dragon flew on to find his master, the madness finally shaking itself free of his exhausted limbs but Hexerne and the now empty chest plummeted forestwards, a desperate wail of sheer disbelief rising from the falling child.

The King of the World had been quietly collecting his thoughts in the privacy of his luxurious tent, after a lively council with his generals, when the feeling of terrible loss and foreboding swept over him. His troubled gaze swiftly fell upon the glimering depths of the Winter Orb, but the only picture it would reveal to him was that of an ugly black rain, falling in an endless downpour from the cloud filled sky. An ominous cry of grief and misery sounded from the Ice Lord's tent, carrying with disturbing clarity over the nearby ranks of idling warriors. A thousand heads turned with alarm to stare at the rambling peaks of the pitched canvas lodging, then a dark stumbling figure growled at them to return to their work before limping his way towards the grand dwelling.

As the crippled form of Wargren hobbled through the opening to investigate, he found his master crumpled into his high backed throne, his crowned head buried in his hands.

This unexpected scene unnerved Wargren deeply and for a few incredulous moments Vrorst's archgeneral was too shocked to speak. Slowly the Ice Sorcerer's head lifted from his palms, his features drawn into a heavy expression of humiliation and contempt. Finally a wry smile wriggled across his tightened lips and his eyebrows raised in disbelief. He spoke almost calmly to his general.

"I have been betrayed," he began, "by she to whom I have given the highest rewards and the greatest trust."

Vrorst rose like an old man from his great chair and staggered towards his subordinate.

"And now she makes a fool of me! So be it, Queen of Witches. We failed in friendship, let us continue in emnity!"

Wargren took a few steps nearer to his master, suddenly fearing that the Ice Lord might stumble or fall but all at once Vrorst reached out and embraced his Fire Orb, and his body swiftly straightened with replenished vigour.

"Have my snowchariot harnessed and made ready, I leave within the hour!" he commanded the dark general.

"What is wrong, Lord?" Wargren demanded. "What terrible fate has befallen us?"

Vrorst stiffened and stared irritably into space.

"There is no time for discussion," he told Wargren. "But I will tell you this. The

Winter Vessel and the crystals it contained are lost to us. Without the power of the blackhearts I cannot destroy the White Ring!"

"Then are we to withdraw from the battlefield before the warring has even begun?" Wargren asked despairingly.

Vrorst suddenly turned on the stooped general and rising to his fullest height, bellowed in his former majestic tones;

"Never! There will be no retreat!" roared Vrorst. "Do you think that now I finally have the Wizards of Light trapped and within my grasp, I shall simply let them go? You my faithful Wargren will remain here and continue the siege, whilst I fly north to Mezereon. There, in Dragonskeep, are consignments of Blackhearts not yet transported to the Throne Citadel. There I shall renew my power and when I am complete, return here and finish the job!"

Wargren suddenly forgot his prudent fear and threw himself at the Ice Sorcerer's feet, his twisted hands snatching at Vrorst's opulent robe, his wretched face haunted by a desperate confusion.

"We have all faced untold dangers for you!" he cried. "All of us sworn to die in your service. I myself have been trampled half to death in the pursuit of your quest. Do you now tell me that you intend to simply jump into your shiny sled and desert us? Stay here and fight! Army to army! We deserve that much from you!"

Sparks of blue fire glittered in Vrorst's eyes as a wave of cold fury surged within him.

"Unhand me, Wargren! Are you mad!" he growled.

The broken general complied with a whimper and crumpled to the ground, suddenly mindful of his master's wrath and his own mortal weakness.

"I shall not kill you, Wargren," Vrorst calmly continued. "You are still of some use to me. Now do my bidding!"

The general very slowly climbed to his feet, bowed respectively to the Wizard and with an earnest attempt to reassemble his air of authority, shuffled out into the forest to command his warriors.

Hexerne fell from the sky like a spinning, fur-clad stone. She screamed with all her might because it was the only thing left to do apart from brace herself for the final impact. The hysterical child was just pondering on the probability of her meeting with a soft landing, when she was suddenly slammed violently from beneath and brought to a jarring halt. The breathtaking experience left her a little dazed but when the stars finally cleared from her eyes, she turned and gazed into the smiling face of Jonquil, her one time prisoner and intended subject for biological experimentation.

Hexerne giggled insanely. She must have been either dead or delirious, because her eyes were trying to tell her that the banf had just caught her in mid-air and was casually cradling her in his arms, hovering above the bristling roof of the forest, courtesy of two magnificent feathered wings. Then the child noticed other floating faces, peering at her with amused interest, more flying banfs. Hexerne could not decide whether to shout for joy or cry with despair, this had to be a dream.

"What have we here?" Jonquil asked merrily. "Too high up for a squirrel I fear, and yet furry enough!"

The other fliers laughed.

"That is the strangest bird I have ever seen drop from the sky, where are its wings?" Judruff cried.

Hexerne glanced from one to another, her eyes wild and staring.

"Are you real?" she finally ventured. "Am I alive?"

"Of course you are alive," Jonquil laughed. "If you were an angel, you would have wings too!"

Hexerne was immediately overcome by a wave of relief which forced glistening wells of water to seep from her eyes. Unfortunately, the embarrassment of being saved by an enemy soon got the better of the novelty of being alive, and with a rash of petulant temper, the child began to beat furiously against Jonquil's arms, bawling at him in indignant tones.

"Then if I am alive, put me down!" she screamed. "You can't keep me hanging up here like a wind-blown leaf. Put me down!"

Jonquil smiled to his brothers and shrugged compliantly and then with a mischievous glint in his eyes answered;

"Whatever you say, my Lady!"

With that the banf heaved Hexerne into the air, where she flew into the swooping embrace of Judruff, a scream of abusive protest erupting from the child's uncontrollable mouth as she was flung through the void. From Judruff, the girl was tossed to Comet and then back to Jonquil and then on again into the arms of the whole group. With every brief flight she made through the air, Hexerne dragged up even worse profanities from the pits of her limited vocabulary to hurl at the fliers, and the more she swore at them, the more Jonquil and the windsprites threw her from one to another. Eventually the indescribable stream of abuse was reduced to a pitiful burble of childish sobs and Hexerne was spared any further torment. Suddenly, a small, sparkling object seemed to leap from the child's deep pocket to plummet down towards the forest. With lightning reflexes that Jonquil would never have dreamed possible when he first flapped his wings, the banf dived from the company and with Comet in close pursuit, flew down to retrieve the mystery possession.

It was a small crystal orb, that shone with a most intriguing and persuasive light. Despite Hexerne's dewy eyed pleading, Jonquil decided that it would be much safer if the apprentice sorceress and her miniature orb were kept apart for the time being, and thinking little more about it, slipped the small globe into his own pocket for safe keeping.

The group of fliers found a conveniently substantial tree canopy and placed Hexerne in the fork of a stout but lofty bough. Once again she squealed in protest, this time without the curses, but was promised that the sooner she told her winged rescuers everything she knew about the great dragon, the chest and the Ice Sorcerer, the sooner she would be free. Jonquil and the others had guessed that some great manoeuvre was afoot when they had witnessed the ferocious aerial exploits of the Winter dragon, and the resultant discarding of the Vessel and the girl. The reason for the bizarre spectacle and the lack of any snowdragon patrol had perplexed the fliers greatly, but now that they had saved the life of the falling Hexerne, they hoped to discover the answers to the puzzle.

Not wanting to incur the anger of her winged saviours and endure another stomach lurching round of mid-air pass the parcel, Hexerne gladly told them everything that she knew. For a good hour or so the fliers perched and listened as she spoke of the siege of the Banf Kingdom, the summoning of the Winter Vessel by the Ice Lord, the heinous betrayal of Tuatara and of course the evil spell of madness that the Ice Witch had cast on Grawlfang. Judruff asked the child if she knew where the great dragon was now. Hexerne told him that the Guardian would seek out his master and rescue him from the battle.

Rescue! The very thought of the terrible and mighty Lord of Ice needing to be rescued from anything was inconceivable, but as the child explained, without the power of the blackhearts, Vrorst was impotent against the strong enchantment of the White Ring.

"Then where will he go?" Jonquil asked. "Now that the Throne Citadel has been taken by Tuatara?"

"To the North, I should imagine," Hexerne replied. "To Mezereon. There are more blackhearts there. In Dragonskeep he will recover his power."

The King of the Falcons prayed that events would overtake the Ice Sorcerer and that the uprising of the dwarfs, carriers and windsprites would successfully deny the fortress of Dragonskeep as a sanctuary for the evil Vrorst. Hexerne, however, predicted a different fate for the rebels.

"The uprising will fail," she claimed, much to the indignation of the attending windsprites.

"How can you be sure?" Judruff demanded.

"Because even as we speak," Hexerne began, failing to conceal a slight glow of pleasure. "An army of goblins ten thousand strong is marching on Dragongorge to reinforce Mezereon's garrison."

A wicked smile enveloped the child's tear stained face;

"Your people will be cut to pieces!" she giggled.

Judruff snorted with rage and his eyes painted a picture that caused Hexerne to almost topple out of the tree as she recoiled from the King's seething expression. Suddenly, the child's eyes were distracted by something moving in the sky behind Judruff and her arms flew out in a gesture of pleading.

"Master!" she screamed.

Jonquil and the others turned to see the gleaming form of a huge white dragon rising from the forest in the far distance, a dark clad figure seated on its back. Even though the rider was too far away to recognise, the shivers of fear that bristled upon the skin of the seven fliers convinced them that it was Vrorst.

Nemesis

For a moment all seven fliers were too stunned to move, their hands gripped like iron to the branches of the tree and each one's heart beating like a restless frog in his chest. In their transfixed rigidity, the banf and the falcons simply sat and watched Grawlfang carry the Lord of Ice into the northern horizon with heavy pounding wingbeats.

Jonquil was the first to wrench himself from the spell;

"We have got to stop him!" he urged.

"Yes!" Judruff cried, "before the dragon climbs too high. Once his wings reach the upper draughts, we will never catch them!"

In a fury of flapping feathers the banf and the windsprites leapt from the naked branches to give chase to the distant Guardian. A howl of protests from the stranded Hexerne caused the last of the fliers to halt and look back.

"What about me?" the child wailed.

The young windsprite, called Merle, was at a loss to know what to say to the young girl, so finally he just told her not to go away and that they would be back as soon as possible. The windsprite's ears stang with the insults of the fuming child as he raced away to catch up with his fellows.

The brave handful of fliers finally caught their deadly quarry as the dragon approached the snow-clad flanks of a lonely forest mountain. Vrorst turned around to look at his winged pursuers with an expression of disdainful nonchalance. He revealed not the slightest trace of concern as the windsprites eased threateningly into Grawlfang's mighty slipstream. It was only when the Ice Lord's scornful eyes fell upon the now winged body of Jonquil that the first twinge of disquiet darkened his imperious demeanour.

Vrorst communicated some urgent instructions to the dragon and Grawlfang's immense white form swept across the path of the fliers in an evasive dive. Jonquil and the falcons followed but foolishly forgot the reach of the dragon's long muscular tail. As Grawlfang dipped suddenly in the opposite direction, a rapid twist worked its way along his endless body, which he enlarged into a violent whiplash to cleave through the close formation of the fliers. Jonquil just escaped the crashing blow of the unravelling coil but four of his companions, including the King's son Comet were slapped like flies by the whistling tail spear and propelled as unconscious bundles into the wind. A cry of dismay rose from Judruff, and the three unharmed fliers abruptly halted from their chase and dropped like stones to try and save the falling bodies before they were dashed on the rocky feet of the mountain. Jonquil and the other windsprite, Hulse, each managed to reach one body, the King caught a third and just succeeded in grabbing the collar of his son's tunic with his other hand, to bring the two stunned fliers safely to the snowy slope.

Jonquil looked back at the sky and his heart sank as the distant silhouette of the Winter dragon disappeared behind the jagged rise of the towering peak. Vrorst would make it to Dragonskeep for certain now, there was nothing to stop him. It had been a vain hope to suppose that a handful of windsprites might have been able to stand in the way of the powerful Lord of Ice, and four fallen brothers was the price they had paid for their lofty ambition.

Judruff and Hulse were busily examining the stricken bodies of the injured, and much to their relief found that all four were alive. With Jonquil's help, the two windsprites tried to make Comet, Merle, Farlin and Dern as comfortable as possible on the powdery snow, flying to and from the nearby wall of trees to fetch soft evergreen branches to make a dry bedding. When the four unfortunate fliers eventually came round, it was discovered that they had been inflicted with a variety of fractures and sprains, the most serious of which was the broken right wing of the King's son Comet who together with the young Merle, who was suffering from several cracked ribs, seemed to have taken the brunt of the dragon's attack.

Suddenly, a great rush of wind roared down the slope of the mountain, a sudden blizzard of disturbed snow powder billowing over the huddled group of winged beings. The storm of eye-stinging particles eventually died down and the windsprites who had been facing into the snowy gust had to blink to try and restore their blurry vision. As Hulse finally regained his sight a gasp of sheer terror burst from his gaping mouth. When the rest of the group turned and followed his gaze, they discovered why.

Towering before them, a short distance up the slope, was the ghastly shape of Grawlfang, his vast outline thinly veiled in the snowy cloud. Standing menacingly before him, the shining Orb of Winter balanced carefully on his fingertips, was the commanding figure of Vrorst, his cold eyes regarding the pitiful scene below him with smug contempt.

Jonquil rose from his fellows and stepped up to face the Ice Sorcerer, the deep growl of Grawlfang rumbling like approaching thunder in the banf's ears. A bitter smile appeared on Vrorst's lips but there was no pleasure in his eyes. The Ice Sorcerer's left index finger rose profoundly from his side and came to rest along the line of his murderous stare. At last he spoke.

"You!" Vrorst roared. "You are the cause of my misery! Tuatara was infected by the light of Old Magic which you carry like a disease! You changed her and she betrayed me. But I am not beaten. I shall rise again and destroy that putrid swamp of enchantment from whence you and your loathsome kind are spawned."

Vrorst paused to stare deep into the shining core of the delicately poised crystal globe, a flickering ice blue flame slowly building within it. Without turning his head, the Ice Sorcerer spoke again to Jonquil.

"You should be flattered, banf! Or is it windsprite now? I see that you have finally found your wings! Flattered, that I have turned from my important journey to Dragonskeep, and flown back here, just to kill you!"

He turned again to fix the banf once more with his merciless stare.

"I should have done so the first time I laid eyes on your wretched form." Vrorst hissed. "Now I am here to make amends."

Towering before them, the ghastly shape of Grawlfang.

Jonquil stood helplessly watching the Ice Sorcerer prepare his doom. Fleeing was useless, Vrorst's lightning bolt would reach him wherever he ran. The banf could only straighten himself to his fullest height, arms clasped to his side and stare defiantly into the face of death. It might make an end worthy of a tale or two, Jonquil decided. He could just hear the likes of Peeli and Finf in years to come, crouched as old banfs before the embers of a dying fire asking if anyone would like to hear the tale of brave Jonquil, the hero of the Banf Kingdom, who died at the hands of the terrible Wizard Vrorst. The children would cry 'Me! Me!' and the great saga would be retold once again, to the everlasting delight of the firelit audience.

The banf's meandering thoughts were suddenly interrupted by a burning sensation on the palm of his right hand. He then realised that without knowing it he had reached into his pocket and clasped the small orb that he had confiscated from the child. Instinctively Jonquil brought it into the light and raised it at Vrorst. For the briefest moment the Ice Sorcerer hesitated and Jonquil knew that Vrorst recognised the small sphere, but then he laughed it off.

"Huh! It will take more than Hexerne's toy to save you!" Vrorst sneered.

Jonquil could think of nothing better to do than sharply pull back his arm and hurl the crystal orb at the Ice Sorcerer. In his surprise Vrorst aimed his bolt of fire at the hurtling globe instead of Jonquil, the force of the lightning blast deflecting the sphere behind him where it struck a smooth outcrop of bare rock and landed undamaged in the snow.

The Ice Sorcerer was just about to launch a second lightning bolt at the banf when suddenly the harsh, wailing voice of Tuatara screeched forth from the small flickering orb. Her terrible spell of madness, which had originally been performed with such devastating effect on the dragonport of the Throne Citadel, had been recorded by Hexerne's toy, which as Vrorst himself once pointed out seemed to have an uncanny affection for the Ice Witch's voice.

The response from Grawlfang was volcanic. His tortured senses which had only just recovered from their last incitement, exploded into a fit of rock shattering roars and a desperate thrashing of limbs. The great dragon's tail rent through the air in wild, flailing blows and his thrashing wings raised a cyclone of snow to swirl about his frenzied body. Vrorst was gripped with a panic driven terror, he commanded his dragonsteed to be still and heed his words but Grawlfang raged on. Finally the Ice Sorcerer's fear ruled his wisdom and he let a volley of searing lightning bolts fly at the rampaging dragon. Grawlfang answered him with a mighty whack of his snaking tail, sending Vrorst flying through the air and crashing heavily onto the jagged spine of an exposed rocky ridge, the glowing Orb of Winter still clutched tightly to his chest.

The dragon roared his challenge at the broken figure lying across the rocks and somehow the Ice Lord managed to prise himself off the jagged points and struggle to his feet. Grawlfang backed away a little, pawing at the ground in readiness to rush in for the final kill. Vrorst staggered his way over to Jonquil, a bloody stain darkening the snow behind him and once more raised his finger to strike blue fire at the banf.

The piercing blue eyes of the Lord of Ice met with the insistent green stare of the simple mushroom dweller. Vrorst hesitated to appraise Jonquil for the last time and as he did so, his left arm suddenly dropped limply to his side, and an expression of miserable disgust fell across his face. He hung his head in despair and spoke breathlessly to Jonquil.

"I could kill you now, Jonquil of the banfs. It would be small payment, for the ill fortune you have caused me. But if I cannot defeat so meek an enemy without the power of sorcery, then it is I who deserves to die!"

Vrorst turned to face the Winter dragon, swaying with the effort to keep himself on his feet.

"Magnificent beast!" he cried. "I created you. Therefore I welcome you as my executioner. Come!"

The Ice Sorcerer threw wide his arms and the dragon lunged eagerly forward. In a few strides he was upon the dark figure and placed a hooked claw at the throat of his master. With his last breath Vrorst seized the cruel spike and held Grawlfang's hateful gaze;

"Find Mezereon," he spluttered. "He must continue it!"

The great dragon bellowed in triumph and despair, the monstrous sound shaking the very roots of the mountain beneath him and Vrorst was no more.

Jonquil was pulled back by his collar and stumbled down the slope to follow the rest of the windsprites to safety. Only Merle, of the four, had to be carried, the rest limped after Hulse and Comet to the shadow of the forest. There they watched the madness finally leave the mighty Grawlfang and the horror of realisation slowly creep in. After wailing with such intensity that Jonquil thought his ears would burst, the dragon seized the Winter Orb in his jaws and stormed away from the desolate slope, swooping low over the forest in two terrifying passes before lifting over the mountain peak and soaring into the North.

Jonquil looked deeply into the green eyes of Judruff and the windsprite king embraced him warmly.

"The King of the Enemy is dead!" he cried.

Jonquil smiled and then turned to look over the crippled and the wounded;

"The King of the Enemy may be dead, my friend," the banf said. "But I am still a long way from home, and until we find our way to the third Well of Hope, we shall not be safe! I am afraid our adventure continues..!"

Swarms of white feathered arrows fell amongst the massed legions of the Winter army, awakening the forces of Vrorst to a new presence in the forest, moving against them, from outside the protection of the White Ring. A chorus of whoops and shouts emanated from an invisible power spreading across the floor of the forest, under a creeping blanket of glistening mist. The unknown enemy of the dark forces approached the black siege like a charging white sea, sparkling arrows, fizzing with enchantment, rising in mesmeric arcs out of the anonymous pale cloud.

Queen Trinia and King Trillil marched with a glittering compliment of fellow monarchs as the combined forces of the whole of the southern fairy realms advanced on the positions of the dark creatures; and trotting proudly at their head was the most remarkable of creatures: Rattajack the Incomparable, the silent diplomat.

Only Rattajack could begin as a prisoner and transform himself into a saviour. After being captured by Queen Trinia's hunters, and brought before the angry monarch as a spy. The terragon had somehow, in his own inimitable fashion, succeeded in completely changing Trinia's opinion of the Three Wizards, and enlisted her help in uniting all of the fairy kingdoms to march to aid the Banf Kingdom. And so they had come, and the sight of the green clad archers, striding forth in pale lines within the milky haze, struck a deep note of fear in the hearts of the enemy. Wargren tried his best to rouse their spirits and rally their courage, but somehow the dark creatures knew that the power was gone.

Suddenly a shower of bright stars erupted from within the Banf Kingdom, and shattered with ear-splitting intensity over the apprehensive black columns. Then a glittering procession issued forth from between the tall stalks of the magnificent White Ring, brightly coloured standards and streamers lifting with full splendour into the sharp breeze. At their head emerged three mighty wizards; green, gold and red. The Three Lords of the Seasons marched from their sanctuary, to claim victory from the Winter armies.

At the sight of the Three Wizards, even Wargren's courage failed him, and almost with one voice, the hounds of Vrorst wailed in despair and fled from the battlefield. The disappointed Gracklins, who had been promised a feast of banf flesh by their keepers, turned their frustration on fleeing goblin warriors, the great beasts casually snatching them in twos and threes from the dark stampede, as they nonchalantly followed the retreat.

The advancing columns of fairy warriors, set fresh arrows to their longbows and heartily gave chase to the shrinking Winter hordes; the rout was on.

Jonquil and the windsprites had just limped their way to within sight of the Banf Kingdom, when the great surge of the Ice Lord's defeated armies thundered towards them. The able bodied fliers could not take to the wing without leaving the injured to perish, so the whole group had dived for shelter within a bank of lush evergreens.

Most of the enemy creatures rushed past, happily trampling on their slower brethren, blinded by their lust to escape. One unusually heavy pair of footfalls however, lingered outside the rash of green bushes, its large scaled nostrils sucking at the air to find more of the strange new scent.

Jonquil and the windsprites stared at each other in fearful silence, hardly daring to breath, lest they should give themselves away. They were soon to find out that they were already discovered. A terrible roar of triumph bellowed through the air as two clawed forelimbs parted the tops of the trees, high above the hiding fliers. The monstrous dagger-laden grin of a gracklin thrust its way into the bower of green branches, and its tiny, evil eyes, rolled in ecstasy as it peered in to the bushy screen and realised that it would be dining on banf flesh after all.

The adventure continues.......................................!

FROZEN

THE FRUIT FORESTS
OF THE WEST

THE MARBLE
FORTRESS

THE GREAT FOREST
OF THE WEST

THE GREAT GARDEN
OF THE WEST

BANF KINGDOM

THE FOREST RIVER

THE SOUTHERNS

BAY OF VOICES

VRORST'S MARCH

FORGOTTEN
ISLAND

LAST REFUGE
OF THE WIZARDS

THE SOUTHERN
OCEAN

THE GREAT
OF THE